Make or Break

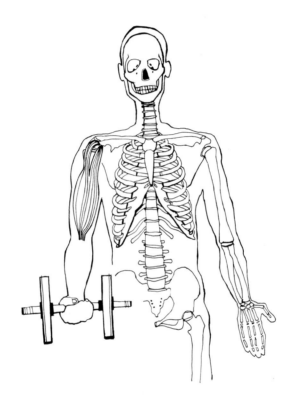

Don't let climbing injuries dictate your success

Dave MacLeod

www.davemacleod.com - blog, training advice, climbing books and films

Published by:
Rare Breed Productions
Grey Corries House
Roy Bridge
Inverness-shire
PH31 4AQ
Scotland

Edition 1.0

First published February 2015

ISBN: 978-0-9564281-3-4

Book design: Claire MacLeod
Cover illustration: John Sutherland www.crofteleven.co.uk
Editing and proofs: Susan Jensen, Barbara MacLeod
Photography: Claire MacLeod
Illustrations: John Sutherland

Printed by J Thomson, Scotland

For Freida

About Dave MacLeod

Dave MacLeod is a professional climber and coach based in the Highlands of Scotland. He has been climbing for 20 years and is recognised as one of the best all-round climbers in the world, climbing 9a sport routes, Font 8B+ boulders, E11 trad routes, grade XI mixed routes and has made hundreds of first ascents around Scotland and the greater mountain ranges of the world. He is also a world renowned climbing coach, writing the popular blog The Online Climbing Coach since 2006. His first book, 9 out of 10 Climbers Make the Same Mistakes is an international bestselling climbing improvement text. He gained a BSc in Physiology & Sports Science and an MSc in Medicine and Science in Sport & Exercise, both from Glasgow University. He has published research on climbing performance in the Journal of Sports Sciences and is a regular contributor to many climbing magazines and websites around the world.

Safety & responsibility

This is not a medical book and I am not a doctor. I am a climbing coach and this is a coaching book. Nothing in this book is medical advice. It is entirely my own opinion based on experience of observing climbers and reading the scientific research of others. Those opinions may be wrong, or rapidly go out of date as new research comes through. The responsibility for what you do with the information in the book is entirely your own and I cannot be liable for any injury you suffer. The book is intended as a starting point for you to see the options you have for dealing with injuries. I recommend that you always speak to a relevant medical professional before taking any action or making decisions on treatment.

This book will help you take control over how long and how far you can push your body in climbing without it failing to keep up.

Contents

Section 5: Psychology of injuries: dealing with the anguish of injury

Section 6: Young climbers

Section 7: The elbow

Section 8: The fingers

Section 9: The wrist

Section 10: The shoulder

Section 11: Lower body injuries

Section 12: Further reading

The author's tale of woe and hope

Glossary of key terms

Thanks

References

Index

For every complex problem there is an answer that is clear, simple and wrong.

H. L. Mencken

Make or break

Section 1

Why the treatments you have tried aren't working, and what to do about it.

If you have bought this book before your climbing has injured you: smart move. The time taken to read this treatise on how to keep yourself healthy for climbing will pay you back in spades down the line. However, the odds are that you have picked up this book because you have either just become injured and are panicking about what to do, or you've been carrying a stubborn injury for ages and despair about what to try next.

If so, the first message from me is to take heart. It is extremely unlikely that you can't beat your injury and regain your enjoyment and previous standard in climbing. However, although injury needn't destroy your enjoyment or performance level in climbing in the long term, it is true that whether you beat the injury or not, your climbing routine will be forced to change somehow. A fundamental message of this book is that injury is your alert that something must change. Your challenge is to figure out what. The potential sources of the problems that you must pinpoint and address are frighteningly diverse. The rest of the book is concerned with highlighting as many as possible. I have focused on the most likely roots of injury, which for reasons I'll explain, are sometimes given the least attention in sports medical literature and practice.

I've written this book because I feel there is a huge gap in the common understanding about how to deal with sports injuries, both generally and specifically within the sport of climbing. In climbing, the problem is compounded by the immaturity of the modern sport and the short epidemiological history of the injuries caused by rock climbing.

The huge gap I am talking about has two components. First, there are several links in the chain of injury management that must be given attention in order for rehabilitation to actually work. However, some of those links are either over or drastically under-used. The reasons for this are numerous; historical inertia, marketing by the sports medicine industry, the outlets where sports medicine is delivered and how certain ideas spread more easily in the media. Far too often, sportspeople and their therapists focus too much on treating symptoms, while ignoring the causes of injury. Thus, recurrence of sports injuries is extremely common.

The second component of the gap is an aspect of rehabilitation that is so underused by all but a tiny, lucky minority that it is essentially missing altogether. That missing link is the world of technique correction. To say this is unfortunate is a bit of an understatement, since incorrect technique is both a fundamental cause of many injuries and the foundation of any long term plan to eliminate injury. A major purpose of this book is to plug this gap for climbers.

To beat injuries you need patience. Yet patiently doing the wrong thing and going nowhere only leads to despair. To beat injuries you also need time and that time can either be filled with positive or negative progress. Doing nothing with injuries often causes negative progress in certain aspects of rehabilitation. Meanwhile, the duration of positive progress required doesn't get any shorter. At best it is only delayed by doing the wrong thing.

The right knowledge is the other key ingredient in successful recovery from injuries. It underpins all the other ingredients such as patience, time, motivation and discipline. The knowledge in this book should help steer you in the right direction, but it is no substitute for patient application over time. Thankfully, the different ingredients above work hand in hand. Motivation and patience are a lot easier to find when you can feel positive progress happening. I won't try to tell you that there are any shortcuts to hard work and patience; there aren't. As you move through the book, you will see how addressing all the variables that are under your control will help avoid the most unpleasant aspects of being injured: lay-off and long term loss of form.

Like nearly every lifetime athlete, amateur or professional, I've suffered a long list of injuries. I have spent 20 years soaking up every disparate piece of information about climbing injuries and what could help deal with them. It might sound strange, but the periods I've spent coming back to full form after injury have repeatedly been the most satisfying of my climbing life and have also been when I've climbed my best. In a sense, the challenge of meeting my climbing goals despite injury have actually added to the satisfaction of working on them.

Perhaps not everyone could see injury in such a positive light and it certainly depends on the injury suffered. However, my goal with this book is to remove as much of the pain from the process as possible.

How to use this book

I have designed this book to be read as a narrative from the start to at least section 6. You'll see from the contents page that descriptions of the specific injuries, and potential interventions to resolve them, are contained near the end of the book. If you have an injury but have yet to find either a diagnosis or a treatment plan that is having some positive effects, perhaps you will be tempted to cut straight to these sections. That's fine. In fact I would recommend you do have a quick look through these sections as it will help to focus your thoughts on exactly what aspects you will need to think about as you come back and read through the earlier sections of the book.

Sections 1-6 contain much of the new, valuable or hard-to-find knowledge and ideas you are unlikely to find in climbing or sports medical literature. It was my own grappling with these issues over a long climbing career with plenty of injuries that first motivated me to write this book. As with my previous book *9 out of 10 climbers make the same mistakes*, this book functions in part to relay some important facts you should know as a climber, and in part to help you understand and change your own sporting habits where they have contributed to your injuries. I have tried to provoke you into thinking in a new way about these habits in order that you fully grasp the magnitude of their effects on your body, and hopefully generate sufficient motivation to change the ones that need changed. That motivation always remains the rate-limiting step!

The parts of the book that involve collating scientific and medical research about the injuries climbers suffer are inevitably quite intense. In places, when it comes to the details of specific conditions and injuries, it reads like a medical textbook. It has to. Digesting all the information you need to overcome your climbing injuries is not an easy task. I have tried to present the information as clearly as possible without oversimplifying the picture to help you make the most informed decisions possible.

This book is as much for healthy climbers as for those who have suffered an injury. In a nutshell, it is a guidebook for how to stay healthy throughout your athletic career. Much of what I write is applicable to other sports as well. It describes the problems people have in response to injuries, the limitations of the sports medicine resources commonly available to them, and what you can do to get around them. In other words, although there is some detailed advice on specific treatments in the later sections, it is a coaching book rather than a medical book. Sports medicine has focused too much on the 'medicine' part at times - treating symptoms at the expense of looking at causes related to the individual sport. Removing causes of sports injuries often needs very detailed understanding of the movement demands of a specific sport. This understanding requires both coaching and medical knowledge.

By far the most common injuries to climbers happen in the fingers and elbows, followed by the shoulders. The available research suggests up to 75-90% of climbers will get an injury at some point[1-3]. The data suggests that a career in climbing that spans over a decade or more may increase this probability even higher. Of the finger injuries we suffer, tears of the pulleys that hold our finger flexor tendons in place are the single most common of all climbing injuries[4, 5]. Strains of the finger tendon units are also quite common[6]. Various tendons around the elbow are commonly injured in climbers, especially at the bony processes (the epicondyles) on either side of the elbow joint[7]. These tendons are among the most vulnerable to injury of the whole body[8]. Climbers also commonly suffer injuries to the tendons and ligaments around the shoulder, which take many forms and have many contributing causes.

Our bodies are not well designed for the repetitive stress to small upper body muscle groups that modern climbing demands. The amazing adaptability of the body and its capacity to heal absorbs a lot of the punishment climbers throw at their upper bodies. Ultimately, however, many years of living beyond the restorative means of the body cannot be absorbed, and injury results.

Outside of this 'A' list of commonly injured joints, tendons and ligaments suffered by climbers is a huge list of potential injuries with more diverse and complex causes internal or external to our sport. These may be related to genetics, lifestyle, occupation, medical conditions and many other reasons. Many of the principles in sections 1-6 of this book will apply to dealing with these less common injuries too. However, with all injuries, the general principles of a healthy, athletic lifestyle must be used alongside extremely detailed and specific knowledge about the particular condition.

Such detailed knowledge about the full list of possible conditions fills many large textbooks and thousands of research papers, far too much to fit into this book. So I have limited this book to giving condition-specific detail to the common injuries experienced by climbers, which form the vast majority of cases. For those who arrive at a diagnosis of something less common, I've tried to provide as many resources as possible to find the information you need to complete your knowledge.

If you have recently picked up an injury, this book has lots of information that might give you clues to what your injury might be and the common treatments that are used. However, please don't use it as a substitute for gaining a professional diagnosis and treatment plan from a qualified sports medic, based on a thorough examination. The body is extremely complex and it is rarely possible for a non-medic to confidently exclude possible diagnoses. An example of this is nerve compression syndromes of the back and neck which mimic exactly the symptoms of elbow tendon pain.

Use this book as a supplement to your consultations with professional medical staff: sports medical doctors, orthopedic surgeons, physiotherapists and more. Take it with you and discuss your thoughts with them to arrive at a diagnosis and intervention that is well founded and specific to you and your sport.

Although this is not a medical book, it does refer to accepted and emerging practice in sports medicine based on peer reviewed scientific research wherever possible. In writing it I have consulted the most recent developments in the scientific literature to understand the pathology and efficacy of treatments for climbing specific injuries and sports injuries generally. Some of the ideas and treatments remain controversial and need further research to reinforce confidence in them. Some practices and treatments will be noticeable by their absence from this book. I have omitted these either because the scientific evidence for their efficacy is absent, equivocal or still very young. In future editions I will look again at these areas for further scientific evidence of their efficacy in the literature.

The real reasons you are injured

A failure is a man who has blundered, but is not able to cash in on the experience.
Elbert Hubbard

Not every injury could have been avoided. Possible contributions include genetic factors or accidents that could not have been foreseen. I will make the case in this book that although many sports injuries are extremely hard to foresee, repeated or prolonged injury problems are to a large extent either preventable or manageable. Moreover, even where injuries do have a component that was not under your control, there are likely to be other components of susceptibility which are. In this sense, if you are able to reduce the elements of susceptibility to injury, you may be able to absorb more of the accidents and mistakes that inevitably happen, without their consequence being a damaged or torn tendon. Even though injuries often seem to be an accidental misfortune, it is likely that the causes are things under your control. You just didn't know it.

Who does know all the factors that you could have

manipulated to prevent the injuries you have or have yet to pick up? No one. In the field of avoiding sports injuries, the full range of causes is rarely obvious even with the benefit of hindsight. However, we must work hard to find and influence as many of them as we can. We must tease them out of the patterns of symptoms and other bits of evidence we can gather from disparate sources.

When an injury happens, the prevailing culture in sport is to lament our misfortune, and then to treat the symptoms as best we can. In most cases, this is a totally inadequate response. Of course it is natural to be frustrated by the pain of an injury and its effects on our climbing. In fact this frustration is exactly the motivational fuel you need to see you through the challenge ahead. It is also necessary to address symptoms as they happen. But this is only for starters. There is a much more important task to address, and it's the bit that is missing from most climbers' response to injury.

Instead of cursing our misfortune and treating only symptoms, we should view our challenge to be a constant quest to unearth new areas of control with which we can manage the stress that sport puts on our body. This is a never-ending process that should begin as soon as possible after starting the sport and should continue before, during and beyond recovery from injuries. However, if you haven't been doing this so far, and you have suffered an injury or even a string of them, now is still the next best time to start!

If you follow sports in general you will surely appreciate that injury appears to plague participants of all levels and in nearly all physically demanding sports. It is a constant battle for both amateurs and professionals. Yet, with the might of modern science and decades of research and experimentation by athletes and coaches across so many sports, the spectre of injury has not diminished. Why should it? Sport by its very nature encourages you to find your limits. And it's at those limits where injuries will always happen. So rather than see injury in sport as a menacing hurdle you hope you never run into, any serious sportsperson must accept its omnipresence at the limits of our performance and learn to live with it, to steer through its hurdles and find the opportunities within it

to learn new things about sporting performance. In a sense, the game of learning from injury to remove its causes is one of the core skills of success in sport.

So what are these hidden, injury-causing factors that lie within our control? Arguably the most important, in climbing at least, is movement technique. Above everything else, the movements we repeatedly perform are those that most directly determine how tissue wear and tear occurs. In any mechanism that does manual work against resistance, damage occurs. In human muscle and tendon, microscopic damage occurs every time we climb. The amount of damage that occurs relates to several different technique-dependent components: maximum force, duration of loading, rate of force development and the mode of contraction (i.e. muscle shortening or lengthening). The efficiency of our positioning and movement on the rock, and the rate of movement errors, determine how much and how hard we can climb before a given level of tissue damage occurs. In other words, with better technique we can climb more and cause less damage. Moreover, an awareness of how our climbing moves are placing strain on our bodies is also important in protecting ourselves from injury by helping us to respond to avoid excessive strain. We might not be able to find a way of doing a move without a really aggressive or awkward pull on a hold, but an awareness that this is a high risk, tendon-crunching move helps us restrict the number of times we attempt it and be ready to let go instantly if the move goes badly. In section 3, I explore the ways in which we can adjust our movements and habits to reduce the wear and tear we suffer from climbing. But the first step is to tune into this channel of body awareness. Climbers generally are not nearly tuned in enough, especially the young ones who have not yet learned the hard way.

Here are a few more factors that affect injury susceptibility, explored in more detail in the following sections of the book:

- Training schedule arrangement/load
- Posture
- Lifestyle
- Diet & nutrition
- Equipment, especially rock-shoe choice

- Warm-up
- Variety of climbing terrain
- Social/competitive environment
- Ambient temperature during climbing
- Body temperature during climbing
- Flexibility
- General stress level
- Activities outside climbing (e.g. your job)

The above list is far from exhaustive, but demonstrates the number and diversity of different variables contributing to or reducing the overall stress on your body through your regular climbing, as well as determining how that stress is spread. If you do not give attention and planning to these factors, you are on a fast track to injury.

In summary, many injuries are the result of failure to accept the likelihood of injury in sport, failure to spread the stress on the body and failure to spot and respond to causes of stress build-up that result in damage.

Stress and injury

Health is when every day it hurts in a different place.
Faina Ranevskaya

Stress is the basic currency of both injury development and healing. In the field of sport and sports injury, stress has a number of different meanings. It is the physical stress placed on a particular tissue by the climbing we do, such as an elbow tendon. It is also the total physical stress placed on all the body parts and physiological systems by our climbing load. It can also include the general psychological stress we absorb through non-climbing aspects of our life. All of the above components of stress are important because they are, to an extent, interdependent. How does this happen?

One measure of stress is the amount of force absorbed by a tissue per unit time. Forces from our body movements create stress by directly damaging the tendon tissue, usually at a microscopic level. The effort of creating the movements themselves, as well as the repairs needed to the tissue afterwards, uses energy and other biological resources, which is also a stress. When we train hard, or just harder than we are used to, there is elevated stress at both the local level in the tissue (repairing the microscopic damage) and the global, whole body level.

Whole body stress is complicated in nature and causes the body to respond on several different levels. The body's general response to stress is managed partly by hormones, such as the general stress hormone cortisol. Cortisol, along with several other hormones, organises and triggers the vast number of biological tasks that must be done to recover from strenuous physical activity such as restoring muscle fuel stores and rebuilding damaged cells. Cortisol is also released as a direct response to the psychological stress we place on ourselves in our work, relationships or difficult learning.

It is really important that we experience the physical and mental cues of tiredness and soreness caused by this general stress response; they remind us that we need a rest to recover. Both psychological stress and the physical stress of sport or training act together (to an extent) at the whole body level to determine how much of an overall stress response the body must make. In this way, the capacity of a particular tissue or biological function in the body is affected by stresses of seemingly disparate areas of our lives. So while a muscle or tendon may be able to absorb a given stress load from the training we do if that was all there was to it, the effect of other life stressors can contribute to the breakdown of the tissue.

Injuries, or at least the potential for them, tend to develop either when the global level of stress, or the local stress on a particular tissue, becomes elevated above the level from which we can recover. In other words, when we are living beyond our means to absorb the stress of our activities. That stress can be instantaneous, such as when the acute force of a strong muscle contraction is simply too high or sudden and the muscle or tendon tears. It can also be gradual degradation of tissue from chronic misuse, or a mix of the two: chronic degradation followed by acute tearing during a contraction that healthy tissue could have absorbed. It follows that once injured, the capacity for the injured tissue to absorb stress is reduced, usually by a large amount. Recovery only happens when the stress level on that particular tissue is also reduced to a level that the body part can cope with.

Although excessive stress causes injury, training stress is also the driving force of protection against injury, both by adaptive strengthening of the tissue before injury and healing and rehabilitation afterwards. In the science of training, the most fundamental law underlying physical adaptation is that of 'progressive overload'. The body improves by getting stronger, fitter or more skilled when the relevant stimulus is just a little more that it is used to. It follows that there is an optimal level of overload of training stress. Too little and nothing happens, or fitness goes backwards. Too much and the body cannot recover quickly enough and improvement stalls. In exactly the same way as the training stress affects improvement, it also affects both the potential for injury and the rate at which existing injuries recover or worsen.

Thus, the goal of any sportsperson who wishes both to increase their performance and sustain a long sporting career is to maximise the stress placed on the body to create maximum adaptation, yet to avoid overloading any one tissue to the point of injury. Inevitably, however, each body part is loaded with training stress differently and also responds slightly differently to a given level of stress. So it is necessary for the climber to take careful note of how each joint or muscle is coping, and to respond by spreading the stress appropriately. Extra effort must be given to increase the stress-absorbing capacity of the weakest tissues to maximise the overall capacity of the whole body to absorb training stress. This can only be achieved by measuring and monitoring feedback from each body part or system involved, as carefully and objectively as possible. However, because this task is so hard to do, it is arguably the toughest part of achieving a long career in sport. The most resilient sportspeople achieve what they do because they are the masters of this never ending game of monitoring, estimating and reacting to every clue they are given about the changing state of every area of their physiology. The tools they use for this science and art are their hard won knowledge, together with intuition and feedback from the body. The

rest of the book aims to help you become a master of this.

The reason you are still injured

Insanity: Doing the same thing over and over again and expecting different results.
Albert Einstein

We've established that climbing injuries rarely come out of the blue, caused solely by an unavoidable accident. Even though the onset of symptoms may be instantaneous, such as a finger pulley rupture, the underlying susceptibility has roots that started long before, often years before. In some well developed sports with a good coaching network and well established training protocols, it is today possible to identify some of the risk behaviours for injury in sufficient time to prevent them reaching the symptomatic level. However, climbing is certainly not one of these sports. The components of good climbing movement for performance are only just becoming understood in our sport. Knowing exactly which movement styles, training practices or particular schedules that either reduce or amplify long term injury susceptibility is largely beyond us at the time of writing. Thus, the first hint that we have overstepped what our bodies can handle comes when it is too late: the damage has already occurred. Too late to prevent the initial injury, and sometimes too late to prevent a long road back from what might be substantial tissue damage. But it is never too late to use the opportunity to investigate and attempt to correct the source of the susceptibility.

It is worth noting here that we are not necessarily attempting to eliminate the use of risky training methods or certain climbing moves. Every aspect of climbing lies somewhere along a continuum of risk for contributing to injury. Moreover, for experienced climbers well adapted to the demands of training, the more aggressive forms of training are chosen precisely because they can bring larger gains, as well as larger risks. The awareness of these risks and how they affect the body as the climber moves through a training programme allows them to be offset by improved quality of recovery and careful progression of loading. Aggressive training can be undertaken safely if it is offset by good planning and recovery. So it is not necessarily the training to blame; it may be down to its timing and the provision of a matching recovery programme.

In well developed professional sports, it is often the role of a professional athlete's coach to gather information about the timescale, location, type and severity of tissue damage. They use this to piece together a case for altering the athlete's game in order to speed recovery and reduce the risk of the injury recurring.

Outside of high level professional sport, this type of investigation rarely occurs. It cannot, because it requires a great deal of highly specialised knowledge and an intimate knowledge about the background and overall game of the athlete. Even within well organised and well funded sports, such as professional football, an underlying susceptibility may be identifiable but may not be acted upon. There may be short term financial or team pressures or a view that the athletes are a commodity to be used in a way that best suits the financial bottom line. But that's another story! Climbers don't usually have to think 'short term' like this (the route will still be there), but they sometimes do.

Sports injury recurrence rates are too high, often because the cause has not been removed. This is a huge area of inadequacy within sports medicine at all levels. It is partly down to the highly complex nature of the causes themselves, the difficulty in measuring them and the lack of sufficiently detailed knowledge in sports such as climbing to be able to pinpoint the causes. However, I think it is also partly down to some avoidable flaws in how we approach sports medicine, and how sports medicine approaches us. It is a problem that the sports medicine field recognises, and urges that sportspeople themselves take ultimate responsibility for sourcing a wide range of support from the numerous links in the sports medicine chain. Furthermore, sports medics recommend that wherever possible, practitioners seeing a sportsperson work together, or someone (ideally the sportsperson themselves or their coach) acts to understand and coordinate advice and treatment coming from different sources. These failures of the sports medicine system

for all but the best supported, usually elite athletes, has several components which I will explore in the next two parts.

The language problem

Some of the terms we use to classify and describe common injuries set us up for making poor rehabilitation choices. The most obvious of these is the term 'overuse injury'. 'Overuse injury' has evolved to be a blanket term among those treating or writing about sports injuries to set these injuries apart from 'acute' injuries such as those caused by direct trauma or from a sudden accident. It's a complicated picture because the two broad types of injury can overlap.

For example, an overuse injury in the supraspinatus tendon of the shoulder, slowly becoming weakened and diseased by impingement of the sub-acromial space over months or years may be producing little or no pain and no effect on sport performance. Then, a particularly 'shouldery' move on a hard boulder problem causes the weakened tendon to rupture completely, taking on the symptoms of an acute injury: sudden and severe pain, swelling and complete loss of ability to perform. The reverse situation can also occur. An acute rupture of an previously healthy finger pulley caused by a sudden foot slip while pulling on a small pocket requires a lay-off and very gradual return to hard climbing. If the climber progresses too quickly, the partially healed pulley will start to suffer accumulation of scar tissue and various other tissue changes that lead to the chronic pain and weakness symptomatic of an overuse tendon injury.

For those practising sports medicine or who are familiar with how the terms have developed and are used, it may not be a great problem. However, for those who have just been injured and have no familiarity with sports medicine language and literature, terms like 'overuse injury' can contribute to poor diagnosis or treatment decision making. The word 'overuse' itself suggests the logical solution: use it less. However, the cause of the injury may not be overuse at all. It is true that the tendon itself may have been overloaded with training, although even this idea is being challenged by studies that suggest the mechanism of tendon damage in certain injuries may be more complicated than this[9-11]. It may be the case that the tendon could have handled this amount of loading if the pattern of loading (the training schedule) had been different, the warm-up had been different, the training environment had been different or the recovery had been different. If so, a more accurate term would be 'misuse injury'. Also, by focusing the mind on the loading of tissue only during training, the term also leads sufferers away from awareness of underlying susceptibility factors which may drastically reduce the capacity of a given tissue to absorb training stress.

An important early message of this book is to be aware that the causes of injuries in climbing or any sport may be extremely complex and to beware of simplifying them just because the injury is classified using certain language. Although it is primarily a problem for sportspeople not at all familiar with the world of sports medicine, it can also lead to poor quality advice from practitioners we encounter at the interface with the world of sports medicine. Often, our first port of call for information might be our general practitioner (GP), or articles online or in magazines compiled by journalists rather than sports medicine specialists. 'Specialist' is really the key word when embarking on your search for a good diagnosis and for advice about injuries from climbing. The following section demonstrates why this is so important.

The practitioner problem

When all you have is a hammer,
everything looks like a nail.
Bernard Baruch

In our sporting careers, most of the highly specialised knowledge we tend to digest relates to improving performance; it is sports science. The most striking thing about sports science, especially for the amateur athlete attempting to improve their level, is the diversity of these fields of knowledge. Climbing is a great example

of this, with an immense array of technical, tactical, physiological and psychological variables influencing how far we get. In my previous book *9 out 10 Climbers Make the Same Mistakes*, I described how difficult it was to give an appropriate weighting of time, effort and importance to each, and how our natural tendency is to focus too much on the factors we are good at, or of which we have existing knowledge.

In dealing with injury in sport, whole other worlds of specific expertise are opened up that allow us to take optimum control over the direction of our recovery and return to normal activity. These include physiotherapy, medicine, manual therapy, surgery and technique correction. In these new fields of required knowledge, the same problem exists: a bias towards the readily available expertise, at the expense of the rest. Let's see how this works out in practice.

When climbers first notice an injury, such as a painful finger following a pulley tear during crimping, they are most likely to visit their family doctor (GP) as they would for most other health issues. The problems begin there because the objectives and expectations of the GP and the climber are not the same. The climber feels that this injury is a serious problem and one that requires an optimal and immediate response regardless of the effort or cost implications. In other words, they are ready to do whatever it takes to get better and expect the advice or treatment given to reflect this. However, the GP's point of view may be very different. In their view, the climber's finger injury is not serious compared to what they are used to, may resolve itself in time with minimal input of medical treatment or therapy and does not present a serious threat to the health and fundamental wellbeing of the climber (i.e. they can still work, and function in daily life). However, the mismatch of expectations often goes unnoticed because it is not discussed. The climber simply trusts their doctor to supply optimal advice and treatment on any medical matter, while the GP may assume that the climber does not expect or even wish to be treated as aggressively as a professional athlete would.

I remember this situation well from my first visit to my GP for a pulley tear at age 17. I was advised, as still is the common prescription today, to take 6 weeks off climbing and take some ibuprofen. Naturally, I returned for a second visit immediately after the 6 weeks was up to discuss with the doctor the seemingly imperceptible progress, and what we could try next. The shock and dawning understanding of being flatly advised to 'try another sport' would have been hilarious if it didn't cut so deep!

Immediately after this experience I realised I had to take control of my own recovery with direct access to the world of sports medicine knowledge. However, although specialist advice in different fields of sports medicine is accessible, choosing between them or balancing their use is a difficult task. Surgeons tend to discuss surgical solutions, physiotherapists describe exercises involving bits of elastic and weights, pharmacists discuss the efficacy of different drug treatments and others see the problem in terms of sticking needles in the right places, massaging knots in muscles or just thinking positively.

What is conspicuously missing when consulting or reading the work of experts in any one of these specialised fields are examples of them pointing athletes in the direction of another specialism. Of course, in certain fields there may be a commercial interest at its source. If you hire a private sports masseur they are unlikely to tell you to go away and see the physiotherapist because they feel they could probably treat you on their own. However, sometimes the reverse can also be true. In many medical or sports medical situations, it is in the vested interest of the practitioner that you go out of the door for the last time as quickly as possible. So what's going on?

The problem is simply that specialists in one area of treatment tend to act out the focused area of their skills and are unlikely to think outside of this for you. In other words, they neither act as managers for the whole picture of your treatment themselves, or check that you or someone else is managing the treatment plan. In professional sport, a sports medicine doctor, physiotherapist, coach, massage therapist and possibly others would ideally meet to plan and manage your treatment response together. In amateur sport (i.e. virtually all climbers) *you* have to manage it yourself. This creates an odd situation. You gain portions of advice and treatments from a range of expert sources around

you. Yet you as the amateur climber, often with little knowledge of how to manage or optimise the response, must weigh up all the different options and priorities for treatment.

When you see your GP, they often simply don't tell you that you'll only receive a fraction of the advice or treatment from them that could make a difference to your outcome. The sports medic might not tell you that a cortisone injection is only one of many treatment options and she is only providing it because that what she's used to doing. Few of the common fields of sports medicine expertise are likely to inform you of recent developments in the other fields, or to explore any underlying susceptibility that might negate the effectiveness of any therapy you are getting.

Unfortunately, it may well be that they fail to offer up to date and comprehensive advice because they are simply unaware of how knowledge from research has moved on. Consider this shocking quote concluding the review of the 2012 International Scientific Tendinopathy Symposium, published in the British Journal of Sports Medicine[12]:

"Achieving evidence-based treatment of tendinopathies is a significant challenge. A compelling example is the persistent use of corticosteroid injections for lateral elbow tendinopathy. In general, it takes approximately 17 years to get 14% of research findings adopted into practice. Moreover, only 30–50% of patients receive recommended care, 20–30% receive care that is not needed or that is potentially harmful and 96% may receive care with the absence of evidence of effectiveness."

This is not necessarily an indictment of each of the sport medicine channels that you might find yourself in contact with. It is merely a natural consequence of their partially independent standing from each other. Moreover, the complexity of the research picture is ever increasing and the resources of medical staff to update their knowledge and thus optimise practice may be stretched. So what should you do about it? Well, I hope that this book will help you gain enough knowledge to at least be aware of the types of interventions available to you for common climbing injuries, so that you can explore each one energetically. In addition to educating yourself on the full range of avenues you might pursue for dealing with your injuries, I hope it will also give you a sense of the relative importance of each, so you know which ones to prioritise.

Unless you are lucky enough to find a therapist, sports medic or mentor with enough specific knowledge about climbing, the first 'take home' message of this book is to recognise that you alone must take overall control of managing your response. That is, exploring, researching and prioritising the full range of possible interventions or treatments. Bear in mind that specialists in any one field may only be able to provide a small slice of the advice and help you need. Try wherever possible to quiz the specialists you do see on what other interventions they would advise. Ask "Who else should I be seeing?" It is quite possible that you will get some really useful advice and contacts that they otherwise might have assumed you either knew already or didn't have access to. Or perhaps they were too busy simply acting out their own field of expertise to talk to you about the whole picture of your rehabilitation response. You are the manager of your injury - it is up to you to squeeze every piece of advice you can from the resources you have.

The sports medicine problem

The sports medical care of athletes is often wrongly assumed to comprise simply the immediate treatment of injuries and of systemic medical problems.
Dr Jacques Rogge -
International Olympic Committee President

The above quote is the first sentence of the rehabilitation volume of the *Encyclopedia of Sports Medicine*[7]. For the authors to lead this text with such a fundamental problem in the scope of sports medicine is illuminating. Yet it so often seems that the limitations of sports medicine in terms of keeping athletes healthy does come down to this problem more than any other.

The trouble is that sports medicine bridges so many fields of expertise. Successful prevention and recovery from sports injuries depends on many of the same fields as mainstream medicine, but with the additional sport specific fields of biomechanics, coaching, sports science and sports therapy, among others. At the Olympic level of professional sport, in well funded countries, collaboration between the practitioners across these disciplines in well organised sporting institutions does exist. This is the cutting edge of sports medicine. But if you are reading this book then it is likely that this level of interface with the world of sports medicine is well out of your reach.

At a push, the vast majority of sportspeople access one or two experts in sports medicine. For those people, the nature of the 'sports medicine' they receive is only part of the picture. Usually, it is the most urgent part - treating the symptoms: a course of anti-inflammatory drugs, a battery of stretching and strengthening exercises to improve the health of the damaged tissue and possibly some manual therapy of one kind or another. Sometimes, if the specialist has more time with you and has good knowledge of climbing, you might discuss the underlying causes and avenues for reducing the risk of having a susceptibility sabotage your rehabilitation. For most of us, this is a best-case scenario.

If you go down the self-help route of researching rehabilitation options for your injury on the internet or through sports medicine books, the focus of the information you find is likely to be even more skewed towards merely treating the symptoms of your injury. It is through this limitation of the way amateur sportspeople access sports medicine that many rehabilitation programs are needlessly lengthened, or fail altogether in the long run.

It is understandable how this problem arises. Much of the science of muscle, soft tissue and bone injury and rehabilitation is transferable across sports generally. Many sports have similar injuries and documented treatment protocols that can be adapted across sports. Medical information about treating symptoms simply spreads more easily among therapists and athletes. Conversely, information about underlying susceptibilities are often very specific to a given sport and involve subtle concepts of movement style and training design. It is often the coaches and experienced elite athletes in those particular sports who hold this knowledge. But this experience is less often written down than the medical aspects of treating symptoms. Undoubtedly, this is due both to the fact that these more subtle concepts are harder to research than, say the effect of a drug treatment, and to the fact that sports coaching knowledge is still passed down, at least in part, by word of mouth through generations of coaches and athletes.

A sport like climbing is even more vulnerable than most sports. It is not big enough to support either detailed research into the patterns of injury occurrence, or have a strong enough coaching structure to ensure that sport specific knowledge is disseminated throughout the sport. The other problem is that it is simply a relatively young sport and there hasn't been time to learn from the mistakes of generations of hard-training climbing athletes before us.

So right now, our task as climbers is first to recognise that we must develop our own sense of where the causes of our injuries lie, using whatever evidence is available or what can be deduced from medical, biomechanical, biological and other fields of science. We must do this at an individual level and as a community within our sport. The individual climber will significantly increase his chances of recovering from, or preventing, an injury by actively experimenting with different strategies which make sense according to the available science of the day. This process of teasing out potential causes and removing them is the missing link of sports medicine for amateur athletes in a small sport like climbing.

The missing link

As a result of the shape of sports medicine discussed above, removing or at least reducing the underlying causes of injury remains little more than an afterthought for many climbers. As a concept, it is poorly defined and extremely hard to know how to actually achieve. Our biomechanical understanding of climbing and its

effects on the body are at an embryonic stage. The later sections in this book are intended to give you as many clues as are available to manage it. However, the first point is the most important: the core of your plan to both prevent and overcome injury should be to reduce your underlying susceptibility to it.

If you read the research literature on the effects of treating symptoms of the sort of sports injuries that climbers get, such as degenerated or torn tendons and ligaments of the upper body, the common theme is the generally poor efficacy of the treatments. In the most recent textbooks concerned particularly with recovery from tendon overuse injuries, more and more emphasis is being placed on establishing the cause of the stress overload on the injured tissue[13, 14]. Removing the cause is steadily being recognised as a mainstay of the potential to rehabilitate many sports injuries, as well as prevent them.

The causes of overuse injury are likely to be a combination of poor technique, poor training schedule design, poor general care of your body (relative to the demands you are placing on it) and possibly issues with equipment. Section 3 of the book explores each of these in detail. Although they are described under a rehabilitation heading, they apply just as much in prevention. Your challenge is to isolate which among these common underlying causes is contributing to your injuries. It is the hardest challenge you will face in your climbing career.

Time, thought and effort into unearthing root susceptibilities to certain injuries, and devising ways to sidestep them, is always time well spent. Here are general ideas to consider and thus ensure you do not suffer from the missing link of an underlying susceptibility going unnoticed and sabotaging all your other treatment efforts:

- Seek to raise your awareness and tune in to each component stressor in your climbing. Innovate ways to change your routine to spread the stress more evenly.

- Get the opinion of the most expert climbing coach

you can possibly afford on what might injure you in the future or how you can change your technique, tactics, training or equipment to reduce or redistribute load on different joints and tendons in climbing. Even a few minutes of advice from someone with the depth of experience needed to see these root causes is rare and precious.

• Talk to another doctor, and another and another. The range of expertise and experience across medicine, sports medicine, physiotherapy and climbing coaching is huge. The more opinions the better. The effort (and potentially cost) of obtaining several opinions will pay off.

• Don't use a consultation with a single expert as a substitute for becoming one yourself. It's too risky. Become an expert yourself, as quickly as possible. Use your expertise to ask the right questions and say the right things when you do meet the expert. An expert working from a meeting a few minutes long, not knowing anything about you, can only achieve so much. Ideally the expert should only be filling in a few of the blanks for you. The probability of settling on a correct diagnosis and treatment plan will be vastly increased.

• If you think that you can recover from your injury and go back to the way things were - just expecting your body to work as you wish without problems - forget it. The luxury of doing your sport badly is over. The sooner you reorientate yourself to this way of thinking, the less time you will lose to injury in the coming years.

Exceptional use: the luxury of doing your sport badly

The art of living is not in eliminating but growing with troubles.
Bernard Baruch

The expectation that your body will put up whatever abuse you can throw at it is a luxury of youth. Almost everyone who has participated in sport for more than one decade will lament this. However, few take advantage of the conclusions that flow from this idea. First, there is a misunderstanding that during your youth, the body fully absorbs all the punishment of poor technique, lifestyle, rest, warm-up, etc, but then fails to do so as aging progresses. It is true that healing and recovery are lengthened with age, but generally later in life than a lot of people assume! What is missing is an understanding that many of the injuries that sportspeople like climbers tend to suffer in their late twenties and beyond are the result of the accumulation of damage done much earlier. In other words: just because you can't feel any symptoms of your body being mistreated now, doesn't mean that it's not happening. Hidden damage done now will show itself later.

A key point is that the onset of overuse injury symptoms is not the same as the onset of tissue damage. By the time microscopic damage is significant enough to reach the pain threshold, it may already be fairly advanced (Fig. 1.1). Even if a finger or elbow began to hurt during a particular session or after a single move that caused further damage, that tissue was likely to have been already weakened by damage caused many months or even years previously. Sports injuries are not just related to the inability of older bodies to recover from the immediate demands of sport. They are also related strongly to the accumulated damage caused over the whole length of your career.

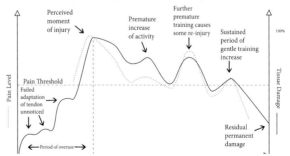

Figure 1.1 Typical progression of tendon injuries.

If your technique, training and care for your body is poor when you are young, that accumulation will reach the point of developing injuries sooner. There is ample circumstantial evidence for this by looking at climbers. Why are some climbers' careers cut short by injury in their thirties or earlier, while others continue to improve and reach their maximum level in their forties or fifties? Those climbers who do peak in their fourth decade of climbing are not always the ones who have been relatively injury free during their careers. In fact, the opposite is often true. Climbers who have suffered serious finger or elbow injuries *younger* than their peers can go on to have long careers. Why? Because the psychological pain of a serious injury teaches a young and fired-up climber an early lesson that the body is not invincible and they start to take better care of it.

Microscopic tissue damage that is occurring below the pain threshold is only part of the problem. The other part is the establishment of bad habits. Poor footwork, lack of warm-up, dependence on crimping or locking-off and poor nutritional practices are all habits of your game that tend to form quickly once you start climbing. The longer you have any of these habits, the harder they are to shake in the years to come. When the injuries that result from bad habits do eventually show themselves, you might be aware of their contribution to the injury, but find them too hard to substitute by then. It is more common that sportspeople subconsciously defend their habits and are reluctant to see them as causes of injury. Instead, they may overplay the effects of unpredictable accidents, like a foot slipping, as being the cause of the injury rather than merely the final straw that brought the damage to symptomatic level.

It takes a great deal of specific knowledge to recognise faults in posture and muscle balance. So it is totally natural that young climbers would be ignorant of these and of the subtle clues of accumulating damage to elbow or shoulders that is happening in the background. So go climbing with some good physiotherapists! It is also very hard to convince humans to change their behaviour before it becomes urgent. Health promotion campaigns have a difficult time convincing people not to smoke and drink to excess, and to have a better diet, in spite of the fact that these behaviours may send them to an early grave.

On the whole, encouraging people by trying to scare them about the future fails. However, within sport, the message will work for a few. That's because sportspeople, who take what they do seriously, are an unusual case. They tend to be more concerned than the general population about what will happen in 10 or 15 years' time. They know they love their sport and want to be able to hold on to it. So it is worth making this plea directly:

Recognise that hard sport is not 'normal' use of the body. Pushing your body's limits through a long career can be seen as an abuse of the body's physical reserves to adapt and cope with physical stress. These reserves of tissue plasticity and capacity to regenerate will absorb a lot of excessive training load and poor self-care, even for many years, if the stress is well spread out. But those reserves do have a limit and will run out unless you offset the damage.

So how can you offset the long term accumulation of tissue damage from years of climbing? Spreading the stress is one part of the answer. An even more important element is to better understand the relationship of training and recovery. Most sportspeople understand that increasing the training load increases the rate of adaptation. However, it is less well recognised that the recovery element of training can also be improved just as the training can. Increasing training load means either increasing training volume or intensity (or both) by an appropriate amount. Likewise with recovery. The effectiveness of recovery is dependent on the amount of recovery time, and what that recovery time is used for.

The term 'recovery' in training is often used interchangeably with 'rest'. Yet the act of taking rest days between training bouts is just one small part of the whole picture of recovery. Absorbing the exceptional stress that hard sport places on the body across your whole lifetime requires exceptional recovery (Fig. 1.2). Those who succeed at it are the ones who take the quality of the recovery as seriously as the training. As you progress in climbing and gradually increase the training load over the years, the volume of training tends to rise; you do more climbing every week. Therefore, the volume of rest

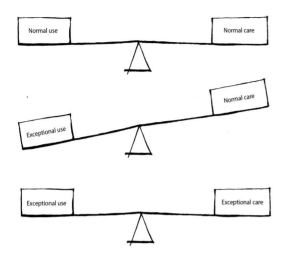

Fig. 1.2 Exceptional use, exceptional care.

must decrease. For many climbers, the intensity of the climbing also increases as you get better. So both the volume and intensity components of the training load are tending to increase as the volume of the recovery is decreasing. This is an increase in three of the four basic factors influencing the amount of stress. The fourth factor - the intensity or quality of the recovery - has to be maximised to protect the body against the tendency to accumulate tissue damage over time under these circumstances.

Those who understand this idea early in their sporting careers have a better chance of avoiding injuries and dealing with them when they occur. However, most of us will only ever learn the hard way, only making a positive effort to spread the stress of sport and increase the quality of recovery when the urgency of chronic injury demands it. For this majority, climbing success in future years is dependent on the speed at which you realise that the ways of your youth, thrashing yourself and never really giving injury prevention or good recovery much thought, are over.

The youthful sense that your body can absorb and recover from anything you throw at it feels great. Letting this go and realising it was really an illusion is

very hard. The practicalities of doing so are one thing, but the psychological shift to seeing your body and its limitations differently does present its own challenge. It is essential to attack this head on. I will deal with this more in the coming sections of the book. For now, let's discuss how to think about preventing injuries generally.

Prevention

There is a fundamental problem with attempting to lead an injury-free sporting career at the highest performance level you can. You are constantly trying to find your physical limits and extend them. Yet, at those limits lie the potential for injury. So in pursuing sporting improvement we are constantly trying to get as close as possible to the potential for injury to occur, without it actually happening. Given that we do not have all the available information to achieve this without some guesswork, is it not inevitable that injuries will occur? I think it is fair to say this is true.

Research on injury prevention suggests that the incidence of sports injuries may be reduced by over 50% through preventative action, although the data supporting this assertion is very limited. Prevention seems to be even more effective in reducing the recurrence of previous injuries. Why is this? On one hand, a previous injury in a given tissue predisposes you to a higher risk of that injury recurring. However, you are much more likely to be able to take preventative action because it has given you some specific information about the areas that are accumulating stress to an unsustainable level.

The strategies to reduce the risk of injury occurrence are very similar to those for rehabilitation, since the primary objective of both is to remove the cause of injury. These should include technique correction, encouraging optimal posture and balance of muscular strength, improved training schedule design, thorough warm-up and adjusting your climbing to take account of your recovery state and the climbing conditions. The last two factors are basic elements of good sporting practice that should be practiced diligently throughout your career, even when it's tempting to shortcut them for immediate gratification during a climbing session. The other factors need more work to implement because they require individual feedback and monitoring over time with very detailed knowledge of what to look for in each individual. Section 3 will deal with each of these in detail. My point in this section relates to motivation.

It is hard to motivate oneself to put effort into prevention of something that hasn't happened yet, even if you have previously suffered the frustration of an injury. The lure of the short term is too strong. The vast majority of us will need a positive motivating factor in order to actually make the changes we need to.

The heartening point is that prevention of injury by learning good technique, posture and training practice also helps your climbing directly. Rather than being a distraction from getting on with your climbing in the here and now, it is just another angle in your quest to improve. Most of the sources of information on preventative measures for injury can be found in the same places as training and performance advice. Indeed, much of section 3 of this book also works as a climbing improvement text! You should view your injury prevention activities as another side to climbing improvement rather than a necessary chore that gets in the way of enjoying the sport.

Your visit to the doctor's

Whoever you decide to see about your injury, a large part of the success of the precious appointment time comes down to what you do to prepare for it and what you say during the meeting. You need to absolutely make the most of any expert source of advice to ensure you get the accurate diagnosis and treatment plan that is so essential to your future of healthy climbing. Here are some fundamental pointers for seeing a professional. In order of importance:

- Actually go and see them! - Putting it off because of laziness, ignorance or even cost is downright

crazy. Seeing a decent sports medicine doctor for a diagnosis and treatment plan is rarely as expensive as you may fear. In some cases it might be highly useful to seek out the world expert in that particular type of injury and that might cost more. But even then, the psychological pain saved per £$€ you have to earn makes it totally worth whatever extra work you have to do to save up for it. As you will see in section 3 of this book, much of the therapy that actually works on sports injuries can be done by yourself, at home. So in most cases, only the first visit is really crucial. Of course, if you can see an expert for subsequent appointments, then do it. But don't miss out the crucial first visit for the diagnosis and treatment plan. If the cost of a private consultation may be a prohibitive factor, at least make sure you find out how much it really is, rather than assuming it would be extremely expensive. It way well be less than a night of drowning your injury sorrows in the pub.

- See the right person - Your family GP is not a sports medical doctor. You need advice from a sports medical doctor, or at least a very good sports physiotherapist. Most cities have private sports medicine clinics which vary in quality and areas of expertise. In the UK it is often possible to get a consultation with a sports physiotherapist through your local NHS GP clinic. A potential problem is that they may not be familiar with the types of injuries climbers get and may not always be on top of emerging developments in the field of rehabilitation. So it can be a gamble, but it is certainly a good starting point if you can be seen within a few days. However, unless you live in the right area, it is more likely to take many weeks to be seen. You can't afford that kind of wait. If you can't be seen within a few days, go for a private consultation first and see the NHS physiotherapist whenever your referral comes around, for a highly useful second opinion.

- See a better person - Once you have homed in on a diagnosis, your job is to track down the most detailed and current knowledge there is on this injury and emerging rehab protocols. In your reading, look out for the names of the leading authors of the research papers on your injury. Often, the leading expert runs a sports medicine clinic. If that is the case, do whatever you can to go and see them. It will be worth the travel and cost involved. The same goes for the 'coaching' side of your rehabilitation. Find the best authority on climbing technique there is. If you can possibly afford it, go and get a session with them. They will be able to spot in a few short hours the technical errors that caused your injury that most coaches wouldn't notice in a lifetime. Climbing coaching is a rapidly emerging profession and many climbing walls now offer climbing coaching. However, the experience of the coaches is extremely variable. Addressing movement technique to remove causes of injury is a highly skilled task and you should seek out the best skills you can. If I were injured, I wouldn't even gamble on coaching advice from a coach without an excellent track record and great experience.

- Set the parameters - Understand that the specialist you see might not have the same goals for your treatment as you do. Assume the worst - the specialist may think that you won't have the discipline to carry out the rehab programme to full recovery (which may be true) and so may lean toward lowering your expectations and to drug treatments instead. That's another problem we'll come to later in the book. The mismatch of treatment goals between you and the specialist means you don't even get the chance to try the long, hard (but effective) therapy that works. So once you have the diagnosis and proceed to formulating a treatment plan, be crystal clear with them exactly how much it means to you to recover from this injury, and that you are after an aggressive rehabilitation programme, no matter what. At least then it will only be your fault when you don't have the discipline to stick to the rehab plan.

- Ask who else you should see - Remember that you are the manager of your rehab program. The specialist you see (let's say it is a physiotherapist) quite rightly sees themselves as one part of the whole picture of your rehabilitation. Yet they won't automatically check that you are exploring all the other avenues of assistance. Ask them who else they think you should be seeing too. Do they know any coaches in climbing who will be able to identify causes? What about specialists in treating that particular injury or giving particular types of therapy? If you don't ask these questions, not only to gain specific information but also to demonstrate your motivation level, you are risking receiving less than optimal treatment. The chances are that whoever you do see about your injury, you will only get one shot. So be prepared.

If you don't prepare suitably for the meeting, the waste of both of your time will be the least of your worries. It is the risk of misdiagnosis that is a real concern. Injuries from climbing can be hard to diagnose correctly even for a really good sports medic with specific knowledge of the upper body injuries climbers tend to get. Remember that the specialist may never have seen a climber before and is working from scratch to piece together the clues of exactly what is wrong with you. Help them out by describing in detail what kind of movements you commonly do in climbing and exactly what causes pain. Take along this book or notes or articles you find about the injury you suspect you have.

Summary

Take control of your recovery. Sports medicine is a complicated, fragmented industry. Unless someone is managing the many pieces of the jigsaw puzzle that includes different experts, treatments to take and blind alleys, you'll get lost. If you have a great coach or sports medic looking after all of this for you, hold on to them! For everyone else, start learning to be a sports medicine expert.

Know pain, or no gain

Section 2

Pain and how to read it

If you are involved in regular sport or training, injured or not, your relationship with physical pain, and an ability to track subtle changes in pain, is one of the most crucial skills you need to master in order to overcome and prevent injuries. Most of the time, pain is a highly useful and sensitive source of clues that inform our decisions in nearly all aspects of sport, especially the prevention and treatment of sports injuries.

As useful as pain is, it is difficult to use. Understanding patterns of pain coming from muscles, joints and tendons and using this to make good decisions about your training or rehab is fraught with complication, subtlety, subjectiveness and potential for misinterpretation. In this section I will discuss the various issues surrounding the use of pain as a tool for gathering information about the state of particular tissues in the body, and what this means for you.

The function of pain is to serve as an alert to danger of damage occurring, encouraging withdrawal from the noxious stimulus. Pain that carries on after an injury has occurred ensures that you pay attention to the damage, seeking treatment and protecting the injured part from further damage. In some situations, pain continues long after its usefulness as a protective agent has become redundant. Such persistent pain highlights the complex physiology of how pain is mediated in the body, and the link to our psychological state and environment. In fact, the exact mechanisms of how pain is experienced and modified by stimuli are still poorly understood[15].

An amazing feature of pain is how it relies on context. We feel pain depending whether or not the brain decides that pain is appropriate, given the situation. In fact, the alarm signals coming from nerve endings near the site of the pain are only one of many inputs that the brain uses to decide what feelings of pain are appropriate. Here are some curious examples of this[15]:

- In battle situations, there are numerous stories of soldiers who have suffered violent limb amputations during explosions, but report feeling little or no pain at the time. There are even cases of war veterans discovering bullets lodged in their chest during routine x-rays, decades after they were shot in battle. They had no idea they were there.

- Acupuncture works best when performed by a Chinese man, on a Chinese woman, in China. It is least effective when performed by a non-Chinese woman, on a Chinese man, outside of China.

- Major surgery has been performed using only hypnosis for anaesthesia. Although the nerve endings in the tissue being sliced are still firing, the brain produces no pain.

- Many of us have suffered cuts that have not been painful or upsetting until we saw the bleeding.

- The shape of the pill influences how effective oral pain killing drugs are. Transparent capsules with coloured beads are most effective, round plain tablets are least effective.

Although we only have clues about the exact mechanisms of pain, three things are clear: the mechanisms are complex, they rely on many inputs and it is the brain which weighs up all these inputs before deciding the appropriate pain response. Have you noticed that young children who fall over tend to react by looking at their parents first before starting to scream? Their young minds haven't yet ingrained their pain reactions. External inputs other than the nerve impulses coming from the damaged tissue cannot be ignored in understanding the pain we feel. Another important observation that stems from this is that all pain is real. Moreover, it is not the same as anyone else's pain. The inputs that cause us to feel that pain can sometimes be faulty, so our goal is to identify and take account of the sources of faulty inputs to pain.

The importance of understanding pain takes on a further dimension when applied to sport. The ability to withstand or ignore the pain of physical exertion is considered a virtue of good athletes. It is true that in sport and training, we must frequently block out the pain of 'healthy' exertion. Yet new, unexpected or persistent pain from a body part gives us a crucial (and maybe the only) warning of more significant damage occurring. Ignoring this is one of the most dangerous and destructive things an athlete can do. Because of this complex relationship to pain, sportspeople can develop extremes of appreciation for pain. Some have trained themselves, often subconsciously, to block out pain of all types. These athletes can have a hard time noticing and managing injuries when they occur. Suppressing the pain of worn out skin on sharp holds or arms burning with lactic acid is useful in climbing. But it is hard to do this at the same time as listening for the early signs of tendon pain. Conversely, some athletes can become very focused on pain, tuning into every twinge and attempting to fit interpretations to it prematurely. This group also have a hard time managing injuries, often resting too much and suffering from tissue atrophy and a self-perpetuating cycle of lack of resistance to their activity and subsequent re-injury. So what is the right path?

Unfortunately there is no universal prescription for how to interpret pain. The number of variables involved, and our subjective sensitivity to pain inevitably leads to some error in the training choices we make based on pain signals. There are several important points in the next section that help to guide you in making good use of pain as a monitoring tool. But it is a never-ending road of learning from experience. Only through years of experimentation do you hone your skills in measuring, monitoring and interpreting pain signals from your own body. This is one reason why some older athletes, despite their disadvantages of age and past injury, can battle on through the decades of body punishment alongside the younger generation - they get better at the game!

There is unlimited potential to outsmart your former youthful, gung-ho self.
Neil Gresham

Seeing the patterns in your pain

Normal physical exertion in sport is often painful. Fatigued muscles during hard exercise hurt from accumulation of the acid by-products of metabolism.

After you finish a hard day of climbing or training, muscles hurt in recovery from microscopic muscle damage. Thankfully, muscle soreness resolves very quickly, in a few days at most. It is also normal in training to cause very minor strains in muscles and tendons from time to time because of particularly aggressive moves or a technical error such as a foot slipping. This causes tenderness and soreness during movement that might last a little longer. For example, if you are training regularly then you might be aware of a minor strain for a couple of weeks, which gradually dies off with each successive training session. These short term 'niggles' are part and parcel of training. It is not really possible to train hard and avoid them, although the goal is to minimise them and prevent them developing into a longer term injury. The athlete with no niggles at all for a sustained period is likely either bad at noticing niggles or undertrained.

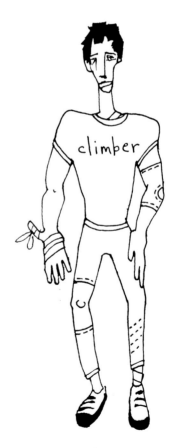

Fig 2.1 It's just a niggle.

While we do need to tune into and monitor everyday fatigue and niggles in muscles and joints, we don't need to worry about them constantly. They simply help to inform our training decisions and regulate how much we do, just as our appetite regulates our eating.

Essentially, all effective training microscopically injures the tissues being exercised. Both muscle and tendon respond to controlled exposure to micro-injury by adapting to the overload. The process is accompanied by some pain, so it is not really whether pain is present or not that is our clue for monitoring injuries. Rather, we have to monitor the patterns of how pain changes. We must learn to 'read' a complex interplay between the training, and the exact location and timing of the pain it provokes in our bodies.

The job of constantly reading the pain feedback from our training activities is just as important in health as it is once an injury has occurred. When a slow-onset injury occurs, we can deal with it earlier if we are constantly on the lookout for signs of a focal overload in one particular joint or tendon. Simply registering that a shoulder feels a little stiff and sore following a training session isn't enough to build up a picture of what is going on in that joint. How does that soreness relate to how the shoulder normally feels? Is there pain in other joints too? Is the nature of the pain different from normal feelings of discomfort after hard training, and how quickly is it changing compared to the post training soreness from other joints?

The objective of this close monitoring is to notice a developing injury as quickly as possible, so you can act before things get worse. You are trying to distinguish between the 'normal' and healthy feelings of soreness after a hard session or series of sessions, and more persistent, lingering pain, even if it is very slight. This is a difficult task. If there is no soreness, then little physical improvement may be taking place. So it is important not to be afraid to give yourself a good workout and really push your body hard if you want to improve. The amount of soreness you feel after hard climbing is not as important as noticing an unusual change in the pattern of pain in one joint or tendon.

However, to be able to notice abnormal pain, it is important to have a fine sense for what healthy soreness after training feels like. The amount of soreness that is healthy is very much dependent on where you are in your climbing development and what your schedule of training looks like.

What is healthy soreness?

When you are new to climbing or if you only climb a handful of hours a week with gaps of several days at a time, it doesn't take much to make your muscles hurt. After training, the mechanical damage to the contractile proteins arranged in muscle fibres gives us delayed onset muscle soreness (DOMS). It is the soreness you feel on the moment of getting out of bed the day after climbing hard for the first time after a break. The most extreme way to give yourself a good dose of DOMS is to run down a big mountain. That's because eccentric contraction (where the muscles lengthen under load rather than shorten) is a much more potent cause of the microscopic damage in muscle tissue that causes the pain. The sports science experiment to demonstrate this was when research subjects were taken separately to the top and bottom of a mountainside. One group was asked to climb it while the other was asked to descend. The subjects climbing the hill used more energy (doing work against gravity) but had much less DOMS in the thighs than the subjects going down hill[16].

However, although exercise involving eccentric contractions is a powerful cause of DOMS, any muscular work that is at an unaccustomed level will give us muscle soreness the following day. In mild cases, the soreness will die off by the end of the first day after the exercise that caused it. The muscles will be mildly uncomfortable if you prod them in the muscle belly rather than the tendons and joints, and even warming up for another training session might be enough to make the soreness dissipate.

More severe DOMS is caused by having a hard session after a complete lay-off of several days or weeks. It can leave the affected muscles feeling sore and stiff for up to five days, with the second day or even third day being the worst. It might sound strange, but this type of muscle pain is a 'friendly' pain. By this I mean that if you really needed to, you would be able to override it without the sensation of causing serious injury to your body. For those accustomed to training, some mild DOMS between training sessions is almost comforting: it is a sign of the body being worked and changes happening within the muscles. The key features that distinguish DOMS from other types of damage are its location in the muscle belly and that if you take rest days, it will diminish steadily each day and be gone after around five days at most. Furthermore, the amount of DOMS will diminish after subsequent training sessions, unless you take another lay-off.

DOMS is to be expected after a break or a change in your training and isn't usually anything to worry about. Once you are well established in a block of training sessions, you may well feel no further DOMS at all. However, even if you are very fit and climbing regularly, you will still experience DOMS if you make even a small change to the content of your workout such as just going to a different crag or climbing wall, climbing with a different partner or on different types of holds. The subtle differences in loading on particular muscle groups are enough to provoke a little DOMS. You can actually use this to tell you if you are mixing your sessions up enough to keep providing fresh stimulus to the body. Or it can let you know if you are especially weak on a particular type of hold, move or rock type.

Persistent DOMS that refuses to settle over several weeks can be a flag that the body is not recovering fully between the sessions. It will often be accompanied by niggling aches and pains in tendons and joints, which stubbornly seem to hang on or get worse. This is not necessarily an error in planning the training. If you have built up to a high training load over many years and have your training plan and body monitoring well tuned, it might be deliberate in the short term to really squeeze out some extra training gains. But if you have these symptoms and are not really training at a high level, this could be a 'red flag' that the training is not having a positive effect. It could be that you have increased the training load

too quickly, or the quality of the recovery is not good enough, or both. It doesn't necessarily mean you have to stop, but it certainly provides a warning that the risk of developing an injury is high and you will need to make some adjustments and be extra vigilant.

As well as causing muscle damage, climbing is also hard on the tendons and joints of the upper body. Hard climbing sessions will often cause mild, transient soreness around the elbows, shoulders and finger joints. While this is certainly a marker of wear and tear occurring, it could be well within the body's ability to recover and to stimulate strength gains in the soft tissue (tendons and ligaments). Again, it is not so much the occurrence of mild soreness that we need to pay attention to but the patterns of it over time. Is one finger or elbow hurting more than another? Is this happening across several sessions? It is this persistence of low level symptoms in one place that let you know the area is unable to keep up with the demands on it, either because of poor training, or because some damage has occurred and the tissue is weaker.

Elite level climbers these days do a huge volume of training and manage to absorb this over many years. They have built up over time to this level of training and have increased their volume of climbing steadily, so the body has had time to adapt and cope with a schedule that would break anyone else if they were to attempt it without the same build up. They have also trained their ability to read pain patterns to an extraordinary level, so they are less vulnerable to making errors and can get away with training closer to their limits, with more soreness. Thus, building up to a high level in climbing is not just about preparing the body's physiology to absorb a lot of training, it is also in learning to read your body's cues so expertly that it becomes a 'sixth sense'.

The general soreness we feel is a useful basic measure of the demands we are placing on the body and how close we are to the line between what we can recover from, and injury. The more regularly you climb and thus the more intimately you get to know your body's subtle cues, the more reliable this measure becomes. The vast majority of people have quite a broken routine of training through the year, with unplanned breaks in activity due to busy periods or just not being motivated or organised enough to keep up a regular diet of training. That's normal, but it causes some problems.

After a break in training, the body is unaccustomed to the hard work and feels sore after training or climbing. Yet, we tend to follow our climbing habits as before without thinking about it. If you did 25 routes in a climbing wall session before, that's what you try to do now. Climbers tend to underestimate the effect of even a week of de-training on your ability to absorb hard physical work. The effects of a short period of de-training might be a little less if you have been climbing for many years, but will probably be more if you climb at a high standard.

The opposite situation is when you have had a good run of a few weeks of hard training. Your confidence is building, soreness is less noticeable and everything feels good. Yet this can cause you to take your eye off the ball and fail to notice a growing niggle. A good run of performance is exactly what you are doing your sport for. It is one of the best feelings you can have and it is important to enjoy it. Who wants to worry about injuries even when they are feeling on a roll? The best athlete is the one who can fully enjoy the good times yet maintain one eye on potential problems in the background. In a sense, this is keeping a cool head even when you are excited.

This monitoring of changes in pain from your climbing will eventually become more and more subconscious. You will barely know you are doing it. But it might take a couple of bad experiences with injuries to force you to consistently pay attention to the cues. Eventually, you should be able to keep a close mental note of changes in how your muscles and joints feel within sessions, between sessions and over the longer term through the whole climbing year. Some people will go further than this and keep a diary of how training aches and pains progress, usually as part of a training diary. In the age of phone apps to help you keep daily training notes, this has never been easier. If you are the type of person who likes to do this, then it will provide a valuable source of objectivity in how you perceive the health of your body. However, not everyone will benefit from such an approach. A badly kept diary is probably worse than none at all. You risk falling between two stools: neither having a complete written record nor honing your ability to keep mental notes.

Understanding your pain

Tuning into the signals coming from the body is crucial for spotting the warning signs of developing injuries. But once we've noticed pain, understanding a bit more about where it is coming from and its influences will help you to make decisions about what action to take.

As we've seen above, there are numerous inputs that potentiate or reduce pain sensations. Psychological and psycho-social influences on the pain we feel are increasingly recognised as being important components of pain[15]. In other words, certain situations, emotional states or social influences directly affect how much our injuries hurt. The ability of these external factors to influence our pain can be conditioned either subconsciously or even deliberately through training. Sometimes persistent pain is felt after the original tissue damage has cleared up, and this lingering pain has to be eliminated by psychological re-education (such as building confidence through graded exposure to the painful stimuli). Recovery status, general life stress, unfamiliar situations and painful memories of past accidents or injuries are all things that are known to potentiate pain. Rest, sleep, supportive environments and certain drugs are all examples of things that may reduce pain sensations. So it is difficult to judge the influence of these factors and get a good picture of the actual tissue damage at the injury site.

The more you rely on written records of these influences, and objective measures such as pain free strength of the injured tissue, scanning and examination with your therapist, the less likely you are to proceed at the wrong pace due to being over-or under-sensitive to any pain from the area.

Even the pain signals coming directly from the injury site can be amplified or inhibited before they actually reach the brain. A popular model of the way this occurs is the 'gate control theory' of pain (Fig. 2.2). Stimulation of the skin (heat, rubbing, etc.) around an injury site can inhibit pain signals on their way to the brain. Sensory nerves from the skin are linked at the level of the spinal cord to pain sensing nerves from the same area of the body. In other words, they 'close the gate' on these pain signals before they reach the brain and cause the sensation we feel. This type of control of pain is increasingly understood to be the mechanism by which massage and other manual therapies reduce pain. This is a crucial piece of understanding, as we can see that their effects are not down to an improvement in the health of the injured tissue itself, but rather as an interference with the pain signals coming from the damaged tissue. In this way, they have similarities to the action of analgesic medication.

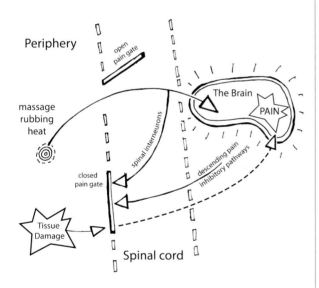

Fig 2.2 The gate theory of pain.

Sometimes pain from a sporting injury such as a damaged tendon can be fairly diffuse: a dull, nauseating ache that is hard to pinpoint. In other injuries, the source of the pain is much easier to pinpoint and feels sharper and more limited to a particular spot. This is down to the neural architecture of the way the body perceives pain. Pain from a location deep below the skin, such as

the brachioradialis tendon in the elbow, seems to cause more diffuse pain and the unpleasant, nauseating ache that is slow in onset during activity and slow to dissipate afterwards. By contrast, golfer's elbow tends to produce a sharper pain, easy to pinpoint during a deep lock-off move but will rapidly dissipate in mild cases if you relax the arm. It is important to bear this in mind when considering a self-diagnosis. It can be difficult to make an accurate guess about which structure is to blame for the pain felt. This underlines the importance of getting a thorough diagnosis from a good sports medic.

So, given all the difficulties in accurately linking pain to the health of tissue, when does pain from a tendon or joint become a concern? There is no clear answer. In noticing developing injuries early, all we can do is look out for pain that persists in one area longer than in other areas (such as the opposite elbow) or unusual feelings of pain or weakness that don't fit with what you can normally handle.

In rehabilitation of existing injuries, we must proceed carefully, tolerating only small amounts of pain and constantly monitoring to ensure that we are not under or overdoing our rehabilitation work. Although we are often advised to proceed at a level that does not provoke pain in a healing injury, recent research is highlighting some possible exceptions to this, thanks to new understanding of the physiology of damaged tendons. So it does depend on the injury in question. The later sections of the book discuss this idea in more detail with reference to specific injuries that climbers commonly suffer.

Going beyond reading only pain

The preceding sections emphasise the importance of tracking symptoms in emerging or existing injuries. This is a basic, pre-requisite skill for being able to recover from sports injuries and resume your normal level of training. To push your limits in sport, you don't just need to be proficient, you need to be a master of reading and interpreting pain signals. We don't merely want to prevent injury. We want to push as close to injury as we can get away with through hard training. And when injury does happen, we want to push the rate of recovery and return to training as fast as possible without tipping progress backwards. To do this, we must go beyond just monitoring pain.

Since rehabilitation often involves using agents that directly interfere with pain signals, so that we can progress with tissue strengthening exercises, we must account for the effect of these agents and develop a balanced view of how the level of pain relates to the actual state of the tissue health.

Just because your pain is reduced by analgesic treatments such as drugs, massage, ice or heat, this doesn't mean the injury is gone. They might allow us to go climbing or perform strength exercises in the immediate term, but we need to override our temptation to push harder than the damaged tissue can handle. Analgesic treatments do have their place in sports medicine. They can be essential in allowing us to break a cycle of chronic pain and poor movement patterns which are perpetuating an injury. We just have to be careful to account for their effects as we estimate the recovery status of injured tissue.

The difficulty of understanding all the inputs that give us clues to the actual recovery status of injured tissue is one of the most important reasons why people choose inappropriate interventions for their injuries and thus fail to recover. Commercial interests in the sports medicine industry, together with our emotional desire to find a quick fix, compound the problem. The fact that a treatment reduces pain leads to a potentially mistaken assumption that it actually promotes healing of the injured tissue. In the marketing for treatments or drugs which reduce pain or inflammation, the implied message is that without pain, you can exercise as normal. This may be true in the immediate term, but the possible consequence is further damage if the injured tissue is not ready. Obviously, tissue healing is the ultimate goal. Some analgesic treatments can help tissue healing indirectly, but they should not be relied upon. Generally speaking, their use lies in allowing us to perform more physiotherapy on the injury to make a real difference in the strength of the injured tissue, and correcting faulty movement or pain sensitivity patterns.

So, as well noticing pain sensations and their patterns, we have to be able to place those sensations in a context of the many possible factors that may be influencing the level of pain relative to the actual status of the damaged tissue. The closer we can get to a good picture of the tissue damage, the more optimal our rehabilitation pathway is likely to be.

Some extra tips:

Call your answer-phone every day and
complain and moan about your life.
Listen to the tape at the end of the year.
Yoko Ono

- Support from family and friends isn't just essential to manage the practical issues of recovering from an injury (exercise withdrawal, laborious rehab schedules, etc.) but it can directly influence the amount of pain you feel. A sympathetic partner has been shown to lower pain thresholds. Share your frustration about your injuries. However, beware of tracking symptoms by verbally recording your daily pain symptoms with your partner *ad infinitum*. They may eventually lose patience and become less supportive when you need it most. It may be better for some to share a review of weekly or monthly changes you have recorded mentally or in writing. Don't forget to share when you feel good. Not only will it be welcome news for you and your family, but just publicly recognising your progress may help reduce the pain directly.

- Sleep on any pain judgement. Since pain relies so much on context, a pain signal that alarms you about a potential new injury or a worsening of an existing one can often be just a transient sensitisation. Experienced athletes normally learn this intuitively and keep a cool head until some time passes and they see a pattern forming that confirms an initial feeling. A 'twinge' one day that feels pretty bad may be forgotten tomorrow when the body has had a chance to get more sleep, a rest day, a break from stress or a change of scenery. It shouldn't be ignored, but neither should every little niggle terrify you. Most of us know athletes that have learned to become oversensitive and never say 'I feel good!'. This state of mind is not good for you in the long term. If you find that you have fallen into it, consciously focus on the positive. When a worrying twinge occurs, reserve judgement. If you find it has died away on your next session or the next week, notice it, feel happy and move on. NB: I'm talking about twinges and aches here. If something tears, feels sharply painful, or shows swelling, still reserve judgement, but quit the session and see a professional as a matter of course.

Summary

- The pain you feel is not necessarily proportional to the damage in the injury site.
- The actual state of tissue health is your crucial link to successful monitoring for prevention and choosing the correct pace of rehabilitation exercises.
- Only by listening to every clue coming your way about the changing status of the muscles and joints, will you be able to notice injuries in good time and nurse them back to health at the correct pace.
- Sometimes a pain relieving treatment is the right choice, but don't forget to account for their effects in your training/rehab decisions.
- The two extremes of a 'no pain, no gain' approach, and avoiding any pain are both likely to lead to problems with sports injuries. Instead, the successful strategy is to understand where the pain is coming from and what influences changes in it. Know pain, or no gain.

One dies of everything, mostly of living.

Frédéric Dard

Removing the causes of injury for prevention and treatment

Section 3

Are you only treating symptoms?

Arguably the greatest failing of modern sports medicine is that it has focused too much on treating symptoms. The reasons for this are, no doubt, complex. For example, the tendency for treatments to become popular where the focus is pain relief is almost inevitable, since the results are so immediate and gratifying for the injured athlete and the therapist. In some cases, there is also a potential commercial benefit if the treatment is unlikely to achieve permanent recovery on its own: the patient keeps coming back for more sessions! The weight loss industry is built around the same economics. The fact that most diet plans allow dieters to lose a little weight in the short term, only to almost universally fail to maintain the weight loss in the long term, means they are always ready to subscribe to next year's diet craze.

Of course treating symptoms has an important role in recovering from sports injuries. Immediate relief from pain allows the sportsperson to commence progressive physiotherapy exercises earlier, which is what stimulates a more complete repair than if it were left to heal on its own. However, pain relief and physiotherapy may well not be enough. This is because many sports injuries occur primarily as a result of an underlying susceptibility. Fail to address this, and your rehabilitation efforts are swimming against a tide that is constantly pulling you towards recurrence.

If you look at this simplistically, participation in the sport could be seen as the underlying susceptibility. Hence one answer to a sports injury is to stop doing the sport. Obviously, the sportsperson quite understandably considers this to be an absolute last resort. Readjusting our goals downwards in response to injury is the one variable we wish to avoid, at least in the long term.

So, we need to look in more detail, separating the component elements of the stress placed on the body from your sport. It is often possible to alter the aspects that are causing the build up of stress on one tendon or joint, without drastically reducing how hard we climb or train overall. This is both a science and an art, with much learning from past mistakes and previous injuries.

In recent years, parts of the physiotherapy profession have made a move from just treating symptoms, and have given more emphasis on removing the causes of injury[14]. One driver for this has surely been the inadequacy of many traditional therapies to achieve complete recovery and bring down appallingly high recurrence rates. At the same time, there has been more research implicating posture, muscle balance and technique in the occurrence of some injuries, and not just in sport. For example, work based manual tasks can be rigid and with little opportunity for workers to influence the movements they must perform. Many cases of tennis and golfer's elbow come from factory workers, who perform highly repetitive manual tasks in which the body positions and movements are imposed by the layout of the machinery or tools in the workplace[17]. Huge numbers of cases appeared to be resistant to traditional therapies such as lay-off, stretching, massage and TENS therapy, and large amounts of money were spent by companies on sick pay[18-20]. This situation fuelled research into improved equipment design and technique training in an attempt to prevent and reduce recurrence of work related injuries.

The ineffectiveness of traditional physiotherapy or medical intervention in treating both sport and work related musculoskeletal injuries has led to several shifts in the focus of physiotherapy over the decades. Today, treating symptoms is still recognised as an important part of the rehabilitation armoury, but it is not even the primary weapon. Let's see how things have changed.

According to Shirley Sahrmann, author of the landmark physiotherapy text *Diagnosis and Treatment of Movement Impairment Syndromes*, physiotherapy practice has shifted from seeing the painful tendon or joint as the underlying cause of the problem, to the dysfunctional movement patterns themselves as the cause of the pain: in effect, a reversal of the way we look at the development of sports injuries. In this sense, the injury is just an inevitable result of incorrect movement patterns, which themselves have a wide range of causes.

Traditional physiotherapy seeks to rest the injured tissue, allowing inflammation to settle, before proceeding to apply strengthening exercises that target the muscle-tendon unit or group in question. The presumed cause is often either simply an inciting event (i.e. an accident) or overuse. In fact, the term 'overuse injury' is still ubiquitously used as a classification of types of injury. On closer enquiry, this blanket attribution of the cause of slow-onset injuries to overuse doesn't stand up to scrutiny.

It is true that one high risk situation for injury is a tired athlete, having trained hard for a sustained period of time. But this is just one of many potential causes. Similar injuries are also common at the beginning of new periods of training, when the athlete is rested and fresh. If more time were given to building up, perhaps the body could handle the loading. However, even when great care is taken to prevent an overly rapid increase in the training load, injuries still commonly occur. So simply calling it 'overuse' is too simplistic. It is overuse only in the context of the current training status of the athlete, and any other underlying susceptibilities.

In both the above scenarios, the injury happens when the athlete feels otherwise well and other joints and tendons are pain free. If general overuse is the problem, why do injuries not more commonly appear simultaneously in several body areas? Why are they not accompanied by the other well-defined symptoms of overtraining? Some tendons become injured while others are not, even the same tendon in the opposite limb. In this situation, overuse may be an insufficient explanation.

The training volume may or may not be an important contributor to the injury. It is equally possible that the injured joint or tendon is a weak point in the body, less able to cope with training than the rest of the body for some reason. The training was certainly the trigger, but may not be the primary cause. In fact, the injury may have been developing for many months or years, with damage slowly accumulating at a level below the pain threshold.

The question to ask is "why could this area have become weaker or prone to injury in the first place?" Getting to the bottom of this question is the subject of this section of the book. The critical point here is that sports injuries may well have multiple contributing causes. Some, like truly unavoidable accidents, you cannot do much about. However, many will have several underlying susceptibilities that can be mitigated, either in prevention or in treatment. Most climbers will never even get as far as addressing their underlying susceptibilities. This is because it is hard to correctly identify and attribute the causes of injuries, even if you involve professional help.

What was really the cause?

With an understanding of the concept of underlying susceptibility and how it can cause progressive tissue damage below symptomatic level, we can see how it is possible to mistakenly attribute an injury to a particular inciting event such as a wild move for a hold when you injured a finger pulley, or a powerful drop down move that tore a shoulder ligament. The inciting event may be a contributing cause, or it may have been merely an inevitable consequence of damage building up.

To prevent injuries, you need to address not only your underlying risk factors, but also avoid the inciting events that trigger tissue failure. Some inciting events, such as a spinning hold, are unavoidable. They are part and parcel of climbing and happen to everyone. Therefore, we have to expect them. But you can mitigate their effects by reducing underlying susceptibility and thus building up resistance to the day to day wear and tear that climbing imposes on your tendons and joints. That resistance comes in very diverse forms, but four concepts in particular stand out as your most important weapons of prevention of the common climbing injuries. The following sections address each of these.

The big four: technique, posture, activity, rest

It isn't the mountains ahead to climb that wear you out,
it's the pebble in your shoe.
Muhammad Ali

Consider one of the most common technical errors made by climbers: that of a foot slipping suddenly. Inexperienced climbers might not even call this an error. They see it as a misfortune that was unavoidable. "I would have done it, but my foot slipped without warning!". The warnings were probably there, but you might not have been able to process them because your concentration was too busy with other high priority movement decisions such as "should I get that hold with my left or right?" In tennis they have a good system of describing errors as 'forced' or 'unforced'. Unforced errors are caused by things like inexperience, fatigue or loss of concentration. Conversely, when a good opponent plays unpredictable, fast and aggressive shots, everything goes too quickly and you are 'forced' into making errors while trying to keep up. This is a good way to think about technical errors in climbing too.

In climbing, errors are forced by the holds being too small or the route sustained, making it harder to maintain control or plan the move ahead precisely. You must focus more on delivery of force and so accuracy is sacrificed. This is of course offset by having a long apprenticeship of technique training: your technique and sequence planning becomes more automatic. You don't need to consciously think about it, so you can operate closer to your absolute physical limit with fewer errors creeping in.

The difference between the error rate found with climbers at a medium level compared to an elite climber is huge. The cost of these errors on the body is also huge. When a foot slips unexpectedly, the fingers, already loaded maximally, are suddenly loaded even further. Even if a significant injury like a torn finger pulley doesn't occur at that moment, there is likely to be tearing of individual collagen fibres within the pulleys. This microscopic damage, or 'microtrauma' is one of the elements which stimulates tissue adaptation. But if your feet slip off or you grab holds 'out of control' too often, the damage accumulates and the pulley becomes vulnerable to a macroscopic failure (a partial or complete rupture).

Thus, the quality of your technique determines how much climbing you can manage without accumulating a critical level of tissue damage. Good climbers can get away

with an aggressive schedule of climbing since their good technique spreads the stress on the body. Meanwhile, novices have high rates of injuries, considering the fact that their volume and intensity of climbing is much lower. The more you can anticipate and reduce technical errors, the lower the probability of exposing yourself to microtrauma accumulation, as well as the inciting events that trigger macroscopic tearing of tissue.

A second major influence on the accumulation of tissue damage may be your posture. Actually, before going any further, it is important to understand this rather unhelpful term a little better as it applies to sport. The word is often used as an overarching term of reference. This is slightly misleading for sportspeople. When people outside of the physiotherapy profession think of posture, they refer to how we hold our body at rest or while doing a static task such as sitting at a computer. In the context of sport, what is important is both the alignment of our muscles and joints (the musculoskeletal system) and how they move. The relevant qualities which come under the banner of 'posture' are postural alignment and movement patterns.

Alignment of the musculoskeletal system deviates from the ideal because of many factors. Some of these stretch back to our childhood and include habits of sitting with slouched posture, sleeping on one side, various routine daily tasks and the effects of old injuries limiting our movements. Many activities in modern life contribute to poor alignment such as driving, carrying a bag over one shoulder, performing repetitive tasks at the limits of joint range and countless other things. There are also some factors within sport that are important. Climbers commonly develop poor upper body alignment due to changes in the strength and length of internal rotator muscles of the shoulder[21-23].

Almost everyone has imperfect alignment, and a significant proportion have alignment which is significantly faulty. The result of poor alignment is more than just looking like a bit of a slouch, or even a gorilla in the case of many climbers. It causes uneven loading on particular joints or tendons which end up either weakened or overworked. The analogy here is with machinery such as a car. When the wheels of a car are balanced and aligned, the tyres wear slowly and evenly. But when the alignment is only slightly incorrect, the wear is uneven and the tyres wear out much faster.

Despite poor posture being so common, many people will last until a relatively old age before the uneven wear on the body reaches the point of causing pain or injury. However, the age at which this happens in sport may be much lower. This is because the exceptional demands of sport compared to a sedentary lifestyle amplify the effects of poor posture on tissue damage. There is an apparent paradox here. In an ideal world, sport and training are healthy and have a positive effect on the body, making it stronger and more resistant to the wear and tear of life. Yet in the presence of poor alignment, the repetitive movements of sport causes body parts to wear out much faster. Looking at it this way, we can see how pivotal the role of good alignment is to the longevity of the body and its resistance to injury.

Technique and posture help determine the tendency for tissue damage from sport to build up. The extent of that build up over time is also dependent on how much sport we do, and how well we rest and recover from our bouts of training.

Microscopic damage to tendons and muscles is actually a desirable outcome of physical training. The body adapts to the conditions to which it is exposed. When tissue damage is super-compensated between training sessions by tissue growth, the health and strength of that tissue will increase. The objective when choosing the correct training load is to give as strong a stimulation as possible, without exceeding the rate at which super-compensation can occur. Since super-compensation occurs during the rest periods between climbing sessions, the length and quality of the rest are critical for maximising the amount of training that can be absorbed without damage accumulating. If the rest is too short, or of poor quality, a training volume which could otherwise have been absorbed will become injurious.

On the other hand, rest periods that are too long are also injurious. It is well understood that training gains in muscle strength and endurance are reversible, and that the losses of tissue status begin within a few days

of ceasing training[7]. However, less account is given for the parallel loss of strength in connective tissue such as tendons and ligaments with extended rest. The rates of loss of strength through disuse in connective tissue are slightly different than in muscle, but the general quality of reversibility of training gains applies. It is for this reason that injuries are just as common when starting to train after a break as when nearing the end of a long, tiring season: the tissue has become weaker during your time off.

The climber who loses the least amount of his climbing career to injury is the one who is the master of monitoring and tweaking the interaction of these four primary influences on the susceptibility to injury. The following sections discuss the specific interventions you can make to achieve this resistance to injury.

Correcting technique

When you watch a video of elite level sport climbers or boulderers on the hardest routes of the day it might be difficult with an untrained eye to see the control they exert even when climbing at their limit on the most aggressive and athletic moves. Don't make the mistake of underestimating that control. Ideally, a good climbing coach will guide you to a level where you can appreciate and wield such control yourself. Improving your technique to reduce the susceptibility to common climbing injuries can be split up into the following areas:

- Reducing technical errors
- Reducing technical risk factors
- Spreading the stress on the body
- Tactics/external factors

Let's look at each of these elements in detail.

Reducing technical errors

The common climbing error that I have mentioned already is feet slipping off unexpectedly. If you have been climbing a long time, it is likely that you've heard of, or even seen a climber rupturing a finger pulley when a foot slipped unexpectedly. It is one of the finest ways you could choose to tear a finger pulley, strain an elbow or damage (even dislocate) a shoulder. Yet, when it happens, climbers often still blame the small hold they were holding for the injury. Reducing the frequency of feet slipping is no simple task. Broadly speaking it involves improving your entire technical repertoire and accuracy of movement. This is a huge area, beyond the scope of this book. If you want to read more, a good starting place would be my first book *9 out of 10 climbers make the same mistakes* which has a sound general discussion of the core elements of good footwork and climbing movement generally.

Support from a good climbing coach (the most experienced you can afford!) is your best shortcut to bootstrapping some of the core skills. But if you are not careful, even this can be counterproductive. Coaching intervention of less than ideal quality sometimes gets sportspeople accustomed to being instructed to perform skills, at the expense of really trying to digest and understand them. Coaching is a catalyst or facilitator of progress, but it can never be a substitute for systematic practice, thought and learning, day in and day out. A thorough understanding of technical skills takes huge amounts of effort and work. It takes an insatiable curiosity about how moves work. You need to develop a habit of critical observation of other climbers to pick up the nuances of climbing movement, followed by systematic experimentation in your own climbing to see what works and what doesn't. Only with real attention to detail will you come to realise how a little more pressure on a foot in a given direction will make the difference between keeping your feet on, or letting them slip off.

In this discussion there are some core skills to highlight with particular relevance to injury risk. Preventing feet slipping is helped by honing a constant mental awareness and monitoring of the friction between your foot and the foothold. If there is too much pressure in the wrong direction, the foot will slip. If there is not enough pressure to create friction, the foot will slip. It doesn't take too long to get a 'feel' for this if you are practising it directly. You can tell when your foot is about to slip. The time when you can't tell is usually not because the

feedback from the sensation at your toes isn't there. It is when you are too busy focusing on other important climbing decisions. You can offset this by developing a 'flag' system where you keep a little part of your mind's eye on what is happening under your feet. If you feel the friction becoming insufficient and the foot is about to slip, a mental 'flag' goes up to give it more concentration and respond accordingly by changing body position.

Many examples of feet slipping are caused by not pulling or hooking with the toes on overhanging ground. Since even novice climbers may be tackling overhanging terrain on indoor walls, this footwork skill (which some might see as advanced) is causing injuries even in novice climbers. Get used to curling the toes downward inside the rock-shoe to grab the most incut part of the foothold with your toes. The amount the toes can actually move might be very little in stiff rock-shoes, but just the action of trying to grab with the toes helps to activate the calves, extending the toes and maximising the force on the foothold. With your toes wrapped over the lip of the foothold, pull your lower body inwards, toward the rock to create and maintain the tension. Body tension in climbing is often mis-attributed as being solely related to strength in the core muscles such as the abdominals. Although it does have a strength component, body tension is first and foremost a technical skill. If you position your body correctly as you move, and engage the strength you already have through your core to your toes, you can get more weight on your feet.

Photo 3.1 Poor grabbing with the toes. Note the heel is dropped and the end of the toes are not making contact with the back of the hold at all.

Photo 3.2 Good grabbing with the toes. The toes are engaged with the best part of the hold by pointing the foot downwards and curling the toes to grab the hold.

Photo 3.3 Body tension. At the moment of grabbing the next handhold, the mind tends to focus on the handhold. But this is also the moment to focus on producing tension through the whole body to the feet so that your feet don't slip.

The other element that contributes to feet slipping is our natural tendency to focus on one movement task at a time. When we concentrate hard on a crux move and go for the next handhold, our mind naturally focuses on grabbing that handhold and generating as much force as possible on it quickly. This is sometimes at the expense of the rest of the body. At this moment, amateur climbers will subconsciously relax their lower body and the feet can slip. When the footholds are awkwardly positioned or the ground is steep and there is a tendency for cutting loose, it is essential to tension up on both ends of the body at the same time. As you sit reading this book, reach out and grab the nearest object such as the edge of your chair or table with your hand. At the same moment, curl your toes into a 'grab' position on the ground. Syncing the timing of this is a learned skill, it takes practice. It is analogous to what drummers must do when they make hands and feet do different things at the same time.

Reducing technical risk factors

Technical risk factors can be anything in your movement style that causes sudden loading or high peak forces on tendons and joints in climbing. High peak forces on connective tissue tend to occur when the acceleration between positions is extreme, or at the extreme ends of the joint's range of movement.

Sport in general demands a great deal of movement at extremes of joint range, making the most of the leverage and reach our limbs allow. Muscles are weaker, either when fully shortened or lengthened, compared to the mid range of joint motion. However, this is offset when muscles are working in a fully lengthened position since the elastic properties of connective tissue such as muscle fascia and tendon are stretched and can thus contribute to the force absorbed or generated[24]. In this position, the stretched muscle-tendon unit has nowhere else to go. If the load it is under pushes it further, it must tear. A further complicating factor is the way the force is distributed within muscles and tendons. Some muscles and tendons 'wrap' around other structures through part or all of their range of motion. This creates friction forces against the muscle-tendon unit and shear forces within it. Both muscle and tendon are remarkable in the way the tissue is organised to cope with this, but they are at their most vulnerable to harmful forces at their extremes of range.

The classic example of a risky move at extreme joint range is the deep lock-off. As we pull up and reach as far as we can with one arm, the elbow of the other arm is fully flexed, placing large forces on the common flexor tendon of the wrist flexors and forearm pronators which cross the elbow. Climbers who have a 'front-on' style, who climb facing the rock and who commonly rely on static deep lock-offs, are especially vulnerable to golfer's elbow where there is damage and degeneration in the common flexor tendon.

Here are some examples of moves which place large forces on the shoulder, elbow or finger tendons:

- Deep locks (common flexor tendon of elbow)
- Wide crucifix 'compression' moves (brachialis/brachioradialis muscles/tendons)
- Gaston moves (common flexor tendon of elbow, shoulder)
- Cross through moves (brachialis/brachioradialis tendons)
- Dynamic moves to small crimps or pockets (flexor tendons, pulleys, finger joints)
- Two-arm pull ups on narrow fingerboard/campus rungs (common flexor tendon of elbow)

While it is not necessarily desirable to avoid these risky moves (dynamic moves to crimps are core climbing moves!), there are a couple of important things we can do to mitigate the risks they confer for injuries. The most important of these is to climb using momentum. Bizarrely, use of momentum has in the past been considered more dangerous than climbing slowly and statically. Yet static climbing movement results in large and sudden spikes in the forces in the upper body, most often at the moment you take one hand off to reach for the next hold. It is true that if you are used to climbing statically and start to climb dynamically, there is a temporarily increased risk of injury while you master the techniques and neuromuscular timing to avoid 'jarring' or uncontrolled moves. However, once you master controlled use of dynamic movement, it is the safest way to climb, generally speaking.

Let's take the deep lock as an example again. If done statically, the force on the common flexor tendon in the elbow is not dangerously high as you pull up with both hands to the locked off position. However, when you let go with one hand to reach, the force on the other hand spikes and must be maintained until you have generated force on the next hold. If a foot slips as you are reaching, the shock loading on the elbow is seriously unhealthy! Conversely, if using momentum, the force during the pull-up phase to initiate the move is higher because the pull-up is performed dynamically. However, the muscle group can handle this better as it is passing through the mid range of motion. As the arms approach the lock-off position and you begin to remove one hand to make the reach, sufficient upward momentum has already been generated so that the force on the common flexor tendon may actually fall during the reach itself. In this way, the high force requirement is transferred from the dangerous end point of the elbow's range of motion, to the safer mid range.

Photo 3.4 Deep lock. If overused in climbing or performed without use of momentum, the risk of developing golfer's elbow may be increased.

The benefit of dynamic climbing using momentum comes from the shifting of force generation towards the middle of joint range of motion, together with smooth accelerations avoiding sudden shock loading. But it is not just producing force with momentum during the initiation of moves that is important, it is absorbing forces during completion of moves too.

Consider the action of a powerful, dynamic lunge to a distant jug. If you catch the hold with the elbow locked in a fully extended position, only the elasticity of the ligaments and tendon across the elbow and shoulder can absorb the downward 'jarring' as your body falls into a hanging position on the jug. If you watch kids and teenage climbers bouldering or climbing steep sport routes, you will see them rely on this move a lot. Older climbers, usually through painful experience of injuries, are much more guarded and are unwilling to dynamically latch a hold at full extension. This can result in them trying to move more statically or refusing to move dynamically at all, at the expense of their climbing standard. However, when you watch skilled climbers, you will notice that they try to latch holds with a slight bend in the elbow, and with the shoulder 'pulled in' rather than fully extended. This is not so easy to spot and takes a bit of close observation. When they catch the hold and their body falls back downward, they absorb the shock as their arm straightens under active resistance, dampening the jarring effect significantly.

This technique is also very useful when doing dynamic, powerful moves to small, fingery holds. If you wish to use a crimp grip on the hold for the following move, it is still often safer to latch it with an openhanded grip, and then adjust into the crimp position as you prepare your feet for the next move. Catching a hold openhanded is not only safer for the pulleys, it also gives you an extra centimetre of reach!

Spreading the stress on the body

The goal of training is to maximise the overload placed on the body without injuring it. Clearly, if the overload is unevenly balanced, with one area receiving too much stress, it can become overtrained and then injured while other areas are actually undertrained. There are several different dimensions across which the training stress imposed on the body can be altered. Some of these are mechanical aspects of climbing, and some relate to the make-up of our training.

Possibly the single most important method to spread the stress of climbing is to vary the grip type we use. Finger pulley injuries are the most common climbing related injury, and occur during crimping. In a crimped grip, the pulleys must absorb huge forces to hold the flexor tendons tight against the bones of the fingers. It is actually amazing they don't injure more easily given what they are subjected to in hard rock climbing. Using an openhanded grip allows the pulleys to be unloaded. In fact, even if you have a moderately bad pulley tear, you might be able to climb without pain using a full openhanded grip[25].

A few climbers naturally develop a habit of alternating equally between an openhanded and crimped grip. However, this tends to be the exception. Most climbers go through a similar progression in their climbing which starts with crimping nearly every small hold, until the day when pulley injuries start happening. Then, one of two things happen. Either they lay-off, lose climbing ability and begin a cycle of climbing with the same reliance on crimping and subsequent pulley injuries and lay-offs. Alternatively, sheer frustration and desperation to climb forces the climber to start using an openhanded grip. Usually it takes a good few cycles of finger injuries to get this to happen. Initially the openhanded grip feels not only totally alien, but also extremely weak. This weakness is because the grip is so underused. The desperation to climb forces climbers to stick with it long enough to get used to openhanding and to get strong on this grip. If you manage to successfully come through this psychologically painful process, you will see that openhanding is stronger than crimping on many (but not all) holds. It is often less strenuous and you get injured a lot less. Once this balance of using both types of grip is established, it is generally good for your climbing, giving you a wider repertoire to suit all the weird and wonderful shapes of hold we encounter.

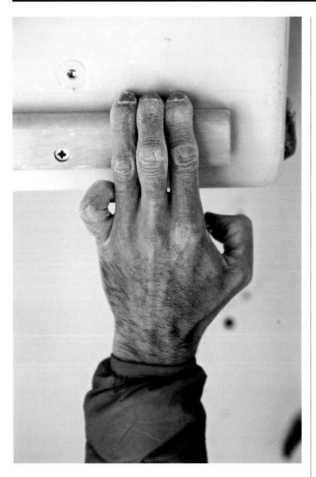

Photo 3.5 Full openhanded grip. Also known as a pocket grip or drag.

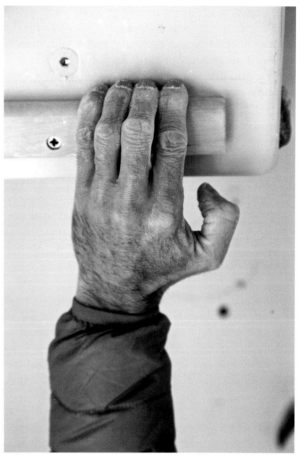

Photo 3.6 Four finger openhanded grip. Note the middle and ring fingers still have a slight flex at the PIP joint, while the index and little fingers are fully open.

Although most will have to learn the hard way, I would strongly encourage you not to. If you are one of those climbers who is so weak openhanded that you barely even understand how it is possible to hang onto holds this way, you will need to start from basics. Go to a fingerboard, or some first joint (20mm deep) holds on a climbing wall and try hanging with both the classic four and three finger openhanded grips. The fingers should only flex at the joint nearest your fingertip (the distal inter-phalangeal or DIP joint) while the middle joint will be only slightly flexed or completely open depending on your finger lengths relative to each other. You will probably need to start with your feet on, even if you can usually hang with your feet off easily using a crimped grip. Persevere with it. Try several sets of straightforward hangs and some pull-ups. On your next session, try a bit more. Then progress to some easy boulder problems or routes where you try to hold as many of the smaller holds as you can with an openhanded grip. You will find that the really small holds (three quarter fingertip pad depth or less) will still demand a crimp grip. Once you get stronger and proficient openhanding, you will be able to use progressively smaller edges without needing to crimp. In fact, where the edge is convex shaped, you

Photo 3.7 Full crimp grip. Necessary on some holds, but overused by many climbers, resulting in damage to the pulley system in the fingers.

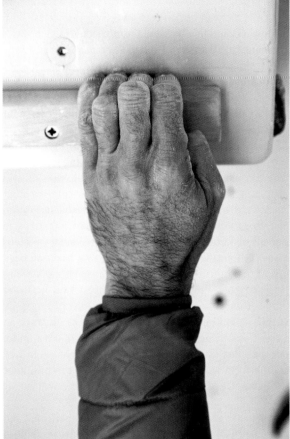

Photo 3.8 Half crimp grip. There is anecdotal evidence from coaches that fewer pulley injuries occur with this grip than using a full crimp.

will often find it stronger openhanded, whereas concave shaped holds with a sharp edge can be better crimped. That said, everyone's preferences settle out differently. The broad goal is to use openhanding at least as much as crimping on small holds. Just by making this change, you will significantly reduce your risk of pulley injuries.

Another key method of spreading the training stress on the body is to add variety to your climbing schedule. Too much of any one component of the climbing diet is a potential cause of point loading and subsequent injury. Here are some examples:

- Always climbing at the same climbing wall or crag (especially on the same route!).
- Always climbing routes on the same rock type or angle.
- Climbing only routes, or only bouldering for long periods.
- Increasing more than one variable of training load simultaneously (volume and intensity).
- Always doing the same basic strength exercises (even varying between campus and fingerboards may be helpful).
- Always climbing problems set by the same route setter, especially on your home board.

A surprisingly small change in some aspect of your climbing diet can be enough to keep the body fresh and responsive, and help prevent tissue damage which was accumulating because of overuse of a particular activity.

Tactics/external factors

Above I described one of the primary inciting events for climbing injuries: that of feet slipping off unexpectedly. Although this is an error which can be mitigated by learning good technique and by monitoring the friction you have on a foothold, inevitably the risk of this happening is also influenced by your rock-shoes. In other sports, the use of the most appropriate and optimised equipment is linked to injury development. Racquet grip size is well known to be related to the incidence of tennis elbow[26]. Running shoe design and fitting has long been linked to a host of lower limb injuries in runners[27-29]. In climbing, rock-shoes are our link to the rock on our lower limbs. They concentrate large proportions of our body weight (sometimes more than body weight) through an area of sometimes only a few square millimetres under our toes. It is extremely important that our shoes fit well and perform as well as possible so that we can minimise the incidence of unexpected slips.

Entry level rock-shoes are, generally speaking, not ideal for this task. Their fit is not supportive enough to concentrate the power of the whole foot through the toes. Their shape is not asymmetrical enough to focus that power under the big toe (the strongest toe). Their soles tend to be stiff and insensitive, making it difficult to feel the 'sweet spot' of the foothold under your toes. Most important, the soles tend to bend upwards slightly near the toe, making it very difficult for the toes to flex into a grab position inside the boot. When coaching climbing, it is painfully obvious how poorly these shoes perform on small or awkwardly positioned footholds, even when the climber using them has good footwork. Unexpected slips happen more often. So if you have started out in rock climbing with a pair of entry level style shoes which are baggy, underperforming and possibly now worn out as well, the sooner you upgrade to a better performing shoe the better.

Don't subscribe to the myth that performance rock-

Photo 3.9 Performance rock-shoes.

shoes are uncomfortable. They needn't be. In fact, if they fit well, they will be even more comfortable than an entry level pair. This myth arises because of faults in the rock-shoe buying process. Firstly, a good rock-shoe has to fit your individual foot shape very closely. Therefore, to find the right fit, you must try on a lot of different pairs. If you haven't found a model that fits you well, go to a retailer that holds as large a range as possible. Don't get fixated on the shoes that are popular at your climbing wall or in climbing films. They may be good shoes, but if they don't fit your feet well they will not help your climbing, and you certainly won't enjoy wearing them.

Differences in rubber quality between manufacturers are outweighed by the benefits you will experience by finding a model that fits you very well. If you like the shoe, but not the rubber, you can always just get them resoled with your favourite rubber, even when new! When you go to the retailer, don't feel you have to stick by the recommendation of the staff. They aren't always well trained. And anyway, how do they know which model is going to match your foot shape best? Don't leave until you have tried on everything. A good retailer will understand exactly why you need to do this, and will take pleasure in selling you the right pair. If you are not getting that vibe, make your excuses and go elsewhere. Your judgement should be based on how they feel when walking up and down and standing on a few footholds (most good shops have a little wall set up for this). Sometimes you will know you have found the right shoes the moment they are on your feet, but not always.

This is particularly true for 'turned down' shoes. These are rock-shoes that are designed with steeper climbing in mind which have the toe turned down to confer more grab on the footholds. Although they sometimes feel very unnatural (even cramp inducing) when you first slip them on, try not to be put off. The shoes are generally very soft and should be comfortable after breaking them in for a session. To get a sense of how they might feel after being broken in, take a good walk up and down the shop floor in them, stand on a few footholds, take them off for a minute or two and then put them back on. Do they feel different? Even a few minutes' wear will start to flatten off a factory fresh pair, bringing them closer to a normal foot shape. The downturn power will still be there when climbing on steep rock, but they will quickly feel more and more comfortable, providing that the shoe shape fits your foot. After having stretched new boots into a normal shape, your feet will inevitably feel a little squashed. But the effect of just taking the boots off for a minute often removes much of this. I also do this when warming up for a bouldering session, as my boots will have shrunk a little between sessions. It really helps! My favourite shoes, the Scarpa Stix, are a good example of this tendency for turned down boots to feel strange out of the box. The first time I tried them on, I dismissed them as being too aggressively turned down for my taste. I had a pair in a box for a year before trying them again by chance to see if they would be good for a heel hooking problem I was trying. Within ten minutes I was kicking myself for not giving them a chance and proceeded to wear Stix almost exclusively for the next six years.

I have also come across an argument that says climbers should wait before moving to performance shoes because they will wear out shoes too fast before they learn good footwork. This argument doesn't stand up. Firstly, it is much harder to learn good footwork in entry level shoes. This is because their inadequacy on poor footholds constantly reinforces a feeling that refining footwork doesn't pay off. So persisting with entry level shoes simply delays the journey to good footwork. Secondly, rock-shoe rubber wears out even with good footwork because the boot is dragged forcefully across the wall during powerful flagging moves. If you do a lot of climbing on an indoor wall that has been friction painted, or on a rough rock type, you will inevitably wear

down rubber a little more quickly. But the difference isn't anything to sweat about. Rock-shoe re-soling, if done by a good re-soler, will make your shoes perform even better than new and costs a lot less than a session with a coach to sort out your bad footwork.

While your rock-shoes are key to influencing the factors that control your feet slipping, what about hands? The friction between the hold and our fingertips is a hugely important factor in controlling the rate of injury inciting events. Just as feet slipping will shock-load the upper limbs, fingers slipping off is bad news, too. When we suddenly 'explode' off a handhold, the rapid unloading of the tendons and ligaments can be almost as bad as overloading, causing high shear and friction forces within the tissues which can easily cause tears. Alternatively, one hand, or even one finger slipping even a little, can overload the remaining fingers or other arm and cause an injury.

Good conditions for friction in climbing are generally found in cold weather with dry air and a good breeze. Cold conditions pose their own risk of interfering with the warm-up, making the tissue more prone to injury. In practice this is more than offset by the fact that unexpected slips are much less common in good conditions. The more advanced your climbing is, the greater the effect of good conditions because you are more able to make use of the control that really good friction offers you in climbing movement.

Of course, the problem is that friction is only partially under your control. You can't help the weather, and even if you ask the climbing wall manager to turn the heating down, he might say no. However, you can make use of any breeze going, and there is a lot you can do to manage how much your fingertips get soft and sweaty. The goal is to have tough, dry fingertip skin for as much of the climb as possible. Here is a list of possibilities open to you, and the more of these you can adopt, the better.

- Keep your core warm but avoid letting your hands get too hot and sweaty.
- If you are overheating, seek out any breeze you can, even if it's just waving your hands back and forth just before you start climbing.

- If your fingertips are getting worn out and thin, try to keep them chalked even between attempts on a problem or route to prevent them getting too soft.
- Keep adjusting your clothing so you can keep cool hands and warm core, and anticipate when your temperature will change. You might need to strip down enough to get a little cold before launching up a long, physical route that might cause you to overheat.
- Use enough chalk. Many climbers don't use enough to prevent injuries.
- If you are trying moves repeatedly and the holds are becoming greasy, remember to brush them regularly with a little fresh chalk on your brush.
- If it is really warm, you might need to take longer rests between attempts to let your body cool down.
- Placing your hands on a cold surface (such as some rock that is out of the sun) before starting to climb will help cool your skin.
- If the climbing wall staff won't turn the heating down, make as good a case as you can to persuade them, based on the injury prevention argument, but don't get frustrated if they won't budge. Sometimes a good fan (They cost £10 or so) placed in the bouldering room is all you need to circulate the air and cool sweaty fingertips. Don't wait until they install one if they are dragging their heels. Just get one and put one in yourself.

There will be plenty of times when conditions are just bad, and despite your best efforts to mitigate it with the tricks above, the holds are greasy and slippery. If you didn't climb just because conditions were bad, depending where you live and climb, you would lose a lot of climbing time to conditions. Provided you take account of the conditions and take extra care, you can minimise the risk posed in greasy conditions. Here are some precautions to take:

- Be ready to let go if you feel your fingers are about to slip off a hold.
- Be more selective about the climbs and moves you will do. Avoid super hard pulls on awkward crimps or small pockets, especially involving deep lock-offs. If you can't avoid them, be extra conservative in your movement; expect the slip.

- Don't spend too long trying the same move, letting the crux hold get really greasy.
- Take extra care to place your fingers really well on the holds. Keep the fingers nice and tight against each other on small holds; separated fingers are less stable on the hold and are more vulnerable to slipping.

No matter what your climbing level is, don't underestimate the size of the injury risk posed by conditions. You only have to look at other sports to see that the frictional properties of the playing surface are heavily implicated in the frequency of injury occurrence. Wet playing fields, different types of grass, the 'hardness' of different playing surfaces and tread design on the soles of footwear are all well known to influence the rate of injuries in many sports.

Here are some more external factors that are regularly lamented by injured climbers the world over. "If only I hadn't…"

- Kept going when I was tired. Keen climbers just don't want to stop. It is understandable. But when you get so tired that your technique is getting sloppy and skin is so thin it just won't go white with chalk anymore, you are getting into the danger zone. Be sensible, and if not, at least be careful.
- Got involved in a stupid competition. Fun bouldering competitions between friends are great. I would never try to tell anyone not to do them. But always keep a cool head. A little part of your brain should be saying "Is this really a good idea?".
- Got distracted. Lots of injuries happen in moments of distraction or shortly after being distracted. If you've just had something happen that has taken your mind off your focus, don't just jump straight back on a hard route. Do a few easy moves first, to 'reset' your focus.
- Got frustrated. Lots of sportspeople are bad at controlling their anger and frustration, usually from failure. Climbers are not much different. If you are having a crap day at the crag, remember it happens to everyone. Don't go home with an injury as well.
- Got hungover and went climbing. If you're going

to get drunk, get drunk before rest days instead. Climbing in a hungover state is asking for trouble.

- Hung on. It is true that to climb at your limit you have to grab every hold like you mean it and not let go. But only with good form. A split second automatic alarm should tell you that you haven't quite caught a hold correctly and that it is going to be dangerous to try to hold on. It will still be there to have another try unless you let it injure you.

Correcting posture

Nature to be commanded must be obeyed.
Francis Bacon

We have seen that the contributing factors for developing injuries are complex, and a clear dominant cause might not be obvious. The role of posture, or more accurately, movement patterns, in developing sports injuries has been increasingly recognised as a significant contributor to many of the injuries climbers get[7, 14, 30]. Common postural faults have been linked to injuries of the shoulder and there are some opinions that it may be important in elbow injuries too[21, 31, 32]. Evidence for this has often come from clinical practice rather than scientific research, because it is both a complex subject and difficult to study scientifically. No research data has been gathered to directly establish links between common postural faults and injuries in climbing. However, many therapists working in climbing agree that it seems likely, or at least plausible, that in time it will become more clear which postural faults contribute to the injuries climbers suffer. Until then, it must be considered good practice to work to improve your posture and movement patterns as part of your climbing training, either to prevent future injuries, or to help reduce existing ones. How we can best do this is a matter of great controversy among researchers and therapists[33]. The 'problem' of exactly how faulty posture and movement patterns might contribute to injuries is not even clear yet, so it follows that any answers are even less clear.

The mechanism by which both postural faults and technical movement errors contribute to injuries is thought to be the resultant misalignment of the body. Two qualities of muscle are responsible for this. Muscles adapt both their strength and their length to match the conditions to which they are habitually exposed. Muscles repeatedly used or held in a lengthened position become longer by adding more muscle protein units in series along their length[24, 30]. Similarly, muscles held or exercised for prolonged periods in a shortened position become shorter. The classic example of this is the shortened calves and stiffer Achilles tendons of women who regularly wear high-heeled shoes[34]. All sportspeople understand that underused muscles become weaker. Groups of muscles work in opposition to each other across joints, both to provide opposing movements such as flexing versus extending an arm, or to stabilise a joint to provide a secure base for movement elsewhere in the body. This opposing muscle group is referred to as an 'antagonist'. If muscles on one side of a joint are allowed to become weak, they cannot provide an effective resistance against their stronger antagonists. This allows the joint to be pulled into misalignment, both at rest and especially during movement. An imbalance of muscles' length and strength across joints appears to cause wear and tear focused on particular areas which cannot cope and are more likely to become injured.

Muscle imbalance is now frequently referred to in common sporting literature and many climbers will have heard of the concept. Yet often it is only discussed in terms of one of the two important variables: strength. Articles recommend strengthening the antagonists of muscle groups commonly used, in order to restore muscle balance and prevent injury. This is good advice but is only half the picture. Correcting altered muscle lengths around a given joint is also essential to restore normal movement patterns and thus prevent build up of wear and tear.

Changes in muscle strength and length often go together. Heavily strengthened muscles often become shortened, such as lats in climbers. Similarly, excessive muscle length and weakness often go together. Indeed, the term 'stretch weakness' in muscles refer to their tendency to become weakened if chronically held in an elongated position, however slight, because of poor posture or movement patterns[30].

It is beyond the scope of this book to fully detail all of the potential upper body postural faults. These are numerous and complex, and large textbooks can be found detailing posture and its faults around the major joints of the body. In the further reading section at the end of this book, I have directed readers to a few invaluable reference texts for identifying postural faults and compiling a program of exercises to address them. However, in this text, I will take you through a brief introduction to some of the more common upper body postural problems that climbers suffer and that likely contribute to their injuries.

The following pages, or indeed the further reading I have recommended, are no substitute for an examination and corrective exercise prescription from a good sports physiotherapist. It is always best practice to go for an examination, because without an accurate diagnosis, you could end up making things worse, if not simply wasting your time by choosing inappropriate exercises. Shoulder mechanics are too complicated for amateurs to accurately diagnose postural faults or sources of pain. However, reading the following section should not only illuminate how the upper body posture can cause climbing injuries, but give you a basic understanding, so you can keep up with your physiotherapist's recommendations and realise how important it is to stick to the exercises.

First of all, let's look at the basics of the field: definitions. In the classic text by Florence Kendall and co-authors[30], *Muscles: Testing and Function with Posture and Pain*, posture is described in the following way:

"Good posture is a good habit that contributes to the well-being of the individual… Conversely, bad posture is a bad habit and, unfortunately, is all too common."

What is clear from this is that posture is a voluntary action. It is something we have control over, even if we are not always aware of it. Just as we can change our climbing technique to reduce the focus of wear and tear on certain tendons and ligaments, improving our posture can have the same effect.

Some actions we can take to improve our posture are simple and will have the effect of reducing the misalignment of the muscles and joints without performing additional corrective exercises. Here are some examples:

- Consciously maintain a more upright back and avoiding slouching the shoulders. It takes considerable conscious effort to maintain this at first, but eventually becomes automatic if you are disciplined enough to stick with it. That old school advice, "Don't slouch, sit up straight!" was good advice then and today. It is not just so you look more civilised, it is to protect your back and shoulder alignment too.
- Adjust your working position and height for sitting in front of a computer screen in order to avoid rounding the upper back and lengthening the trapezius muscles of the upper back. The screen should be at or below eye level, arms resting on supports on your chair (not on the desk) and feet should have a foot rest. Try to break up long periods of sitting at work with even a few minutes of activity as often as you can.
- Vary the working position to avoid repeatedly twisting or leaning in the same direction (e.g. to answer a phone).
- Adjust your seat position for driving.
- Use clean technique to perform repetitive lifting in daily life (children, shopping, etc.).
- Sleep on a good mattress and avoid positions that contribute to injury pain.
- Simply be more active. It has been argued that since our relatively inactive lifestyles involving long hours of sitting in front of screens and steering wheels in positions that cause postural strain, simply increasing the volume of varied, basic activity we do may be the best solution we have for poor posture. If climbing is your only sport, simply doing more of this might not help, as you will see below. Involvement in other sports, or a discipline such as yoga or Pilates may be useful to add variety to your movement and break up periods of inactivity on days you are not climbing.

The effect of simply making these changes should not be underestimated. For some, these changes may be enough on their own. However, once significant alignment faults are established, they may well require some additional corrective exercises to treat them. Moreover, many of the sport-specific contributors to poor posture in climbing are difficult to avoid. They are part and parcel of doing the sport and require climbers to do a little extra work to keep their upper bodies in alignment. In essence, climbing in its modern form with repetitive pulling and twisting in the same directions is an activity which the body is not designed to perform. From a musculoskeletal point of view, it is an unbalanced activity. By isolating the particular postural faults that it tends to create, and by performing some simple exercises to correct them, the muscular system can be kept in balance.

Climbing has a number of habitual movements and positions that may, hypothetically, contribute to postural faults. Obviously, these are very complex and have not been well researched, but here are a few examples:

Photo 3.10 Twist lock move with internal rotation of the arm.

- Twisting and reaching requires us to perform powerful internal rotation of the holding arm, to extend the reaching shoulder (Photo 3.10). The internal rotators of the humerus (lats, teres major etc.) are frequently well developed and shortened in climbers, while the external rotators around the shoulder can become weak and lengthened. The frequency of internal rotation in activities of daily life (e.g. driving, reading, keyboard work) further contribute to the problem.

- Carrying heavy rucksacks over one or both arms is known to cause depressed shoulders by lengthening the upper trapezius muscles which can contribute to impingement syndrome in the shoulder. This is also a problem for women with ill-fitting bras where the straps run too far out from the neck, towards the shoulder. The long lever-arm pulls the shoulder downwards.

- Even having long or very muscular and therefore heavy arms can contribute to shoulder alignment faults (abducted scapulae).

Upper body alignment and misalignment

Now that we have established how alignment is affected by posture and habitual everyday and sporting movements, let's go into some detail on what tends to go wrong with upper body alignment in climbers. Even if you have regular visits to a good physiotherapist to monitor your alignment before injuries occur, it is important for every climber to have a basic working knowledge of their upper body anatomy and its common alignment problems.

The first key concept to grasp is that the demands on strength and range of motion of the elbow and forearm are dependent on alignment further up the kinetic chain, at the back and shoulders. There are four key areas which are particularly important in upper body posture and movement for climbers:

1. The upper back. A rounded upper back and poor flexibility in the spine causes the scapula (shoulder blade) to become tilted forwards (anteriorly) and internally rotated (Fig 3.1). This forces it to have to move further than normal when reaching overhead. If the shoulder range of motion cannot

compensate for this, the scapula gets in the way of the humerus reaching overhead and the shoulder joint becomes impinged[14]. In this way, poor posture in the back contributes to impingement syndrome in the shoulder.

2. The scapula. The function of the scapula is to support the arm as it moves. It is very prone to misalignment, causing a complex range of movement impairments and eventually injuries.

3. The humerus. Alignment of the humerus (upper arm bone) is dependent on the scapula, and on the length and activity of several key muscles.

4. The forearm. Forearm movement is dependent on the humerus and therefore the scapula, and may be affected in climbers due to postural faults in the shoulder and back[26, 32].

The shoulder is a particularly important root cause of many upper body sports injuries as a result of its unusual construction. Most joints in the body achieve their stability and alignment because the bones are literally stacked on top of each other and locked together at joints. There is a trade-off between mobility in a joint and its strength and stability. The shoulder is at one extreme end of this continuum, with exceptional freedom of movement compared to other major joints of the body. It achieves this because the shoulder is essentially a floating system of bones and muscles. In fact, the only bony attachment of the shoulder and arm to the rest of the skeleton is via the clavicle (collar bone). However, this small, weak bone doesn't hold the shoulder in place against gravity, it merely holds the shoulder away from the body midline. Instead, several muscles and ligaments

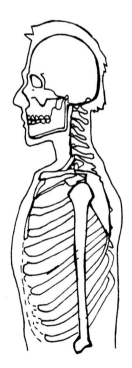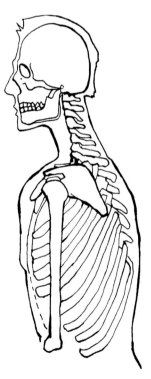

Fig: 3.1 Good and rounded upper back posture. When the scapula is tilted forwards by a rounded upper back, it cannot tilt backwards (posterior tilting) enough when the arm reaches overhead, contributing to shoulder impingement.

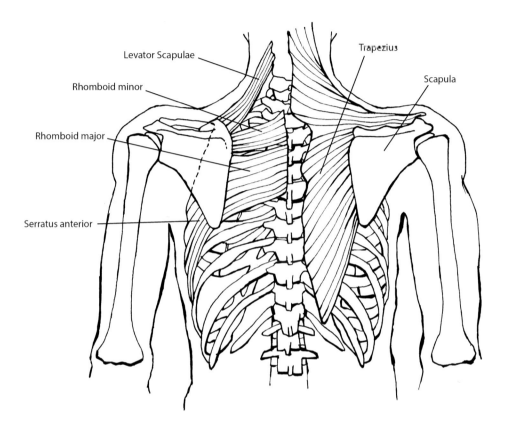

Fig. 3.2 Muscles holding the scapula in alignment.

hold the shoulder up and control its movement (Fig. 3.2). The benefits of the great agility of our upper bodies come at a cost. Since muscles are plastic tissues which readily adapt their length and strength, the shoulder is particularly vulnerable to poor alignment and injuries.

It is important to carry a basic understanding of the shoulder's anatomy and function to be able to identify faulty alignment before it causes an injury. The most obvious place to start an assessment of your shoulder function is the position of your upper back and shoulders at rest.

The scapula (shoulder blade)

The scapula must rest at the correct height, angle and distance from the spine in order to be able to move properly and support the arm through its full range of motion. Various postural faults and muscle imbalances can alter any of these variables. When the arm reaches overhead, the scapula must elevate, swing away from the spine (abduction) and tilt backwards (posterior tilting). Movement impairment of the scapula causes a knock-on effect of loss of range of movement in the shoulder and various shoulder injuries, as well as chronic neck and shoulder pain.

At rest, the inner (vertebral) border of the scapula should sit approximately three inches from the midline of the spine, running parallel to the spine and flat against the chest wall (Fig. 3.3). Deviation in either direction can occur, but it is more common for the scapula to sit too far from the spine. If your scapulae sit too far from your spine, try squeezing them together and holding the shortened position repeatedly through the day. Such 'inner range holding' exercises strengthen and shorten the muscles between the scapulae, bringing the vertebral border of the scapulae back to where it should be. Adjusting your car seat so that you can rest your scapulae on the back of the seat will also help reduce this postural fault.

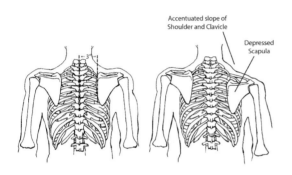

Fig. 3.3 Scapular positioning at rest; normal and depressed.

The scapula should also rest at the correct height in order to be able to support the arm properly during movement. The top of the scapula should rest level with the second or third thoracic vertebra (T2 or T3). If you are unable to identify this yourself, you can get a hint of whether your shoulders are elevated or depressed by using more simple clues. If the clavicle (collar bone) is resting horizontally rather than tilting upwards towards the shoulder, this may indicate depressed shoulders. The angle of the upper trapezius muscle will also form a steep slope from the neck to the shoulders, giving the appearance of a long neck. Spotting misalignment by yourself may be easier if you have one shoulder which has more marked misalignment.

As well as the resting position of the scapula, it is necessary to observe its position at full abduction (reaching vertically upwards with the arms). The scapula should rotate to 60° and elevate so that its top is level with the C7 vertebra on the spine (Fig. 3.4). Both elevation and rotation of the scapula are often impaired by muscle imbalance. The result of this is that the shoulder joint itself (where the humerus joins the scapula) must move more to obtain maximal overhead reaching, which causes shoulder impingement, the most common painful shoulder condition.

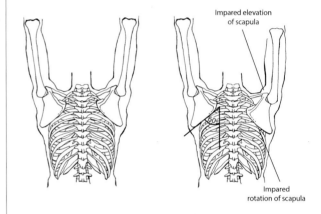

Fig. 3.4 Scapular positioning overhead; normal and depressed.

Shoulder impingement

What exactly happens during shoulder impingement? Depressed shoulders and various muscle imbalances limit both the rotation and elevation of the scapula. In addition to this, inadequate posterior tilting further contributes to movement impairment. Posterior (backwards) tilting of the scapula is limited if the scapula is anteriorly tilted at rest. This occurs when you have a slouched, rounded back (Fig. 3.1). Anterior tilting at rest means the scapula has further to tilt during overhead reaching and cannot achieve full tilting. The bony process on the top of the scapula that forms the 'roof' of the shoulder (the acromion) cannot get out of the way of the humerus and impingement occurs. In other words, the head of the humerus literally bumps up against the acromion, squashing the tendons of the rotator cuff, especially the supraspinatus, which attach here. This may be compounded by a genetic susceptibility, since different individuals have been shown to have variations in the shape of the acromion[24]. A hooked acromion (decreasing the size of the sub-acromial space) would seem to increase the risk of developing impingement and is seen much more frequently in rotator cuff tears.

As well as impairment of scapular movement, impaired movement of the humerus also contributes to impingement. How this happens is explained below. The symptoms of shoulder impingement and interventions for prevention and treatment are described in Section 10.

The humerus

To maintain the acromial space during overhead reaching, the humerus must also move in a coordinated motion with the scapula. The head of the humerus must be pulled down and rotated during movement to prevent the humeral head bumping up against the acromion of the scapula. The group of four muscles responsible for this action are collectively called the 'rotator cuff'.

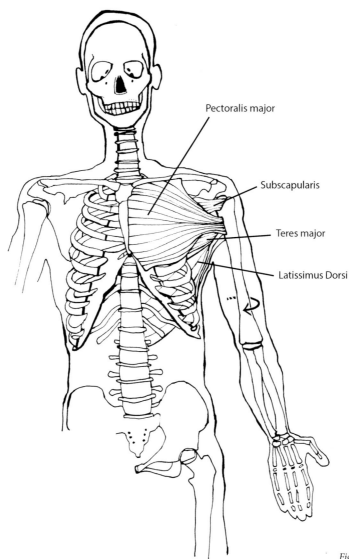

Pectoralis major

Subscapularis

Teres major

Latissimus Dorsi

Fig. 3.5 Internal rotator muscles.

The rotator cuff muscles run from the scapula to the head of the humerus and are individually activated depending on the angle of humerus movement. The small rotator cuff muscles that externally rotate the humerus must work in opposition to much larger muscles which internally rotate the arm. This, combined with the fact that many activities of sport and daily life involve internal rotation of the humerus, means that the large internal rotators tend to tighten, while the external rotators are stretched and become weak. The result of this is poor control of the humeral head during arm movements (with resultant impingement of the acromial space) and possible imbalances in the workload placed on the muscles around the elbow and forearm.

Two of the largest internal rotators of the humerus are pectoralis major (pecs) and latissimus dorsi (lats) (Fig. 3.5). The action of the lats is to pull the arm backwards and downwards. The lats tend to become well developed and often shortened through training for climbing. Teres major is another internal rotator which becomes well developed, and shortened in climbers. Pectoralis major, attaching to the humerus and running across the front of the chest, does not seem to become well developed in climbers, although it is often short, giving climbers a 'hollow chest' appearance with the shoulders pulled forward[21]. Pectoralis minor is a smaller muscle that sits behind pec major and also tends to become short in climbers. It is particularly troublesome if short as it is very difficult to stretch. Like pec major it pulls the arm forward. It actually attaches to the scapula and not to the humerus as pec major does.

Stretching of these commonly tightened internal rotators and simultaneous strengthening of the weakened external rotators is thought by many therapists to restore normal shoulder function and reduce the risk of many different shoulder and elbow injuries[21, 35]. Stretches and exercises for these muscles are described in section 10. In addition to the muscle imbalances, poor posture and years of progressive misalignment can cause the shoulder joint capsule to become tightened (reducing range of motion), or lax (reducing stability of the joint). This may be caused by the fact that climbers spend large amounts of time hanging passively from a straight arm, with the tension being transmitted through the joint

capsule rather than the muscles[21]. Abnormalities in the capsule must be assessed by a physiotherapist who can determine its laxity by assessing the 'end feel' of shoulder stretches.

The elbow and forearm

The effects of faulty upper body alignment on the muscles and tendons of the elbow and forearm are poorly described in the scientific literature. There is some limited evidence that weakness further up the kinetic chain in the core, shoulder and upper arm is associated with tennis elbow[26, 31]. There is also anecdotal evidence from physiotherapists that correction of shoulder range of motion and muscle imbalance appears to reduce symptoms of golfer's and tennis elbow[32]. Although the mechanics are not fully understood at present, it does seem plausible that postural and strength impairments of the shoulder and upper arm musculature contribute to elbow and forearm injuries.

The reason why weakness of more proximal muscle groups might throw stress onto distal areas such as the elbow relates to the kinetic chain principle. The body can produce very large forces from sporting movements when power is generated from the core and transferred with use of momentum to the extremities. Greater use of the large proximal muscle groups in sporting movements reduces the contribution required from distal muscle groups in the limbs to achieve adequate force generation. Moreover, when movements are performed at speed, better use of multiple body segments allows forces to be developed or absorbed with better control and less rapid accelerations in distal muscles. Any climber who has strained their arm from 'exploding' suddenly off a hold or breaking a hold off will understand the damaging effects of excessively fast changes in muscle length.

Where momentum is used in climbing movements, there is better use of the whole kinetic chain during climbing. Unfortunately, use of momentum in climbing is poorly understood, even by some high performing climbers. So it is not surprising that elbow injuries are suffered by climbers at a lower level who do not train heavily. However, even where technique is good, faulty alignment or poor range of motion may interfere with the transfer of force through the kinetic chain, throwing excessive stress on particular muscles or joints.

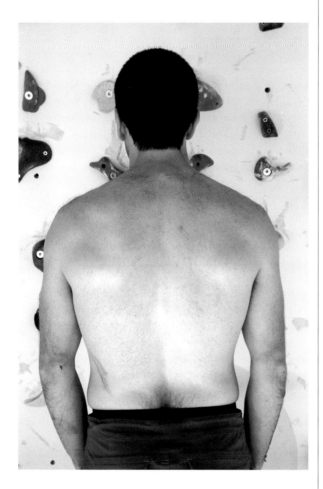

Photo 3.11 Shortness of the internal rotators is common in climbers. In ideal alignment, the olecranon of the elbow should face backwards with the arms resting at your side. Internal rotation causes the olecranon to face outwards and the elbow crease to face more inwards, towards the body.

It is common for the humerus to operate in an internally rotated position due to shortness of the internal rotators of the arm (Photo 3.11). The implications of this for forearm muscles during climbing are not yet understood. It is possible that there may be increases in the force demands and changes in the the length at which these muscles are forced to work. As well as the wrist flexors and extensors which are the most commonly injured area (golfer's and tennis elbow), climbing also involves forceful pronation and supination of the forearm. Injuries to both the pronator and supinator muscles have been reported in climbers. Pronator teres may be involved in up to 40% of golfer's elbow cases[36].

Sleeping position

We have seen that driving position and various everyday, occupational or sporting habits contribute to underlying postural faults such as rounded or depressed shoulders. Sleeping position is a particularly important aspect of everyday activities that can also play a role. Since we spend so much time sleeping, the potential effects on reducing postural strain by altering sleeping position are quite good.

If you sleep on your side, try to avoid letting the bottom shoulder slide forward. Instead, try to rest your scapula underneath and behind you to maintain a more normal shoulder position. If you sleep on your back, and have short pectoral muscles, your arms dropping down onto the bed can contribute to anterior glide of the humerus. If you prop your forearms up on pillows, lifting them off the bed, the humerus will rest in better alignment. If you sleep on your front then it is a good idea to place pillows under your shoulders to prevent gravity pulling them forward. Experiment with different positions and note the effect on any shoulder pain you have.

Conclusions

If you are reading all this functional anatomy for the first time and are unused to visualising the three-dimensional positioning and movement of bones and muscles in your body, hopefully two things will have struck you about the subject. Firstly, it is far from simple. So many variables of muscle length and strength affect posture and movement, especially when it comes to the shoulder. Secondly, faulty alignment in a proximal (close to the midpoint) area of the body may have knock-on effects down the chain to the forearm.

Both these points reinforce the need to seek professional help from a physiotherapist to maintain good alignment throughout your athletic career. A quick check of your shoulder alignment with the basic landmarks described above will very likely reveal some visible faults. However, planning a programme of exercises to address these specific faults requires detailed knowledge of all the muscles involved and specific tests for their function. An experienced sports physiotherapist can offer a tailored programme of corrective exercises. This minor expense (in the big picture of your whole climbing career) is likely to be well worth it. Be aware that correct diagnosis and exercise prescription for poor shoulder alignment can be challenging even for physiotherapists. So unless you have chosen your therapist via sound recommendation, seek a second opinion wherever possible. If you have no injuries and feel that your alignment is good, you might be able to train hard without injury for many years by simply keeping up a small programme of protective antagonist exercises. Basic corrective exercises for shoulders are described in section 10. However, poor choice of exercises or non-completion of exercises may contribute to gradual wear and tear that will eventually result in symptoms.

Two big problems for athletes are the un-motivating nature of corrective exercises for postural faults and the difficulty of reversing poor posture that is constantly being reinforced by our everyday sporting activities. Some authors question whether it is even realistic to correct postural faults in this way for general populations outside of sport[33]. Athletes display high levels of motivation when they are convinced of the benefits on offer for sporting success. However, the science has not yet reached a point where we can make clear, well researched conclusions about how best to improve our posture. One of the few things that therapists agree on is that variety of activity is protective against both poor posture and injury in general, and long periods of inactivity or positions of postural strain seem to contribute to injuries.

Therefore, if it proves too difficult to discipline yourself to complete corrective exercises for posture, simply taking part in some alternative movement activities such as yoga, pilates or basic functional exercises may be a useful alternative. If you enjoy doing the activity, it will be more likely to get done. For those who have more

advanced postural faults or already have pain from the neck, shoulder or elbows, corrective exercises should still be strongly considered. For many injuries, a little work can go a long way to reversing the problems and can easily be fitted in to your existing program of training for climbing.

Until this aspect of climbing biomechanics is better understood, the available evidence that links faulty alignment or weakness in the shoulder and upper arm with injuries should encourage all climbers to invest time and effort on these aspects, both for prevention and treatment of upper body injuries. However, the subject is not without controversy. The shift in approach by physiotherapy to see alignment as the root of injuries has been questioned. Many athletes have poor posture but no injuries. Moreover, simple stretching of shortened muscles (rather than active exercise) may not have much effect on posture[37]. Yet, therapists routinely experience success in treating injuries by prescribing exercises which are designed to correct faulty alignment. This underlines that the picture is not simple. It may be that in years to come, biomechanical contributions to sports injuries are valued less highly than training schedule design and movement technique. Let's hope sports medicine makes some progress in this area over the coming years.

Activity

In order to plan and implement an injury rehabilitation plan it is crucial to understand the importance of activity levels on the health of human muscle and connective tissue. In this discussion, I use the term 'activity' instead of 'training' to emphasise that all forms of activity need to be considered in judging the load on weak, healing tissue: training, therapeutic exercise and activities of daily life. Most sportspeople understand the basic training principle of 'use it or lose it'. In other words, tissue adapts dynamically to the demands placed on it, and any increases in the strength of muscles, tendons and ligaments gained through training are reversed if that training stimulus is removed.

The same principle applies in injury as in healthy training. Muscle and connective tissue which are exposed to lay-off tends to decrease in size and strength. Many people experience poor recovery from injuries by falling foul of this law of human adaptation. The mistake they make is to rest completely, rather than just rest from the intense demands of of normal sport participation. Of course, tissue which has been severely torn and hasn't had time to complete the early stages of healing is very weak and prone to further injury if not treated gently. So, in some cases, complete lay-off from sport is required for a while especially when the loading pattern cannot easily be reduced, such as in running or competitive sports. However, without the stimulus of movement and appropriate progressive loading as imposed by healthy training, recovery to previous levels of strength will not occur.

For most injuries where a single tendon is strained or partially torn, a short period of complete rest from loading is recommended. However, unloaded movement should be commenced as soon as pain allows. The duration of complete rest obviously depends on the injury and is still debated in sports medicine. However, the general trend is for initial lay-offs from all activity to be kept very short: sometimes only a day or two. The primary rationale for this is to limit detraining of the affected muscle-tendon unit (not to mention the whole athlete!).

Where a tendon or ligament has ruptured completely, a period of immobilisation in a splint or cast may be necessary to allow the tissue to knit together and get onto the first rung of the ladder in restoring tensile strength. Again, this period is kept as short as possible and the general trend has been for immobilisation periods to be reduced and physiotherapy exercises to start earlier (with some specific exceptions).

It is not just therapeutic exercise of the injured tissue that is important here. Maintenance of an anabolic state (stimulated to repair and strengthen tissue by regular use) of the whole body is important to make sure healing progresses optimally and to minimise losses of tissue strength in other areas[7]. It has been demonstrated clearly by experiment that exercising the opposite limb to one which has been injured or immobilised in a cast prevents loss of muscle tissue and the functional adaptations of training in the injured limb[7]. These effects occur because the mechanisms which promote tissue growth or atrophy occur at both the local and whole body levels The hormonal system plays a critical role in managing tissue adaptations to the demands placed on the body.

There is also some limited evidence that cross-training (that is, training which is quite remote from an athlete's normal training, such as running or biking for climbers) during a rehab program can slow some of the losses of training adaptations. However, it appears that the effects are less important if the athlete is more highly trained[7]. It is likely that running or other such activities will do little to slow the losses of upper body climbing fitness while an injury heals.

For these reasons, the objective of the injured athlete is always to find ways to maximise the activity and loading that can be safely performed on both injured and non-injured tissue, without causing further injury. It follows that the term 'rest' in the context of sports injury rehabilitation must be further clarified as 'relative rest'.

How to rest

Apart from the initial days after a significant new ligament or tendon injury has occurred, complete inactivity can actually worsen the situation for the injured athlete. Although the correct volume and intensity of stimulus that the injured tissue can handle may be laughably small, it is crucial to apply that stimulus to optimise the path to rehabilitation.

In the case of climbers recovering from mild soft tissue damage in a finger, elbow or shoulder, a relative rest protocol means an adapted regime of climbing, together with repetitive rehabilitation exercises to strengthen the injured tissue and correct any postural contributors. Many injuries will demand that the amount and intensity of the climbing decreases by a large amount at first, but once you are past the initial stages and the rehab program really gets under way, the reality of an optimal rehab regime is rarely restful. Optimal progress will require you to work at least as hard as you did in your healthy training, but the content of the training will be different. In fact, the main complaint of those motivated enough to follow a good rehabilitation plan is finding the time to complete the work. The detail of rehabilitation plans is discussed later in the book for specific injuries.

As you plan, monitor and adjust your rehab plan, the overarching approach is to use 'workarounds' to maximise the climbing intensity you can achieve. While this allows you to minimise disturbance to your climbing and hence your sanity, it is dangerous.

Firstly, the very fact you are climbing at all creates the enormous temptation to act as if you were not injured and make your injury worse. This takes great discipline and usually supervision from a coach to pull it off. This is one of the reasons your doctor will prescribe a complete lay-off from sport to let your injury heal. It is well known that without supervision, any participation in the sport creates a great risk of overdoing it and causing re-injury.

Secondly, the total amount of work the injury can absorb will be grossly limited and the specific rehab exercises must take priority. Too often, climbers who feel the injury is not coping with the demands placed on it will hold the climbing volume steady while skipping the rehab exercises to bring the total load down. Don't make this mistake. Perform only the climbing your injury can handle without reducing the volume of rehab exercises. The nature of basic rehab exercises tends to be fairly low intensity and high volume. A typical routine might involve a daily workout lasting an hour or more. For many climbers, it is a challenge to comply with a daily exercise regimen if they are used to enjoying a climbing session 2 or 3 times a week and doing little or no exercise on other days. The fact that most rehab workouts are very simple and can be performed at home ought to make them more palatable to comply with. Yet in reality, there is a psychological effect which counteracts this; if you don't have to go to a gym to do it, it is somehow easier to make an excuse to skip it.

Finding the workarounds that allow you to maintain

some level of altered climbing will take some imagination and experimentation. The later sections of the book have many suggestions for specific injuries. Generally speaking, they fall into two categories: changing your technique or changing the climbing terrain. It is your job to continually experiment and monitor what you can manage without aggravating the injury. The subtlety of the differences in climbing which can or cannot be tolerated should not be underestimated. For instance, golfer's elbow is often badly aggravated by the last few degrees of a deep lock-off. Hard bouldering on a 45° board where full locks are very rarely performed may be tolerated at a surprisingly high load before the injury is aggravated. Conversely, onsight trad climbing on vertical terrain, which involves a lot of locking-off to place gear in breaks may be much worse, despite the fact that the trad climbing 'feels' less intense overall. In the case of finger pulley injuries, holding a small hold may be tolerable as long as a fully openhanded 'drag' grip is used, whereas holding onto large jugs may provoke pain despite being easier to hang on to. You might have to hold onto the edge of jugs as if they were first joint pockets!

Altering your climbing technique in this way always feels awkward at first. It will probably take many sessions or even weeks to get used to it, and even then will take great discipline to sustain. Moreover, you will need to be aware of the limits of your own discipline and choose climbing situations that you are certain you can keep control over. Stressful climbing situations such as hard onsights, bold routes or friendly competition with friends at the bouldering wall are almost sure to cause you to become 'lost' in the moment and revert back to automatic habits. If you have weak, healing tissue, it may only need one momentary lapse of concentration to cause much more damage and turn a partial tear into a complete rupture needing months of lay-off. Proceed with extreme care.

To establish what or how you can climb without provoking pain in your injury, start by simply standing on the ground, pulling gently on some holds. Does a certain grip or body position provoke pain? Once you feel confident you can pull on the rock at all, you can climb some very easy moves as if you were warming up, all the while 'listening' for pain in the injury in certain moves. Once you have thoroughly tested the affected limb with a range of move types, you will have an idea what limitations you must to place on your climbing movements in order to climb safely. Be aware that pain in many soft tissue injuries, especially slow onset injuries like epicondylitis, will diminish significantly with warm-up. So continue monitoring the pain after the climbing session, and reserve judgement on what it can handle until at least the next day. If you feel the injury is sore after the session or on waking up the following morning, the session may have been too intense. Increasing pain signals across a number of sessions is the clearest indicator you can get that the intensity is too high. But remember, you might be able to experiment more with climbing differently, so you can maintain the same overall climbing load while causing less aggravation to the injury.

Warm-up and injury

Sports science has struggled for some time to find conclusive evidence for the importance of warm-up for both sport performance and for injury prevention. Several studies have shown that maximal performance can be produced in certain situations with very little or no warm-up. However, there are now several strands of evidence available that support the effect of warm-up on physiological, psychological and biomechanical aspects of our performance. This fits with the experience of most athletes who are convinced that their performance is better and more consistent after warming up. However, although the arguments for warm-up for maximal performance are now well supported, we are concerned in this book with its effects in preventing injury.

One of the primary effects of warm-up is literally to increase the temperature of the exercising muscle groups. It does appear that muscles and tendons that have been heated beyond normal resting temperature are more elastic and more resistant to tearing[38]. It is important to note here that whole body temperature does not change in a uniform manner. At rest, blood flow in our muscles is much lower than during hard exercise. Moreover, if our core temperature is on the low side such as when

standing still on a cold day at the crag, blood is moved away from our periphery and pools in our core, in order to limit further losses in core body temperature, which must be maintained. So it is possible to feel comfortably warm in our core when the muscles in our limbs are significantly below optimum temperature for hard exercise. Any climber used to sport climbing in the cold will have experienced this effect after a long shift belaying. Even when you feel reasonably warm in your core, if you step straight back onto a hard route without a good pulse raising warm-up jog or climb, your climbing level is far below what it could be.

The other important effect of warm-up is on our psychological readiness for performance. Proprioception (our awareness of the position and movement of limbs and joints) has been shown to increase with warm-up[39]. This is obviously a critical skill for injury avoidance since it allows us to anticipate, even during moments of extreme concentration, when a joint is being overloaded/overstretched so that we can respond by re-adjusting or letting go.

Warm-up also serves to focus the mind on the task in hand, clearing our consciousness of peripheral thoughts and becoming tuned in to the the cues we need to listen to in order to complete a hard climb with fewer errors and with awareness of dangerous positions. In addition, the warm-up provides a rehearsal of general climbing movement. If we are trying a hard redpoint of a boulder problem or route, it might even offer the chance to rehearse specific moves and reduce the errors such as feet slipping which are common triggers for injury.

So the importance of warm-up for injury prevention is fairly uncontroversial[40, 41]. However, what the warm-up should contain so that climbers can maximise the protective effect from injury has not been well researched. Where sports science research is unavailable, we must fall back on the experience of athletes and coaches and follow what seems to work well through others' trial and error, as well as adaptation of what is known to work in other sports. A warm-up routine which consists of progressively more difficult movements specific to the sport has been shown to reduce injury rates[41]. For climbers, a progressively more difficult series of routes or boulder problems will serve to increase blood flow to the upper body muscle groups and tune the mind into the kind of moves we will be doing during the session. The optimal length of the warm-up will depend on a number of factors. Climbers often report that a shorter warm-up is needed if climbing on consecutive days. Indeed, it has amazed me many times how little warm-up is needed to resume attempts on a hard boulder problem after taking an extended break of a couple of hours or more during the climbing session, when local muscle temperature may have declined significantly. In a bouldering session, a warm-up of 30-60 minutes of progressively more difficult climbing seems like a fair rule of thumb. That doesn't mean you can't try hard moves during the warm-up. After completing 20 minutes or so of easy moves, it's usually OK to progress to trying single moves or sections on a hard problem. This is a good rehearsal for your maximal efforts to link the problem once you are fully warm and climbing your best after 30-60 minutes. Age, climbing schedule, grade level, experience, the ambient temperature and many other things will all influence the amount of time it will take to warm up on a given day.

The key skill is to develop a 'sixth sense' for when you are warmed up and climbing well. Most climbers understand this intuitively and don't go far wrong with warm-up. Errors in the warm-up routine that cause injuries occur in those exceptional situations when you really should have spent more time warming up but didn't for some reason. Here are some examples:

- Lack of time, like a lunchtime climbing session.
- When it is really cold and feels like a chore (exactly when you need it most!).
- When your friends arrived earlier than you and are already warm and trying the hard stuff.
- After you took a long break for lunch or just a really long rest during the session.
- When there aren't any easy routes at the climbing venue.
- When you tried a warm-up route that was harder than you anticipated and were too lazy or self-conscious to come down and start on a more appropriate route instead.
- You were just too keen for the harder climbing to discipline yourself and complete the warm-up first.

The above reasons have been lamented by countless climbers who have paid dearly with serious finger, elbow and shoulder injuries for the sake of a few extra minutes spent doing a warm-up that would have helped them climb better anyway. At least you've only got yourself to blame if you don't listen to that inner voice telling you, "maybe I should warm-up a bit more before trying this".

One popular aspect of warming up I haven't yet mentioned is stretching. The importance of stretching in warm-up is a little more controversial. Stretching is a mainstay of injury prevention in popular sporting culture. Its popularity as part of the warm-up routine is not borne out by the available evidence[42]. Studies have repeatedly failed to demonstrate clear evidence that fewer injuries are caused when the warm-up included static stretching[43-45]. It appears that the value of stretching, if any, for injury prevention may lie in restoration of normal length of shortened muscles which have been altered by postural strain.

Lifestyle

One of the main messages of my climbing improvement book *9 out of 10 climbers make the same mistakes* was that the tiny details of training plans and exercises are often the main focus of climbers' attention, yet the bigger gains lie in stepping back to look at the 'big picture' factors of lifestyle and routine. Most of us are keen amateur athletes and in many ways we have a harder job than the tiny minority of fully professional athletes, which includes only a handful in the sport of climbing. Amateurs are essentially attempting to lead a double life, one with family and work commitments and another of training.

Although it is often possible to fit work, family, social time and hard training into the weekly routine, the aspect that is most neglected is time for adequate recovery from training. Moreover, it is not just recovery from the physical training that is needed. Since injuries are often caused by poor concentration in tired or distracted climbers, recovery from the general stresses of life is important too. Safe training needs time not only for muscles and tendons to recover, but also our ability to focus and concentrate.

The demands on our time and resources are varied and complex, so there is no single path which is best for us to follow to make the best use of our time. Moreover, 'real life' is a constant source of upset and upheaval to any lifestyle plan. So in this section I have set out some general ideas to guide your decisions about how to best plan your routine and make inevitable adjustments, both big and small.

Sleep

Since it is very difficult to test scientifically, the effects of decreased quantity and quality of sleep on athletic recovery and risk of injury are not fully understood. However, lack of hard scientific evidence at present does not mean we should underestimate the potential importance of sleep. There are plenty of sleep studies which demonstrate serious health problems caused by even small sleep deficits. Athletes and coaches across the sporting world testify that poor sleep has been a precursor to injury, and improvement in sleep reduces injury occurrence and improves performance. Although individual differences exist, good practice is to aim for at least 7-8 hours of restful sleep every night. Many athletes report better long term health and performance with as much as 10 hours per night, and there is evidence to support this[46]. Various aspects of recovery and repair such as growth hormone release happen mostly or only during sleep. The opinion of many sleep experts is that athletes ideally should simply sleep until they wake up. Those with an inflexible start time for morning duties will have to adjust their evening routine accordingly. Unfortunately, many in the western world allow themselves a mere 6.5 hours or even less. Even modest sleep deprivation results in poor health and performance scores across a whole range of measures[47, 48]. The period before you go to sleep is extremely important too. It should include time to relax and wind down, preferably without taking caffeine, to ensure that the quality of the sleep is optimised. Moreover, the blue light of digital screens is known to affect melatonin levels and cause significant problems getting to sleep for those who use computers and smartphones in the evening. Emerging technologies such as computer programs which reduce the blue light emitted by digital screens in the evening may have much potential for improving our sleep. It is also critical for sleep quality that your sleeping environment is optimised. The room should be completely dark, quiet and cool. Even the LED lights from digital clocks or standby buttons can be enough to interfere with sleep quality

Intermittent training

Rapid increases in training load are strongly associated with the onset of new injuries. The increases need not come from taking your training up a level from your previous limits. In fact, usually the problems arise when resuming training after a work, study or even injury enforced period of reduced training. The temptation to overtrain is far greater in this situation since it is the level you were used to before the interruption. As a rule of thumb, the time you should take to increase training back to a previous load should at least equal the length of the interruption in training. There are some workarounds to this by manipulating the volume-intensity ratio, but the general message is to give your body time to work back up to a previous level of conditioning. If it were not for the temptation among athletes to resume hard training too quickly after a break, intermittent training would be a healthy part of a training cycle. Periods of reduced training load are the basis of periodisation in training. So when life gets in the way of training and you need to take a few days, weeks or even longer out of full bore training, don't sweat too much about it. Yes, you'll need to build back up to where you were, but the break may well help push you to higher levels of performance in the long term. However, jumping back into hard training too quickly is an effective way to make your training break much longer than you had bargained for.

Non-sporting injury contributors

Our jobs and other activities of daily life often contribute to both the onset of new injuries and prolong the recovery from existing ones. Try to think of activities which could be contributing to your injuries. Contributing factors are not necessarily heavy physical tasks; it is more the repetitive nature of every day movements or positions that build up over months and years. Driving position, sitting position at work, lifting young children or carrying awkward items are all examples of activities which can cause injuries in otherwise healthy tissue. If you have an injury, you will probably already have noticed that you have to change aspects of your daily routine to relieve the stress and allow healing to make progress. Usually, all that is required is being more careful while performing these habitual tasks or movements or using a slightly different technique in order to minimise aggravation. For instance, If you have tennis elbow, you will know that lifting a kettle and belaying provokes pain. Washing your hair can be enough to irritate golfer's elbow. Your sleeping position can be a strong aggravator of shoulder injuries. If you are injury free, it is prudent to give some thought about which activities or aspects of daily life could potentially build up tissue damage that might eventually contribute to an injury.

Alcohol effects

The short term effects of consuming alcohol during the recovery period are poor rehydration and replacement of glycogen stores, resulting in a reduction in the amount and intensity of training that can be completed during the next workout[49]. But in this discussion we are concerned with the longer term effects. It has been suggested that the vasodilatory effects of alcohol may contribute to undesirable swelling in sites of muscle or soft tissue damage following training[49]. However, perhaps the greater concern is the knock on effects of alcohol consumption on sleep and diet quality. Sleep quantity and quality tend to be reduced. Alcohol contains many calories which have little nutritional value and alcohol consumption is associated with choosing poor quality, high energy foods which compound the effects on overall nutrition during recovery from training. There is no hard evidence to relate chronic alcohol consumption at different rates with injury occurrence in sport. However, it is fair to say that successful athletes, with long, relatively injury-free careers rarely consume much alcohol. Conversely, it would be possible to build a case, based on anecdotal evidence of high level athletes known to consume large amounts of alcohol, that it contributes to short and injury prone sporting careers. A further

concern, perhaps the greatest worry for climbers who enjoy drinking alcohol are the effects on coordination during the hangover period. Climbing or training during this period causes marked loss of fine motor control and seems likely to be a potential cause of injury inciting events. Good athletes rarely worry much about having a beer or two if the occasion arises. Because they tend to do it fairly rarely, the long term effects are too small to be a concern. The potential for problems arises when trying to combine regular nights of alcohol consumption with training over the long term.

Rushing

Trying to fit your training into a busy routine is, on the whole, a good thing. On one hand, keeping up regular training rather than allowing a full schedule to force breaks in your training will help protect you against injury. On the other hand, if 'rushed' sessions cause you to shorten your warm-up or climb without having time to focus on the job in hand, it creates a big risk for causing an injury. If you have to rush from work or have an unpredictable routine that throws out your planned training time, at least take the following steps to reduce the risk. Firstly, take a few minutes before you start to climb to focus. That means just sitting quietly and 'off loading' what you've just been doing and getting into your climbing mindset, or having a coffee, or just wandering round the climbing wall; do whatever works for you personally. Secondly, if you know you have little time left to fit the workout in, be more structured with your warm-up routine to avoid going off too hard. Have a planned series of steps that you mentally tick off. That might be an allotted time, a certain number of routes or problems, or a set progression of grades. Do whatever works to suit your individual needs so you know you are powered up, loosened up and feel safe to pull hard.

Training tired

For some, not training tired means not training very much at all. There is no doubt that training when tired is very risky for injury. It doesn't matter whether the tiredness is from previous training, from a busy day, or simple lack of sleep. The effect is broadly the same: you are less aware, less coordinated and likely weaker, too. So take all steps you can to avoid it. If you must train when tired, at least have a long warm up to fully stimulate body and mind. Some caffeine may help[50], but if you need chain espressos to drag you out of a sleepy stupor it is likely to be counterproductive; too much caffeine makes you jittery and prone to errors. Also, be realistic about what you can achieve with your limited resources of energy and time. Rather than squeezing out a 2 hour training session when exhausted, it may be better to sleep an hour later in the morning and have only 1 hour of training in a better rested state.

Poor equipment

Earlier in the book I discussed in detail the huge effect of bad rock-shoes on injury risk. Failure to upgrade or replace your rock-shoes quickly enough can be a lifestyle choice. Some people choose to squeeze every last drop of use out of a given piece of equipment. With something so important, I would argue there are probably better places to skimp. If you have never used a rock-shoe re-soler, you should try it. The results are really good and inexpensive. The same goes for any piece of equipment you use. Is it really a good idea to shiver every night in a cold sleeping bag on your sport climbing trip and then try to climb hard every day? Will the quality of your recovery be optimal? If cost really is the limiting factor, that's fine, but not if you are lining up beers in the campsite bar every night! It's not just a salary that encourages older climbers to have a big, fluffy, warm sleeping bag, or to sleep under a roof on trips. They have learned from hard experience that not recovering properly leads to trip-ending injuries.

Even if you cannot fully remove from your routine the lifestyle causes of injury that I have described above, simple awareness of them will help you reduce the risk to an extent. If you know it is risky to train tired, or under time pressure, or without good rest, or with a slight hangover, you will adjust your climbing and the content of your climbing sessions to match. The adjustment may be very subtle; just being ever so slightly more ready to let go if a move goes badly, or winding down the difficulty of the boulder problems a few minutes earlier in the session.

There is no getting away from the fact that when taking care of our bodies to maximise performance, making amateurish choices give amateur results. The first result, failing to reach your climbing potential, is easier to live with because it is harder to see. You will never truly know just how much harder you could have climbed if you had made a better routine for yourself. However, the second result, that of contributing to injuries you could have avoided or recovered from more quickly, you will certainly notice, but might still mistakenly attribute to bad luck.

Nutrition

It is universally accepted that a good, varied diet is essential for optimising both performance and health in sport. A healthy 'athlete's diet' is not radically different in nutrient content from that which is recommended for the general population. The demands of training do increase tissue turnover and energy requirement. But in most cases (within the sport of climbing) we don't need to take care to eat more than we feel like eating, since appetite efficiently ensures energy requirements are met by increasing the volume of food eaten. Although research evidence is far from complete, it appears that the best way to eat for prevention of or recovery from injuries is to consume a balanced diet including foods from all five food groups: meat, dairy, cereals, fruit, and vegetables. An adequate supply of amino acids (the building blocks of protein) is essential for maintenance of all muscle and tendon tissue, including the collagen that gives tendons their tensile strength[49, 51]. Vitamins A and C, magnesium and copper are important in collagen synthesis and can all be obtained in adequate quantity with a healthy diet[8]. Achieving adequate intake of many nutrients is achievable with a balanced diet and so supplementation may be unnecessary in most cases[49]. However, four groups of athletes tend to end up deficient in key nutrients and at risk of poor performance and injury: those undertaking high volumes of aerobic endurance training, those attempting to maintain a low body weight, those who fail to consume a balanced diet, and those with specific health problems[51].

The athlete's balanced diet

Many climbers consume a sub-standard diet with nutritionally poor food choices. The food industry does not help, as misleading marketing and labelling of food will fool you into making poor choices unless you know exactly what to look for. Those who feel unable, or not motivated enough, to educate themselves on good sports nutrition practice should have their diet analysed by a dietitian, to identify areas for improvement. Here are some basic points that will help you achieve an adequate intake of nutrients for good muscle and tendon health:

- Eat less processed and 'fast' food. Generally speaking, processed food tends to lose valuable nutrients. Fast food tends to be high in calories from saturated fat and refined sugar and are nutrient poor. These fill you up and make you less likely to eat high quality foods. As discussed in the lifestyle section, avoid replacing calories from high quality food with calories from alcohol and the bad food you tend to consume along with it.

- Eat plenty of fruit and vegetables to ensure adequate consumption of micronutrients such as vitamins, minerals and antioxidants for their anti-inflammatory properties. Better still, eat them fresh and raw. Many vegetables such as spinach are great sources of protein too, which might become important if you are vegetarian. Large amounts of fruit can contribute to an increase in calories. Two fruit portions per day, eaten around training, and 1-2 portions of vegetables per meal is a good ratio to aim for.

- Ensure adequate protein intake. Healthy cuts of meat, offal and fish are a good way to achieve this, but legumes and certain vegetables will also help. Eggs, natural yoghurt and milk are also great healthy protein sources. These sources are preferable to supplementation as they are also micronutrient rich. Thanks at least in part to successful marketing by the sports nutrition supplement industry, many athletes consume excessive amounts of protein for their weight and training load[49]. If you choose to consume extra

protein in the form of protein powder shakes, choose them carefully as many also contain refined sugar, large amounts of caffeine and other ingredients which may be unnecessary. However, if excess protein is consumed without extra fat or sugar, there may be no effect on body fat[52]. In a normal diet, it is not difficult to achieve adequate protein intake for most climbers' routines. However, certain amino acids could end up being deficient if the dietary protein sources are not varied enough. Protein intake could be deficient during a food restricted diet for weight loss (see section below).

Weight management and injury in climbers

There are a number of issues which relate injuries in climbing and body weight. Performance in climbing is heavily dependent on strength-to-weight ratio, and climbers are generally keen to maintain as low a body weight and body fat percentage as possible. That said, there are probably more overweight recreational climbers than underweight. It has been suggested that carrying a lot of excess muscle and/or body fat is, in itself, a risk factor for injuries since the high loads place greater stress on the upper body and relatively delicate finger ligaments and joints. It is a plausible hypothesis, but there are no data available in support or otherwise. It does seem prudent for overweight climbers to reduce excess body fat to within the normal athletic range of 5-15% for males and 10-25% for females.

For many climbers, chronic attempts to maintain low or very low levels of body fat appear to confer an increased risk of injury, although the mechanisms for this remain unclear. There is anecdotal evidence from other activities which are dependent on low body weight, such as distance running, gymnastics, and ballet, that both nutrient deficiencies and injuries are more common than in non-weight dependent sports[53]. Sports nutritionists take this issue extremely seriously and it is for good reason that they recommend any athlete wishing to maintain a low body weight to do so under the supervision of a professional dietician.

It is possible to achieve realistic goals of low body

weight and fat percentage without serious performance and health consequences if great care is taken over the diet and methods used to lose weight[54]. Here are some general points which should be observed:

- Use modest restriction of calories together with increased energy usage (through exercise) to achieve a negative energy balance without a drastic reduction in food intake. Intermittent fasting on alternate days of very low and normal calorie intake, together with exercise may be a useful strategy for climbers[55]. However, there are several different methods of safe and effective weight loss. Which method is best depends on individual needs, circumstances and preferences.

- Good quality sources of protein ensure that protein availability for tissue repair is not limited during weight loss, as well as limiting loss of muscle mass during reduced training. Protein feedings should be spread throughout the day to maintain protein levels in the blood. Protein also has favourable effects on appetite reduction[56].

- Eating plenty of fruit and vegetables greatly helps to achieve adequate micronutrient intake. The low calorie density and high fibre content of these foods also make them one of the best ways to achieve weight loss.

- Fats are essential to health and recovery from training and injury, particularly the omega 3 fats found in oily fish. The easiest way to reduce overall fat content in the diet is to reduce processed or 'fast food' consumption.

- Overall carbohydrate consumption should be reduced but with care to practice nutrient timing to ensure there is an adequate supply to fuel your training and recovery. If you are not motivated to research nutrient timing for sport, a sports nutritionist will be able to help you plan your eating routine. Matt Fitzgerald's books *Racing Weight* and especially *Racing Weight Quick Start Guide* are good texts to get a handle on the details of nutrient timing.

- Large portions should be reduced; more of a 'grazing' approach of healthy snacks and smaller main meals helps to improve diet quality[57].

- Be careful when choosing processed food products labelled 'low fat'. These products such as ready meals, bars, sauces or baked goods are often loaded with refined sugars so they remain tasty despite having slightly less fat. Various ideas have been proposed as to how refined sugars such as sucrose and high fructose corn syrup appear to contribute to weight gain, including that they may fail to stimulate satiety hormones. However, researchers have failed to show firm evidence for this and continue to point to general overconsumption of calories and lifestyle factors as being the important factors[58].

Supplementation

While supplementation may be unnecessary in climbers with an optimal, balanced diet, there are certainly some strong arguments for supplementation where the diet is restricted for medical or other reasons. A general multivitamin and mineral supplement may be a good precaution to ensure adequate micronutrient intake if you are restricting calories or feel unable to maintain a balanced diet[51]. Whey protein or leucine may be useful supplements to achieve adequate good quality protein intake without the extra calories in its dietary sources such as milk, yogurt, cheese and meats. It is true that typical modern western diets can be deficient in many nutrients. Supplements should not be taken as an alternative to improving diet quality. A full discussion of nutrition supplements for health and performance is beyond the scope of this book. However, there are a few injury specific supplements worth singling out for discussion here.

Glucosamine is involved in the repair of cartilage and it has been suggested that its supplementation as Glucosamine Sulphate (often with Chondroitin) could aid cartilage healing and maintenance. It has become popular among osteoarthritis sufferers as an alternative to anti-inflammatory medication (which has severe long term side effects). But it has also been marketed to the sporting community as promoting 'joint health'. Several early studies showed some evidence of beneficial effects on arthritic joint pain and this has propelled the supplement's global popularity, with $2 billion in global sales in 2008. However, a recent review of the research evidence for its efficacy in the British Medical Journal (BMJ) has shown that it appears to have no significant effect[59]. The BMJ review recommended that it should not be prescribed by the medical profession for joint pain. Studies which have shown benefits were generally small and poorly designed, thus their evidence is questionable. When larger and better designed studies were carried out in the 2000s, they failed to show any beneficial effect. The BMJ review recommended further study to address some remaining questions about the specific conditions in which glucosamine could be useful, but the authors felt that based on the existing data it was unlikely that future research would find beneficial effects.

Omega 3 fatty acids are often deficient in a typical western diet. Omega 3 has important circulatory and anti-inflammatory effects which may be useful for injury rehabilitation. Many of us do not eat enough oily fish or other omega 3 sources and so supplementation may be useful. The best sources of omega 3 are salmon, sardines, mackerel, chia seeds and flax seeds. A further complication in the story of omega 3 involves a similar essential fat: omega 6. A typical western diet has too much omega 6 and the two types of fat have opposing effects. In other words, too much omega 6 negates the benefits of the sparse omega 3. Omega 6 has a pro-inflammatory effect in the body. An ideal ratio of omega 3 and omega 6 is 1:1, which was probably achieved with the type of diet our hunter-gatherer ancestors ate. However, in western diets it may be more like 1:40. Thus it is important to address the excess of omega 6 in our diet as well as consuming more omega 3. Omega 6 is commonly found in processed foods, especially in vegetable oils such as soybean or sunflower oil.

The amino acid arginine is a precursor of nitric oxide (NO), which has been implicated in tendon growth. Transdermal NO donation via skin patches has been shown to improve recovery outcomes in tendinosis under certain circumstances. NO donation is discussed in section 4. It has been suggested that supplementing arginine could assist with availability of NO for healing tendons[60], but there is no good evidence of a beneficial effect. Arginine is a non-essential amino acid which can be synthesised by the body. Arginine is also used by body builders in the belief that its supplementation leads to increased growth hormone levels and subsequent anabolic effects. However, this only appears to occur with large intravenous doses which could not be taken orally without gastrointestinal upset[61]. Moreover, a larger growth hormone effect can be achieved simply by doing some training!

A specific warning for female climbers

Females naturally have a higher body fat percentage than males and different consequences of attempting to maintain artificially low levels of body fat. Moreover, gender differences in the patterns of fat storage and metabolism appear to make it harder for females than males to lose body fat. Males tend to store more body fat in the upper body and abdominal areas and fat is more readily metabolised in these areas during exercise. For these reasons, it seems possible that females could be particularly vulnerable to the injury consequences of needing to use severe calorie restriction to achieve weight loss.

The serious health complications experienced by female athletes attempting to maintain low body weight have been well documented and need to be highlighted. Maintenance of a low body fat percentage in females leads to menstrual cycle disruption below a certain threshold. The threshold varies greatly between individuals, with some females maintaining body fat at 11% without problems, while others experience menstrual upset below 20% body fat. Therefore, the body fat percentage which represents a safe minimum for females depends on the individual. Although low body fat percentage is associated with menstrual dysfunction or absence (amenorrhea), it appears that it is the low energy availability from calorie restriction actually triggers symptoms. In general, females should maintain a body fat percentage that allows a normal menstrual cycle to proceed. Young female athletes maintaining low body fat percentage are at risk of delayed onset of puberty and menarche. Apart from the reproductive problems caused by low body fat in adult females, the major consequence of concern is early onset of osteoporosis[62].

Osteoporosis is caused by athletic amenorrhea because the ovarian steroid hormones stimulate calcium uptake into bone. Bone loss has been widely reported among female distance runners and there is some anecdotal evidence of the condition in female climbers (avulsion fractures from simple falls onto bouldering mats). It has been suggested that if amenorrhea is allowed to persist over time (over 3 years) then bone loss becomes irreversible, with serious implications for later life. Bone mass tends to decrease throughout adult life and should only reach a critical threshold for fractures in the elderly. The occurrence of fractures in the elderly is associated with loss of independence and general deterioration of health in late life. Osteoporosis can also be an extremely painful and debilitating condition: degeneration of the spine causes chronic and severe back pain. Females attempting to minimise body fat should take care to ensure adequate calcium intake in the diet, and consider supplementation if this is cannot be achieved. Vitamin D is also critical for bone health, and should be supplemented if the recommended intake cannot be met by exposure to sunlight and dietary sources. However, supplementaion is no substitute for increasing body fat percentage to a level that allows resumption of regular menses, and thus normal hormone function.

In summary, if you have suffered one or more injuries, the quality of your diet is one of the places you should look to identify a possible contributing cause. Poor diet quality and maintaining low body fat for sport have both been shown to predispose athletes to injuries. Fortunately, the solution - to eat a balanced diet of good quality food - is attainable for almost all climbers.

Make your next move from where you actually are.

Frank Kuppner

Rehabilitation of climbing injuries - treating both causes and symptoms

Section 4

Acute rehabilitation

If you pick up a regular sports medicine textbook and turn to the section covering the immediate response to a new injury, it will generally provide advice for sudden onset, traumatic injuries which are common in many sports. On the playing field, injuries to tendons or ligaments often come from falls, impacts or sudden changes of speed or direction, causing soft tissue to tear. Climbers have this sort of sudden onset injury too, such as a ruptured finger pulley or torn shoulder labrum. However, many climbing injuries are slow onset injuries where you notice the symptoms increasing over one or several sessions. Injuries can even be a mix of both, where progressive microscopic damage, perhaps below symptomatic level, precedes a sudden worsening with macroscopic tearing of the weakened tissue.

Sudden onset of symptoms is referred to as an acute injury. Healing from acute soft tissue trauma follows three broadly defined stages: inflammation, proliferation and remodelling (Fig. 4.1). Proliferation and remodelling are the formation of a collagen scar and adaptation of this scar back into normal functional tissue. These stages will be discussed in later sections. The initial acute or inflammatory stage is essential in managing the body's response and initiating the later stages of healing. The inflammatory stage may not actually occur if the injury is a slow onset injury such as tendinosis. This is one of the reasons why slow onset tendon pain is so reluctant to heal.

If you do suffer an acute tear of soft tissue, there is a well defined protocol to respond in the initial days, known as the RICE protocol: Rest, Ice, Compression and Elevation.

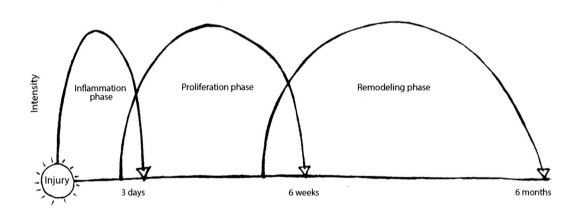

Fig. 4.1 Stages of healing.

The purpose of the initial rest is to protect the area from further damage. This aspect is normally applied automatically after a sports injury since pain dictates immediate withdrawal and protection. However, this is not always the case. Partial tears of finger pulleys can occur without much immediate pain. Even complete ligament ruptures are not always painful enough to stop you climbing immediately. Thus, although the climber has noticed that something is wrong with a finger, the temptation to continue a route or have another attempt is there. Don't do it! I have heard numerous stories of complete or even multiple pulleys rupturing when the climber has failed to stop after a minor tear. Ice packs applied to the injured site reduce bleeding and reduce further tissue damage, as well as providing pain relief. There is no consensus on the best protocol for applying ice packs. In general, the deeper the injury site and the more fat tissue the athlete has, the longer the application has to be to achieve adequate cooling. Ice should be used for 20-60 minutes every two hours in the first two days post injury[63, 64]. There are various methods of applying ice including ice baths, bags of ice and water. Don't apply ice directly to the skin as this can cause an ice-burn.

Ice does not reduce swelling which has already occurred - a point which is not well understood among sportspeople. Its effect is merely to reduce further increases in swelling and slow tissue metabolism. Compression, used in combination with ice and elevation of the affected limb prevents accumulation of excessive swelling. Movement of the affected area is by far the most effective way to reduce existing swelling. The accumulated fluid can only be drained via the lymphatic system. Lymphatic veins have a valve system and hence the pumping action of physical movement (unloaded passive movement is sufficient) assists drainage.

Aside from the obvious benefits of preventing further tissue damage, the concept of intervening to reduce of the extent of inflammation itself during the acute stage has been the source of great debate in sports medicine over the years. The inflammatory response is an extremely complex biological phenomenon, which has evolved to initiate the healing process immediately after injury. Inflammation greatly sensitises the area making any movement painful, ensuring that further trauma is avoided. However, because sportspeople tend to have well vascularised tissues, bleeding into an injured area may become excessive. Excessive, uncontrolled bleeding and swelling into an injured area brings its own problems[7]. Thus the rationale for reducing excessive inflammation is to limit bleeding and allow the injured athlete to progress more quickly to mobilisation and then strengthening exercises. It may be safe to intervene to reduce inflammation so long as the rehab activities that follow are at a suitably low intensity. As well as RICE, anti-inflammatory medication such as ibuprofen may be useful in the 24-48 hours following a traumatic soft tissue tear to help reduce excessive inflammation, although the rationale for this is still controversial[65]. Beyond the initial couple of days its use is generally not recommended as it may interfere with biological initiation of tissue growth and subsequent healing.

The RICE protocol should be followed for any sudden onset soft tissue injury. In the case of finger pulley tears, visible swelling and even pain on unresisted movement may be minimal. However, the area may still benefit from ice to reduce bleeding and certainly the injury should be rested for several days to allow the acute stage to be completed without causing further damage.

Inflammation is usually complete by 3-5 days with minor trauma and at this point the priority for rehabilitation shifts to getting the injured area moving as it begins to grow an immature scar which must be remodelled by progressive loading into healthy strong tissue.

When to move beyond acute care?

Ultimately, it is loading of the injured tissue which forms the driver for restoration of full tensile strength of tissue weakened by injury. So the short answer to the question of when to move from rest and immobilisation to movement and progressive exercise is as soon as possible. The faster therapeutic exercise can begin, the more rapid the progress of strengthening the injured tissue occurs and the problems of excessive, tight and weak scar formation can be avoided. However, when you add human error to the equation, things get more complicated.

In the ideal sports medicine scenario with athlete, coach and sports medic working together to assess the injury and implement a carefully applied program of therapy, the athlete might commence exercises after a couple of days post injury. The first collagen fibrils of the immature scar are not laid down until the fifth day of a traumatic injury. However, it is also important to limit tightening and weakening of healthy tissues around the injury.

The initial days (even weeks for more serious injuries) of exercises should be very gentle, simply moving the injured limb under no resistance at all. The purpose is first of all to allow a good scar to form which is not damaged by overly enthusiastic rehab exercises and is long enough to maintain full range of movement. It is also probable that some of the inevitable losses of form are offset even by the most gentle exercise, compared to complete inactivity which causes rapid loss of both muscle and soft tissue strength.

Under this sort of care and supervision, the athlete might use some anti-inflammatory medication in those initial days to permit the exercises to begin. For all except the most knowledgeable, disciplined and experienced athletes, this is a risky practice because the danger of overdoing it and making the injury worse is always there. In the initial days when an immature scar is forming in the damaged tissue, it is very vulnerable. Dulling the pain warning from an injury at this time will contribute to the danger of re-injury. In addition, there is a tendency for the athlete to not yet have fully accepted the new situation of being injured. There is a strong (often subconscious) desire to ignore the injury if possible and carry on as normal.

It is for this reason that a good period of complete rest is often recommended before rehab exercise commences. So what balance should you strike between risking further damage to a fresh injury by an early and over-zealous commencement of therapeutic exercise, versus complete rest and the problems of loss of tissue strength and tight or weak scarring?

The answer depends on several factors, most notably the location and severity of the injury. For strains and partial tendon/ligament tears where the injured part can essentially still function, but only at a low level of load before pain is provoked, exercise may be safely commenced under no additional load after a few days. This sort of timescale is practical for climbers anyway, since we don't usually have a sports medic to hand when we get injured. It will probably take a few days after you are injured to source and attend a consultation with a good sports medic for your diagnosis, and to read everything you can get your hands on about the injury, so that you become an expert on it.

For milder injuries such as a partial pulley tear, it will have settled down a little after a few days and probably be pain free to move the finger under no load. So you will be able to test the level of load that it can handle without provoking pain. Yes, it will probably be very little! But you have a starting point for your return to full strength and you can begin to do the exercises which are going to drive the progress in strength gains.

If you do attempt a tentative start to some unloaded or very low load exercises but the pain gets noticeably worse, don't be afraid to step back and give it another week of lay-off. Taking some more days or weeks to allow it some breathing space will do little harm compared to the damage you can do with exercises that progress too quickly. Also, if you have had a diagnosis from your sports medic and been given a green light to begin moving and exercising, but this causes unexpected pain, make sure you go straight back and see them again to update the situation. There is always a chance that the initial diagnosis or estimate of the extent of injury was wrong.

Some readers may have picked up this book having already taken many weeks or months of complete lay-off from climbing with no physiotherapy and be worried that this was a wrong move. It is true that complete lay-off means that healing does not progress nearly so well for many soft tissue injuries. It is also true that the surrounding healthy muscle and soft tissue will lose strength during the lay-off. So no matter how late it is, get going with a physiotherapy program now! The losses of tissue strength are still reversible and although a large, weak scar will have formed, its function can be dramatically improved with diligent work. At least the tissue has had breathing space to form a healing scar without further damage and you can start afresh, albeit from a low level. The biggest thing to worry about now is your mindset for returning to climbing. You have endured months of psychological torment in your self-denial of climbing, your injury is pain free in normal life activities and now you feel like you've earned your return to climbing. But the reality is you are still near the starting blocks. Your injury may have healed back to the level of a non-climbing (probably fairly sedentary) lifestyle where little demand is placed on it. Without the program of progressive increase of load you ought to have started weeks ago, re-injury is a big risk. On the face of it, this might seem disappointing. But as long as you adopt the rehabilitation mindset (section 5), you will be fine and will probably enjoy the coming challenges.

For slow onset injuries such as elbow tendinosis, the injury pathology is essentially non-inflammatory. Unless you have ignored symptoms until they have progressed to a severe injury, the acute response of complete rest is bypassed and corrective and strengthening exercises can be commenced as soon as symptoms are noticed. In mild cases of tendinosis, a period of lay-off may only compound losses in strength of the affected tendon through disuse atrophy.

Goals of mid-late rehabilitation

Nobody ever made a greater mistake than he who did nothing because he could do only a little.
Edmund Burke

After five days following a soft tissue tear, the immature collagen scar will begin to form[24]. This second 'proliferative' phase of healing can last from a few days to many weeks depending on how severe the injury has been. This scar consists of weak collagen fibrils which are loosely arranged and disorganised. In practical terms, immature scar tissue is the 'scaffolding' on which healthy tendon or ligament tissue is restored. Without a rehabilitation program, the scar will remain weak and bulky and will tend to tighten. The aim of the rehabilitation program is to encourage progress of the scar to normal healthy collagen which is much stronger, with fibrils densely packed and aligned in the direction of force transfer.

Progressive loading promotes this transformation which is known as remodelling. Proliferation of immature scar tissue and the subsequent remodelling stages overlap, and hence progressive loading from a low level can begin almost as soon as the scar starts to form. The priority early on is to ensure that the scar does not form too short, so that range of motion is protected. So early mobilisation is very important, even under no load. Later, regular therapeutic exercises must be used to train the immature collagen back to full tensile strength. The remodelling phase may take up to one year to complete. Unfortunately, it often takes even longer because over-zealous progression back to sporting activity is common, causing re-injury.

The idea of progressive rehabilitation exercises conjures images of repetitive, boring, basic exercises in the physio room for many months. Most rehab programs do include some of these. However, despite their repetitive nature, they can often be performed at home and combining them with some other work or entertainment activities ought to mitigate much of the boredom. Moreover, if athletes fully grasped just how important these exercises are, they might not seem so much of a drag.

However, basic exercises are just one part of the picture. Climbing, being a non-competitive, varied and flexible activity allows a significant part of many rehab programs to be done by actually going climbing, with obvious benefits for the psyche. It is a dangerous business, because great discipline is needed to avoid re-injury. By using workarounds for how you move in climbing, the actual climbing can be relatively intense, while keeping the loading of the injured area to a minimal level.

As you read through this chapter, I hope you will notice that the level of work and commitment required for optimal progression back to normal function is very high. One of the key messages of this book is for climbers to leave behind the idea of a rehab program being about relieving inactive boredom by watching DVDs and drinking beer. For most, the problem is fitting it all in. Hopefully climbers can reorientate themselves towards this idea and get ready to put in the hours.

Modern understanding of tendon injuries and recovery

Tendons don't like rest or change.
Jill Cook, International Scientific Tendinopathy Symposium 2012

Much remains unknown about what happens at the cellular level in injured and healing tendons. In fact, research over the past two decades has opened more new lines of enquiry than it has resolved[8, 12, 66]. Part of the problem is that tendons injured in sport are hard to study scientifically. Much of the research has been done on animals involving tendons that have been cut and then the healing response observed. The slow, progressive damage that precedes many sports injuries is difficult to replicate in animal research models and so the details of the cellular changes can only be estimated in humans. Acute traumatic tears to both tendons and ligaments appear to heal following the well understood progression of initial inflammation, followed by early collagen scar formation and, ultimately, remodelling into mature tissue. It appears that full restoration of healthy tendon tissue is never achieved. However, tendons still show ability to become strengthened and enlarged by training, so full function can often be restored and pain reduced or eliminated, despite the tissue itself showing the evidence of past injury.

So what has been learned from recent research? Perhaps the most important development has been better knowledge of the role of inflammation in slow onset tendon injuries. Chronic tendon pain used to be referred

to under the blanket term of 'tendinitis', suggesting that inflammation plays a critical role in the condition. It is now accepted that the classic inflammatory response and healing progression of acute traumatic injuries does not occur in slow onset tendon injury and there is now ongoing argument about which, if any inflammatory mediators are involved in the process[67]. Although some of the body's inflammatory chemicals have been found in chronically painful tendons, the response is not the same as acute injury[12, 68]. Hence the term 'tendinosis' superseded the old terminology for slow onset tendon pain, to describe what is thought to be a combination of degenerative and inflammatory changes in these injuries. Today, researchers use the term 'tendinopathy' (tendon-pathology) as an overarching term to describe painful tendon injuries including acute tendinitis and degenerative tendinosis[66]. There is continued debate over the cellular changes that occur in painful tendons[67]. New theories suggest that chronic tendon pain is most accurately described as a 'failed healing response' to chronic damage to the tendon[68]. The irony is that accumulating microscopic damage in overstressed tendons can be much more difficult to rehabilitate than complete traumatic rupture because the classic healing response is not triggered. It is not known why the normal inflammatory response is reduced or absent in this type of injury.

Although a distinction needs to be drawn between slow onset tendinopathy and acute tearing of tissue, it is important to recognise that the former may lead to the latter. Healthy tendons are not thought to be routinely activated anywhere near their maximum breaking strength. Tendons are about four times as strong as the maximum force of their attached muscle. However, they behave in an elastic manner, storing energy by being stretched during dynamic movement. It is thought that tendons rarely rupture without underlying damage being present, even if this damage is below the level of pain. Climbers rarely suffer tendon ruptures although ruptures of rotator cuff tendons do occur when shoulder impingement is not corrected. However, microscopic damage that accumulates without pain for many months can cause acute ruptures of small focal areas within tendons during maximal loading. In this way, a climber who has a sudden onset of tendon pain after a slip or a particularly aggressive move may assume that an otherwise healthy tendon has torn, when in fact the tear is merely the inevitable result of progressive tendon damage.

Why would tendons in healthy, active people develop this kind of damage? This question has not been answered by the research, but some interesting ideas are emerging. Training tends to increase the size and strength of tendons, while disuse causes atrophy and weakness in them[7]. Numerous hypotheses for tendon damage have been offered, relating to the characteristics of the frequency, magnitude and speed of exercise loading. Ruptures of tendons often occur during the transition from concentric to eccentric movement. Eccentric and sudden maximal muscle activation increase force transfer through tendons. This is likely why uncontrolled movement (poor technique) and excessive or premature use of plyometric training such as campus boarding precedes injuries in climbers. Rapid unloading of tendons also appears to damage tendons by creating shear forces between tendon fibrils[8]. 'Exploding' or slipping suddenly from a handhold creates this scenario in climbing.

Microscopic damage in both muscles and tendons is essential in training, as it is the stimulus for subsequent supercompensation and strengthening. However, if the rate of damage outstrips the rate of repair and growth, injury results. Given that different sports cause predictable patterns of injuries to particular tendons, it seems possible that general overuse caused by the pattern of training loading may not fully account for the injuries that result. The picture appears to be more complicated than simple overuse. For example, as well as tensile loading, tendons can be subject to compressive loading as well. Where compressive loading is excessive or sustained, it appears to be damaging.

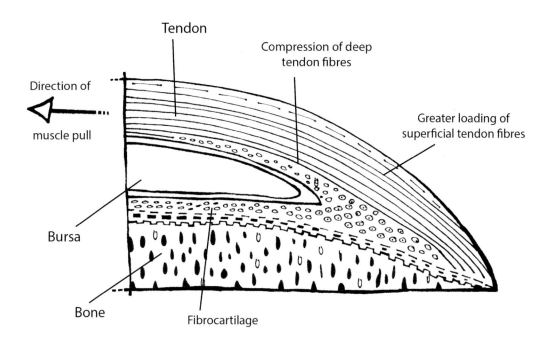

Fig. 4.2 Compressive forces in tendons.

An interesting theory that has emerged through the study of patellar tendinopathy (runner's knee) is that tendons are subjected to damaging compressive and/or shear forces when repeatedly exercised at certain joint angles[9, 69]. Tendons are often loaded while wrapped around bone or soft tissue at certain joint angles (Fig. 4.2). This creates shearing within the tendon and compression from the tissue it is wrapped around[70]. Both of these variables change with joint angles. Many sports are characterised by very repetitive maximal loading at the extremes of joint range of motion, for example when locking off with the elbow maximally flexed. Zones within the cross-section of the tendon may become overstressed and suffer micro-tears as a result[71, 72]. Meanwhile, other parts of the tendon are underused ('stress shielded') and become atrophied and vulnerable to tearing due to their weakness[11, 73, 74]. There is also the possibility that compressive forces within the tendon compromise blood flow, compounding the unfavourable conditions for tendon health. Even the high levels of heat generated in localised areas during exercise have been proposed in the research as a possible mechanism for tendon damage[71, 74]. Much remains unknown at present and so there are no definitive answers about why sporting activities result in tendinopathy.

There may also be causes at the individual level[71]. There is limited evidence that tendon injury rates are higher in those with blood group ABO and O[71]. Genes that encode for the structural collagen of tendons lie near the ABO gene. Women have less tendinopathy than men, although post menopause, there are higher rates of Achilles tendon rupture in women. It is suggested that estrogen may promote tendon health and this is supported by evidence that hormone replacement therapy improves the health of Achilles tendons. Body composition may be important too, as there is evidence that tendinopathy rates in the lower limbs are higher when body fat percentage is higher. It's not known if this is due to direct effects on tendon tissue or because of the additional loading.

Finally, increasing age predisposes you to tendinopathy, but does not necessarily directly cause it[8]. Aging tendons don't appear to degenerate so long as activity and optimal nutrition are maintained. However, changes in the cross-links between collagen fibres does mean that tendons become stiffer with age. While high levels of training should still be possible, the loss of elasticity may mean that older tendons are more likely to be damaged in the same circumstances of sudden heavy loading or unloading.

Treatments for damaged tendon tissue

In previous decades, rehabilitation programs offered by sports medicine focused very much on treating the injured tissue directly with drugs such as steroid injections, or a collection of treatments known as 'modalities'. Modalities include ultrasound, ice, heat, laser, pulsed electromagnetic current, electrical stimulation, acupuncture or manual therapy (massage). There is a detailed discussion of these later in this section. The most remarkable thing to note about all of these treatments is their ineffectiveness in delivering long term recovery of tendon health on their own[66, 75]. Part of the reason they became so popular was the absence of any better treatments. Many of these treatments have good short term analgesic effects and, occasionally, limited research evidence that they improve recovery outcomes.

Ultrasound is still commonly used by physiotherapists today, but is controversial[66]. Some studies have shown small effects on tendon healing, while others have failed to show any effects[75]. The picture is similar for many of the available types of modalities. They give moderate pain relief in the short term, but very limited evidence for long term positive effects on the injured tissue. Short term analgesia may have a more useful function than previously thought given recent advances in understanding of the effects of tensile loading on healing tendons and their increased pain sensitivity[12]. The role of analgesia as a facilitator of therapeutic loading of the tendon may be important or even critical to optimise progress of rehabilitation.

Apart from the role of inflammation in tendon injuries, the other major development in the field has been the understanding that therapeutic loading during rehab is essential for restoration of normal function[76]. It is now considered to be the mainstay of tissue treatment for tendon injuries. As well as the understanding that disuse is bad for tendon healing, it has emerged that the mode of exercise loading also seems to be important.

A combination of experiments on different modes of muscle contraction and a better understanding of the sources of pain in tendinopathy have resulted in the most promising treatment to date for tendon pain: eccentric exercises. Muscle contraction can be either isometric (maintaining tension without movement), concentric (shortening) or eccentric (lengthening under tension - such as lowering down from a pull-up). Research in the early 1980s started to report very promising results by using eccentric exercises in rehabilitation[8, 77]. Patients who had suffered from chronic tendon pain for several years, having tried multiple rounds of anti-inflammatory drugs and modalities, experienced resolution of symptoms after as little as six weeks (in some cases) with carefully applied eccentric exercise programs. This remarkable result prompted several more studies which reproduced the positive effects and explored in more detail the actual tissue changes as well as optimisation of the exercise therapy[78, 79]. Some studies have shown that following a program of eccentric exercise, tendons become larger, have an appearance and cellular makeup closer to normal and are much less painful. Moreover, rates of recurrence of tendon pain after return to sport are much lower compared with traditional drug or modality treatments, or surgery.

Precisely why eccentrics work is still unknown. One hypothesis is that they break up adhesions of scar tissue within and around the damaged tendon. Another is that they reverse the ingrowth of pain sensing nerve endings within the tendon[78]. Yet another hypothesis is that this mode of exercise simply stimulates the whole tendon cross-section in a way that eliminates the 'stress shielding' described above[79, 80].

Although it is an exciting development, as usual the picture is not simple. The effectiveness of eccentrics may not be uniform across tendons or areas of the tendon tissue. There is evidence that healing is poorer if the site of the injury is at the tendon-bone junction (insertional tendinopathy) versus tendon mid-portion injury[78, 81]. Moreover, while the results from studies on achilles tendinopathy have been quite promising, studies

on elbow tendinopathy have been less consistent. It is possible this merely reflects the quality of the studies done on elbow tendinopathy which have tended to be small and lack the gold standard protocol of medical research, with randomised controlled trials. Another issue is that there is no consensus on the most effective design of the eccentric exercise programs. Different studies have used quite different protocols for the volume and intensity of the exercises, some supervised by therapists, some not. A notable review in 2012 suggests that eccentric exercise may not actually improve the tendon structure, whereas heavy slow resistance training (concentric and eccentric contractions under heavy load) did improve tendon structure[82]. This highlights the fact that no clear prescription for the mode of exercise most likely to achieve healing has been delivered by the research. The only firm conclusion at the moment seems to be that appropriate loading with exercise of some sort is better than no exercise[12].

The most striking research finding from studies on eccentric exercise protocols was that results seemed to be better when injured tendons were given eccentric exercises that were intense enough to elicit pain[83]. It had been a foundation concept in sports medicine that therapeutic exercises for soft tissue injuries should progress at a level low enough that the work can be completed pain free. The idea is that if pain was present, the intensity was too high and more damage was being done. It is possible that this hypothesis still holds for rehab of acute injury to torn muscles and ligaments, both of which tend to recover when exercises are kept pain free. In the case of slow onset chronic tendinopathy, however, painful loading appears to be important to elicit a healing response.

Tendinopathy appears to cause great sensitisation of the tendon to any loading[12]. An obvious benefit of this from an evolutionary point of view is that the condition becomes self-limiting: it forces you to avoid the activity which caused the original injury. This sensitisation is still not fully understood, but it has been shown that damaged tendons grow many new blood vessels (known as 'neovessels') and these are copiously lined with new pain-sensing nerve endings. When injured patients undertook painful eccentric exercise programs, the level of pain experienced during multiple (20-30) rehab sessions tended to stay stable and eventually decrease while the forces applied to the tendon were progressively increased. Early research studies used exercise protocols consisting of around 40-50 eccentric contractions per day (for example 3 sets of 15 eccentric wrist curls or heel drops). Later studies had even better results when the amount of pain tolerated was slightly greater and the volume of exercise was much greater[84]. Today, the recommended protocol for achilles tendinopathy from some researchers is 180-250 eccentric repetitions (heel drops) per day with moderate pain tolerated. Whether this protocol can be extended to other tendons such as golfer's or tennis elbow has not yet been established by research[85], but the opinion of at least one prolific researcher in the field is that it can. However, Dr Julian Saunders, an experienced climber and osteopath, reports a 100% success rate for supervised treatment using 60 reps x 5 days per week (3 sets of 10 reps, morning and night)[86].

This idea of undertaking painful rehabilitation exercises is still controversial, although the research evidence is increasing in strength. To both tendinopathy sufferers and some physiotherapists, the idea of painful rehab exercise still 'feels wrong'. It does appear to walk a fine line between providing sufficient stimulus for progression and causing further injury. There is also the issue of individual pain thresholds and problems determining the correct intensity by feel. This would be compounded if sufferers were using analgesic treatments which would 'mask' the pain sensations coming from the tendon. Thus, it is important that the rehab program is designed and at least initially supervised by a good physiotherapist who has taken all these aspects of the individual case into account. Despite these problems and the fact that more research is needed to learn more about painful eccentrics, they remain the most promising development in recent years for tendinosis and are of great benefit to many climbers, particularly those suffering with golfer's or tennis elbow.

The following sections will explore in detail the efficacy and protocols of therapeutic exercise, modalities, surgery, drug and other emerging treatments for damaged tendon tissue.

Therapeutic activity - basic exercises

The first point to make about basic corrective or strengthening rehab exercises is that they are critical to the success of most soft tissue rehab programs. Most programs will need to include exercises that strengthen the injured tissue directly as well as exercises or stretching of other muscle groups, to address underlying causes and strength deficits in the whole area. The next aspect that may be surprising is just how much physiotherapy is needed to optimise recovery. It is a big commitment. However, this is outweighed by benefits of a greatly reduced time to return to healthy sporting activity and probability of recurrence.

In the case of some ligament or tendon injuries, stretching may be the earliest exercise to start with following an injury. Gentle stretching can begin at day 4 or 5 following an acute tear, maybe even earlier so long as pain allows, or immediately in slow onset tendinopathy. The main purpose of stretching is to lengthen the muscle-tendon unit if it has become shortened either before or following the injury[8]. Where length is normal, stretching may not be necessary or even desirable. There is no good quality research data demonstrating that stretching has direct effects on tendon tissue healing in tendinosis conditions such as tennis elbow[65, 71].

Following an acute ligament or tendon tear, the new collagen scar tends to form in a contracted state, and may adhere to surrounding tissue. Stretching it as the collagen is laid down would theoretically help it to repair at a normal length and also reduce vulnerability to re-tearing as the progressive loading is applied in the later stages of rehab. Stretching is also thought to help rearrange the disorganised collagen fibres of the immature scar to be aligned in the direction of force transfer. If the whole muscle-tendon unit is short, this is a separate issue and should be stretched to correct alignment and eliminate this potential cause of the injury. Whether stretching needs to be done routinely once an injury has recovered is debatable. It is now thought that static stretching during warm-up does not reduce the risk of injury (see section 3: warm-up and injury).

The correct time to commence loading of the injured area

depends on the type and severity of the injury. For acute tears, gentle loading can begin as soon as the injured part can tolerate load-free movement through its full range of movement without pain. It is at this point that one of the first dangerous periods in the rehab program is reached. Sportspeople routinely start the loading with too much resistance and further damage is caused. The supervision of a physiotherapist is invaluable here. Starting off too hard serves no purpose other than to put you back at square one or worse. Choose a load that allows you to complete the whole workout without more than mild discomfort. A little stiffness or aching in the morning is acceptable, but if it gets worse as the exercise sessions progress, that should be a flag to reassess the intensity of the program. The duration of the program obviously depends on the severity and type of injury. Ligaments tend to respond more readily than tendons and moderate tears may resolve to allow virtually normal sporting activity in as little as six weeks. More severe tearing, or repeated re-injury from overenthusiastic loading may lengthen the process greatly and although return to altered sporting activities might be possible quite early, full strength may not be achieved for a year or more.

For slow onset tendinopathy, the recommended loading pattern is very different. Since significant inflammation or traumatic tearing of tissue is unlikely to be present, the initial lay-off may be unnecessary. However, in severe cases, a short lay-off may be advisable to let pain subside with support from analgesic treatments. Opinions differ on the correct length of this, from two days to two weeks or more. Unless the area is too painful to exercise at all, eccentric loading should commence. Sample protocols for exercises, and suggested exercise volume for specific injuries are discussed later in the book.

Current opinion of some researchers is that chronic tendinopathy should be treated with high volume (180-250 reps daily), high load eccentric exercises. The exercises should isolate the eccentric phase of muscle contraction. The concentric (muscle shortening) phase should be performed unloaded. For example, if wrist curls are performed for golfer's elbow, the concentric phase of lifting the weight back up to the flexed starting position should be done with assistance from the other hand (see section 7). Although opinions on the level of

pain that should be tolerated still differ, some researchers advocate an intensity that provokes moderate pain; level 5 on the VAS pain scale. The VAS (visual analogue scale) is a 1-10 scale which provides an index of subjective pain ratings. 1 represents very slight pain and 10 represents unbearably severe pain. Clearly, the subjectiveness of rating pain during exercise creates difficulty in estimating the most effective intensity. The best strategy may be to concentrate on the word 'moderate' to avoid overdoing it as well as monitoring changes in the pain experienced across multiple sessions. Slight worsening of the pain in the first 2-3 weeks is thought to be acceptable and doesn't require backing off unless the symptoms are getting rapidly worse. However, in later weeks (providing all aspects of the program have been followed correctly) the pain level should stabilise and eventually decrease if healing progresses. If no pain is provoked in the exercises for this type of injury, little or no progress appears to be the result. In my opinion, my own rehabilitation for golfer's elbow faltered for this reason. I had read the research emphasising that the eccentric loading must be intense enough to elicit pain. I persevered with moderately painful eccentric wrist curls for a week or two but experienced a slight worsening of the pain and backed off as a result, ceasing the exercises for a few weeks before resuming them again. When I eventually continued with daily eccentrics at VAS level 5 despite slight early aggravation of the injury, under the advice of Dr Nicola Maffulli (one of the foremost researchers in the field), I finally experienced an improvement after six weeks and eventually remission of symptoms. I found that the moderate discomfort in the affected tendons became gradually worse during the sets, but the sensitivity of the tendons returned to normal or better within half a day. Completing the exercise protocol daily caused no increases in sensitivity over the days and weeks of the exercises. After the third week, I found that I could increase the intensity of both the eccentric exercises and my climbing training while maintaining stable levels of sensitivity and pain in the tendons. After six weeks, I found that only the most aggressive eccentrics could provoke pain and all climbing exercises were pain free.

Where all underlying causes have been identified and removed, therapeutic exercises such as eccentric wrist curls may be unnecessary once full recovery has been achieved. However, in many cases the athlete might not be able to pinpoint or remove all the contributing causes, leaving some underlying susceptibility. Complete resolution of symptoms in the long term is not always achievable and periods of flare up and remission are the common picture[12, 87]. Even if symptoms do not appear again at a later date, it may be prudent to continue eccentrics indefinitely to maintain the strength of the vulnerable tendon[86]. In my own case, intense periods of training must be matched with corresponding therapeutic exercises to prevent symptoms recurring. Normal climbing on its own is fine, but as soon as I add heavy manual labour such as chopping wood, cleaning new routes, or basic strength work such as pull-ups or campus boarding, I get symptoms of golfer's elbow unless I include eccentric wrist curls as well.

It must also be noted that the responsiveness to eccentric exercises for tendinopathy seems to be dependent on the exact location of the damaged tissue in the tendon. If the damage is very close to the attachment to the bone (the enthesis), recovery rates are significantly lower. It may be that an altered program of exercises may help to improve recovery rates for damage to the enthesis. There is some evidence that using eccentrics through a more limited range of motion improves recovery rates for Achilles tendinosis[81]. I have made some speculative suggestions for how this could work for different tendons later in the book, but the basis for designing tailored rehab programs for specific tendinopathies is still hypothetical rather than evidence based.

Therapeutic activity - climbing

One of the biggest negatives of experiencing an injury is the spectre of needing to take time out of the sport you love doing. Increasingly, sports medicine has recognised that lay-off brings with it many problems of its own[12]. Cessation of activity causes marked reversal of training adaptations, with muscles, tendons and ligaments weakening rapidly. Moreover, for chronic tendon conditions such as golfer's elbow, lay-off seems to be ineffective as a treatment. Another problem is that lay-off is often followed by premature and over-zealous return to training and performance, so recurrence of the same injury is very common.

As a result, the lay-off times recommended for many tendon and ligament injuries have become dramatically shorter and the focus has shifted towards altered or reduced participation in the sport during recovery, so long as the loading is carefully controlled. Apart from being more effective, this is also good news for the injury sufferer simply because it makes the rehabilitation period more palatable.

Climbing is particularly well suited to altered participation during recovery since it is non-competitive and has such great variety of forms of the activity. However, it remains that the primary reason that lay-off has been recommended for sports injuries is that participation while carrying an injury frequently results in excessive loading of the injured tissue, causing further damage or at least delayed healing. Extreme care and discipline are needed to walk the line between optimum healing and negative progress.

When commencing a rehab program that involves some climbing, there should be a clear decision that you are setting aside immediate performance goals. Instead, the climbing has several key purposes which must be fulfilled:

- Keeping you from going insane. Not only will you be easier to live with as you go through a roller coaster of emotional upset, but you will be less likely to dive back into normal climbing too aggressively and get re-injured.

- Stimulating the injured tissue at an appropriate level (much lower than normal) to promote healing.

- Maintaining a general anabolic state in the body to maintain tissue strength and fitness so that injury risk is not increased on resumption of more intense load.

- Assessing and retraining technique to reduce or remove contributing factors to the injury development.

Exactly what climbing you can do depends entirely on the injury. A moderate flexor unit strain in a ring finger might allow you to train almost normally, simply avoiding dropping the little finger on holds. In contrast, a completely ruptured pulley will certainly require several weeks of complete lay-off followed by very gentle and restricted climbing at slow speed on big holds. The key point is that the intensity is dictated by the strength of the injured tissue, together with the extent to which you can change the climbing to temporarily work around it. Most soft tissue injuries will require several weeks of fairly gentle loading unless the damage is mild. If the available workarounds can successfully unload the injury, such as climbing completely openhanded with a partial pulley tear, or, as in the above example with a flexor unit strain, overall loading can remain quite high and your climbing might feel relatively normal. However, you must remember at all times that it not normal climbing; it is rehab climbing. It only takes one lapse of concentration to revert to normal movement habits and make the injury much worse.

Identification of technical causes of the injury and retraining of technique are probably the most important purposes of therapeutic climbing. The causes may be related to a strength issue which then dictates your technique. The most obvious example is very poor openhanded strength forcing you to crimp most small holds. The rehab period forces you to climb openhanded to unload an injured pulley and meanwhile you learn to become more comfortable using this grip as well as balancing out your strength. If you have suffered a string of finger injuries, it is prudent to question whether some aspect of your movement technique could be a contributor. For less advanced climbers, footwork and not using momentum will likely be the primary contributors. Advanced climbers will need to look in more detail at their use of momentum and body tension to maintain clean controlled technique on hard and risky moves, or identify certain move types on which they are particularly weak, either physically or technically.

Technique training takes the form of drills to correct either basic movements such as raising the arm overhead with the shoulder joint moving as it should, or practising common climbing movements to prevent over-reliance on a certain movement style such as deep locks. This type of training is referred to in physiotherapy as proprioceptive training since it requires increasing awareness of how different parts of the body are affected by climbing movements.

Proprioceptive training

Proprioception is the ability to to sense the position of the limbs and joints in space in different positions or during movements. The sense of proprioception is mediated by various nerve endings in muscles and joints. The idea overlaps with the concept of movement technique in sport. Good technique is defined as movement that promotes maximum energy efficiency and performance, and proprioception relates to reduction of stresses on the body and maintenance of good alignment during movements.

Proprioceptive training is really just training the mind's eye on body position during movement. We do it all the time without being aware of it. Simply practising a move repeatedly, or noticing a particular body area or movement while climbing is proprioceptive training. Good proprioception is good for both performance and protection against injury[42]. When injury has occurred, or you have been climbing less, proprioception diminishes.

While normal sporting activity increases proprioception, more specific proprioceptive exercises, which are basically technique drills, may be essential to correct faulty movement that is contributing to an injury.

Some examples of proprioceptive training for climbing injuries:

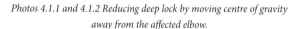

Photos 4.1.1 and 4.1.2 Reducing deep lock by moving centre of gravity away from the affected elbow.

- Retraining scapular movement with a physiotherapist to reduce shoulder impingement. Improved recruitment of rotator cuff muscles and greater awareness of scapular motion can improve scapular elevation and rotation within one session in some cases. The resultant retraining can provide rapid relief of pain and irritation of the supraspinatus tendon.

- Reducing the last few degrees of 'deep lock' while reaching, to relieve stress on golfer's elbow. This involves moving the trunk more laterally over the opposite foot to the locking arm, keeping the

the same time, the shoulder girdle is tilted more and the reaching shoulder is further extended (Photo 4.1). This achieves the same reach while avoiding the last few degrees of elbow flexion that are particularly irritating for the affected medial epicondyle. This requires the climber to concentrate on putting more tension through the opposite foot, as well as focusing on the trunk and shoulder girdle.

- Greater recruitment of core and upper body prime movers to generate more momentum for climbing moves. This reduces the peak force on the smaller distal muscles of the forearm. Good use of momentum from the core also protects the upper limb from jarring onto a straight arm or upper body muscles operating at their vulnerable limits of range of motion. If force such as the swing when catching a hold after a dynamic lunge are absorbed eccentrically through more muscle groups in the kinetic chain, forces on any one muscle or joint in the chain can be reduced.

So what proprioceptive training should climbers do? To answer this it is necessary to understand how proprioception is learned. There are three overlapping stages of learning. Stage 1 is referred to as the cognitive stage. This is the stage of thinking about and trying to understand what is required in the movement, and what accessory movements should be eliminated. Complex motor skills such as those described above often require demonstration and detailed feedback from a coach or physiotherapist for the athlete to actually notice the sensory cues during the movements. The movements are broken down into smaller component actions and practised slowly. Stage 2 is where the athlete is able to perform the basic movement effectively then begins to refine the timing, force and speed applied and is able to recognise mistakes without outside help. The final stage is when the movement is consistently accurate and automatic and can be performed in demanding and varied settings with many other tasks going on at once (e.g. reading the sequence ahead, danger, finding protection, etc). During this phase of learning, the speed of the movement can be increased without sacrificing accuracy.

Many climbers today still do not routinely use a coach, or see a physiotherapist in the event of injury. Without expert supervision or input, proprioceptive training often involves a stage 2 approach when the climber is really at stage 1. The result is that learning stalls and poor movement patterns persist, hence the recurrence of injuries despite treatment of symptoms, not to mention lack of performance gains. Ideally, inexperienced climbers should have as much contact with an experienced coach as possible, to gather awareness and receive demonstration and feedback about efficient and protective movement technique in climbing. Climbers should also have some contact with a sports physiotherapist to ensure that basic shoulder movement is optimal, unless the coach is qualified to assess this also.

For some athletes, it is possible to progress from stage 1 of proprioception in many crucial movement skills without the help of a coach or therapist. Those who succeed are characterised by diligent self-driven research, observation and practice of the skills involved for climbing and injury avoidance. For instance, if a climber is prepared to read textbooks outlining the detailed anatomy and optimal movement of the shoulder, and to practise shoulder movement with careful assessment of key landmarks using a mirror, basic shoulder function can be improved. In climbing, lengthy and systematic observation of skilled performers, together with knowledge of anatomy and physiology and extensive discussion with peers on what works and what doesn't, can allow self-learning of these complex skills. Even then, self-diagnosis of movement errors contributing to injuries is extremely difficult.

The most successful strategy is to strive for understanding of the movements required for good performance and injury avoidance using a combination of self-learning and professional advice.

The training itself usually takes two forms: basic movements and climbing-specific drills. Basic movements such as shoulder abduction (reaching overhead) while monitoring scapular motion may only be necessary if symptoms of poor movement are evident. Once good shoulder movement has been retrained, recruitment of the rotator cuff muscles may persist without regular drills. However, if short mobiliser muscles such as lats and teres major are contributing to muscle imbalance, then continued exercises will be necessary to counteract recurrence. In the absence of injury, general climbing technique drills which promote use of momentum, good footwork and controlled dynamic movement should be performed as part of your everyday training routine. Most climbers achieve this by focusing on movement during the warm-up routine and then working on a varied range of move types and angles. Good discussion and feedback between peers, or even video feedback, is essential for making the most of proprioceptive training. Post-attempt analysis between climbers working a boulder problem together is probably the most common form. Feedback should be as descriptive, detailed and systematic as possible. Both errors and improvements in the speed, timing and position of the trunk and limbs during moves should be fed back to the climber to help him visualise what works and what doesn't. If using video feedback, be sure to compare movement between both poor and good attempts so that the differences are noted.

In summary, most of our everyday climbing and training routines include elements of proprioceptive training. Climbers should not be put off by the term - it is simply correction of poor, unhealthy, or overused movement patterns by observation, feedback and practice. Making the most of these opportunities is essential for both performance improvement and correction of the poor movement patterns that cause injuries. If you have access to professional help from a climbing coach or physiotherapist to get beyond stage 1, that will be of huge benefit and may well be pivotal in the ability to successfully remove injury causes. If poor movement patterns are corrected with good proprioceptive training there is potential to reduce symptoms of many climbing injuries without any further treatment, as well as prevent future injuries. However, it is more likely that proprioceptive training will be only one of the interventions required to recover from an injury.

Walking the line of rehab ups and downs

Most injuries to ligaments and tendons will show a gradual increase in strength and resilience as a well-designed and monitored rehab program progresses over weeks and months. However, there are two main reasons why it never seems to go quite like this while you are working through an injury rehab program.

Firstly, many rehab programs suffer from setbacks where weak or immature scar tissue is re-injured. Secondly, since the slow progress of soft tissue healing is measured by subjective pain signals which are complex in nature, it is not always easy to see that progress is actually taking place.

So it is more normal to feel that there are 'ups and downs' of intermittent progress as the weeks go by. There are often periods of a few weeks where you are surprised by how much you have stressed the injury with climbing or rehab work, with little aggravation in response. This makes you feel excited that the rehabilitation is progressing and you are getting further along the path to recovery.

Yet often these good periods are followed by periods of equal length where you seem to be getting more pain for doing less, sometimes inexplicably. Older athletes who have already experienced several cycles of injury and protracted rehab back to full function will be much less disappointed by the bad patches in rehab progress. They understand that for many injuries, they are just to be expected.

This phenomenon of apparently intermittent progress means that tracking progress is not as simple as might be hoped. The problem is that several variables influencing the pain you are using to measure recovery status are changing at once.

If you are good at keeping a mental or written note of these variables, it can be possible to correctly attribute the most significant cause of a change in the pain coming from the injury. Making conclusions from your measurements about the health of the tissue is tricky, and very much an art. It is especially difficult if it is your first injury or you are early in the rehab process, because you don't have experience on your side. For instance, if you have golfer's elbow, you may find that it becomes more sensitive and painful after taking several days' rest. This might seem counterintuitive at first, but not when you understand the difference between tissue health and sensitivity. In this situation, you must readjust your expectation of the level of pain you feel for a given load on the tendon following a few days or more of rest, because another variable (training load) has been changed. For any injury, pain will also be influenced by peripheral factors. If you are not aware of these, it will appear that you have made progress or gone backwards for no obvious reason. For instance, injuries generally feel more painful when you are tired, nervous, or stressed. It is up to you to notice, record and then anticipate the patterns in your progress.

Your task is first to be aware of the variables influencing the pain you record from the injury, and then to tread a line between progressive loading of the injury and re-injury from over-doing it. Even with the best efforts, it is likely the progress will not be entirely linear. Moreover, because progress in tendon healing is so slow, stagnation or apparent negative progress for several weeks at a time may just be part of the process. If stagnation happens, you should look again at your whole rehab plan and everything you are doing, in order to root out any mistakes. If none are to be found despite diligent work and professional help, keep the faith and keep at your rehab work and progress will likely show itself again.

A common response to lack of reasonable progress in rehab is to back off the intensity of rehab and sporting activity. This approach is well founded, generally speaking. Over-doing it, especially with sporting activity, is a likely cause of failure to progress. However, there are some exceptions to this such as with elbow tendinosis where rehab exercises involve noticeable pain. Therefore, it is important to maintain contact with a good sports physiotherapist who understands your case and will be able to offer ongoing advice.

Therapeutic modalities

Not everything that counts can be counted,
and not everything that can be counted counts.
Albert Einstein

The term 'therapeutic modalities' covers a broad range of treatments which are also referred to by the more descriptive term 'passive physiotherapy'. They include various manual therapies such as deep transverse friction massage (DTFM), ultrasound, sports massage, dry needling, trigger point therapy, heat, ice, electrical stimulation and others. Taken as a whole, these treatments are very popular. Physiotherapists and other manual therapists recommend their use, and sufferers commonly seek them out and return for continued treatment, even though it can be expensive.

Unfortunately, there is a gross lack of hard, scientific research evidence for their effectiveness in achieving long term recovery from soft tissue injuries[66, 68]. The experience from clinical practice is that many of these therapies successfully reduce pain in the short term. Indeed the mechanism of their action has been identified in many cases as acting directly on pain sensing pathways in the nervous system. However, there is little evidence that they have positive effects on the health of the injured tissue, at least directly.

For acute injuries, modalities can be extremely useful for allowing the athlete to get started quickly on joint movement and exercise therapy, avoiding the complications caused by rest, immobilisation and excessive bleeding within the injury site. However, for chronic injuries, the short term effects on pain may be either desirable or undesirable depending on how the sufferer responds. Sometimes pain relieving therapy is used as a denial technique to permit short term, continued use of the injured area and cause distraction from actually addressing the injury itself. In this way, they can prolong or worsen an injury. However, modalities can also act as facilitator in sensitised tissue, to allow therapeutic exercise to progress more quickly and achieve real improvements in the health and strength of the injured tissue. In other words, the pain relieving effects of modalities must be used carefully as part of a wider rehabilitation plan, to ensure long term success. This issue is compounded by the fact that modality practitioners do not, or cannot always advise injured athletes on how to fit the given modality into their wider rehab program. Your massage therapist may not tell you that the pain relieving effects of a back massage will do nothing to correct your shoulder misalignment and muscle imbalance and therefore the pain will soon return if the modality is discontinued. It might, in fact, be bad for business to do so! Having said that, it does appear from clinical practice that modality use does sometimes precede complete resolution of symptoms in some individual cases. Perhaps this only serves to underline the complexity of the body's responses to pain and injury.

Taking the aspect of pain and limitation of acute inflammation to one side, it is still debatable whether modalities are required at all in the later stages of sports injury rehab if the causes can be successfully corrected and weakened tissue strengthened with active physiotherapy. Broadly speaking, their most important role may be as a facilitator to active physiotherapy, thus speeding up the process of rehabilitation. In the following section I will go through some of the popular modalities and assess the rationale for their use in different situations.

Sports massage

Therapeutic massage is the manipulation of body tissue with the aim of restoring function. Evidence for its effectiveness in soft tissue healing is anecdotal, although that may be because it is extremely difficult to evaluate scientifically. One of the few uncontroversial effects of massage is that it makes athletes 'feel better' in the short term. Even therapists themselves accept that a significant part of the positive effects may be a psychological effect. The question for athletes to consider is whether equivalent or better effects could be achieved by using other forms of therapy, especially where massage is expensive. However, there are some proposed direct effects on tissue with plausible mechanisms that could be worthwhile for injured athletes in certain situations.

One of the main suggested benefits of massage is increased blood flow to the area massaged. Massage does increase skin blood flow. However, deeper blood flow to the muscle or soft tissue underneath may not increase[64]. In fact, it may even decrease if blood is shunted towards the skin during the massage. The most effective way to increase muscle blood flow is active exercise, even if light in intensity. When tissue swelling is involved, blood flow is not the only concern. Swelling, once present, is not removed by the vascular system. Rather it is drained via the lymphatic vessels, which have a valve arrangement preventing back-flow. Again, exercise, even just light movement of the limb, is the most effective way to stimulate the pumping action and resultant lymphatic drainage. However, if pain prevents this, then stroking or kneading ('effleurage' and 'petrissage') massage does result in increased lymphatic drainage.

Massage is a good inhibitor of pain. Reduction of swelling and interruption of muscle spasm is one mechanism for this in acute injuries. But there is also a direct effect on pain sensitivity via the gate mechanism (see section 2) which will likely have effects in chronic injuries too.

The role of massage in sports injuries is still debated and it has been argued that it is overused in both organised sport (athletic or team sports with therapists assigned to them) and individual athletes who may mistake the pain relieving effects for improvement in the health of the injured tissue. In the later stages of the acute phase of injury, some sessions of massage may well assist clearance of swelling if movement and exercise are still too painful. In chronic injuries, it could be used as a facilitator to reduce pain and thus allow more volume and intensity of therapeutic exercise. However, it may be unnecessary if the rehab program is appropriate for the injury. In fact, if it is used as a crutch to continue participation in climbing and ignore the injury, it may well be counterproductive.

Deep transverse friction massage (DTFM)

DTFM is really a separate form of massage both in the technique used and the mechanism of the effects. It is the application of deep pressure perpendicular to the angle of ligament or tendon fibres to create a shearing force between fibres. Rather than being applied to the whole area of muscle as 'regular' massage is, DTFM is applied directly to the site of the injury, usually a tendon or ligament. There are several proposed beneficial effects.

Firstly, DTFM is thought to break up fibrous adhesions within the injury site. Adhesions are caused by the disorganised arrangement of collagen scarring in a recovering injury. Collagen fibres attach to nearby structures such as tendon sheaths, adjacent tendons or other structures and these are thought to cause pain during movement. It is thought that the shearing caused by the strong transverse pressure literally breaks these adhesions and promotes reorganisation of the fibres to normal alignment and mobilisation of the scar relative to the surrounding tissue. It may also improve local blood flow to the area.

DTFM is also hypothesised to provoke an inflammatory response in non-inflammatory chronic tendinosis, 'kickstarting' the normal healing process and reversing the degeneration that has occurred. It also has a strong analgesic effect, with five minutes of DTFM providing 48 hours of significant pain relief.

Evidence for direct effects on healing tissue from DTFM is very limited, and opinions differ on whether this is a useful treatment in chronic injuries. However, a recent review of the available research concluded that there was some scientific evidence that it is beneficial, and pointed out that there is much anecdotal evidence for its effectiveness[88]. The strongest case for its use may be where a bulky scar has formed following a sprain or tear, or in chronic tendinosis. It has the advantage of being an easy to perform self-treatment and treatments do not take long, so experimenting with the technique may be worth considering.

DTFM should not be used in the acute stage of a traumatic injury as it may worsen existing inflammation and cause further mechanical damage to fragile healing tissue. If the injury has an acute onset, such as a pulley tear, the time to consider DTFM is later in the healing process, when pain and any swelling have settled well and the tissue can already handle resistance exercise.

Photo 4.2 DTFM technique for golfer's elbow.

The technique for DTFM involves using the fingers, knuckles, elbow or a hard ball to apply firm deep pressure with short stokes across the tendon fibres. The skin should move with the therapist's fingers as one unit and be of sufficient force and sweep to affect the desired tissues. Discomfort or pain during the treatment is normal and athletes treating themselves often do not use sufficient force because the technique feels very aggressive. Very firm pressure is essential to mechanically break up the collagen adhesions. However, care must be taken not to cause excessive irritation by over-zealous frictions. It is normal for pain to diminish slightly as a treatment session progresses. Apply the frictions for 1-2 minutes and assess whether pain has increased. If pain has increased, reduce the force amplitude. Treatments are generally given for 5-10 minutes every other day or perhaps less. No scientific data exists to promote one loading protocol over another. If the injury becomes more sensitive in subsequent treatments, then the force amplitude or frequency of treatments can be reduced.

Trigger point therapy

Myofascial trigger point therapy has become increasingly popular in recent years with anecdotal evidence of relief from muscle and tendon pain. However, the causes and importance of trigger points in musculoskeletal pain are still controversial.

Trigger points are defined as an area of hyperirritability which is tender if compressed and may cause referred pain in nearby areas. Trigger points can occur in skin, ligaments and tendons, and muscle fascia. Muscle fascia (myofascial) trigger points are most commonly described in sports medical literature and are treated with various manual therapies.

A myofascial trigger point can sometimes be palpated as a noticeably tight band of muscle, often about the size of a pea[89]. It may be constantly tender or may only be tender if pressure is applied. Common trigger points correspond remarkably closely to traditional acupuncture points from eastern medicine, although the two treatment methodologies have developed completely independently and under radically different principles. The extremely high correlation between trigger and acupuncture points on the body lends weight to the existence of trigger points in muscle, which otherwise suffer from the lack of a well-understood physiological basis. Science has so far not even come close to understanding what changes occur in a trigger point, why this causes pain, or why trigger points might occur in certain common locations in the body.

One of the biggest problems with this field is accurate diagnosis of whether painful trigger points are important in a sports injury. They may be either associated with, caused by, or even mimicking the symptoms of an injury. It is also possible that painful trigger points are the sole clue to an underlying postural fault or overuse of a muscle or joint. Trigger points are most commonly found in postural muscles in areas such as the upper back and neck, which are easily affected by faulty alignment and poor postural or movement habits. However, there are reports of climbers experiencing relief from golfer's elbow symptoms with trigger point therapy. Some therapists believe that trigger points exist alongside many common sports injuries, and routinely experience good results by administering trigger point therapy[89].

Possible causes of trigger points (according to the clinical experience of therapists)[89]:

* Injury or pain in general.
* Postural faults or strain, causing abnormal muscle length.
* Fatigue or overtraining.
* Inactivity, especially prolonged occupational sitting, or bed rest.
* Stress.
* Prolonged cold exposure.
* Poor nutrition.
* Smoking.

The treatment for trigger points can be performed using a variety of techniques. Continuous deep pressure on the trigger point from the therapist's fingers, elbow or massage equipment can be used to 'release' the tight band in the muscle, allowing it to relax and reducing its sensitivity. Alternatively, a slow, deep pressure, stroking massage technique called 'muscle stripping' can be used. Both techniques are thought to cause increased blood flow or mechanical disruption of spasm within the trigger point, which allows the chronically contracted

band of muscle to relax and hence no longer cause pain. However, this idea is consistent with a theory of 'trigger point cause' which is disputed. Another technique is to apply ice or a cooling spray to the trigger point and then apply a slow progressive stretch of the affected muscle[90]. These techniques are possible to apply as a self-treatment for many trigger points with appropriate training and massage tools.

Photo 4.3 Using a tennis ball in a sock to apply trigger point therapy at the exact spot.

Dry needling is another popular method of treating trigger point pain. The technique is similar to acupuncture, but where acupuncture needles are inserted superficially into the skin, dry needling involves the needle being placed deeper into the muscle, directly into the trigger point itself. Thin acupuncture needles are inserted to locate the most painful area. The needle then causes gradual relaxation of the muscle and relief of pain. Pain relief may last several days with initial treatments and more for subsequent sessions.

The limitations of trigger point therapy may be similar to other forms of manual therapy in offering only short term pain relief, at least in some cases. If the underlying cause of the pain is not investigated and removed, long term pain relief and recovery may not be achieved. The pain may simply return when the treatment is stopped or when training is increased. It is thought that trigger points may be caused by postural or movement faults or as a complication of another injury (which has caused compensatory movement patterns or postural changes). However, the causes are poorly understood. The true benefit of the treatment may be as a facilitator to therapeutic exercise which then restores the health of affected muscles and hence normal muscle activation patterns.

The possibility of trigger point involvement should be investigated when an injury is examined for diagnosis. Readers who wish to investigate self-treatment of trigger points rather than see a professional therapist are directed to the textbook *Therapeutic Exercises for Musculoskeletal Injuries*[90]. It is important to be aware that trigger points can cause referred pain at a distant site. Thus, applying therapy at the site of pain will be ineffective in theses cases. Either a consultation with a trigger point expert (hard to find) or careful reference to trigger point texts will increase your chances of successfully locating trigger points.

Therapeutic cold/heat

Superficial application of both heat and cold are frequently used to treat injuries, although there are many misconceptions about their effects. This section refers to the use of heat/cold during the treatment stage of rehabilitation, as opposed to immediate care of a new injury (RICE protocol, described earlier).

Superficial heat, in the form of hot packs or warm water immersion, are used to increase blood flow to the injured area in an effort to assist the healing process. Heat application does increase blood flow, but the increase is only significant in tissue less than 1cm deep, so is only thought to be useful for superficial injuries such as tendons which lie just under the skin[64]. Moreover, the blood flow increase is much less than that caused by simply exercising the area. Hence, exercise will likely be more effective if the injury can cope with movement or loading. Arguably the more important use of superficial heat is its analgesic effect. It provides rapid pain relief (although not as much as cold application) and reduces the stiffness of tissue. So it is particularly useful as a aid to warming up an injured area ready for exercise therapy or stretching short muscles or tight scar tissue. However, if used as a treatment on its own, it may be ineffective compared to exercise.

Cold application, such as ice packs or cold water immersion, was traditionally considered only to be useful in the first 24 hours after an acute injury, with the purpose of limiting swelling and thus secondary injury to the tissue. However, cold therapy (cryotherapy) is also useful in the later stages of soft tissue healing in certain situations.

Its primary use is to offer immediate pain relief in order to tolerate more exercise in the early stages of rehabilitation. In ligament sprains cryotherapy, as a facilitator to commence exercise therapy earlier and more vigourously, is known to reduce healing time and prevent permanent loss of function (range of motion or tensile strength). Cold is a powerful analgesic and application of an ice pack or cold water for 10-15 minutes reduces pain in an injury to the point where more exercise or mobilisation is possible. The cold application is merely a facilitator. It is the exercise that follows which stimulates the tissue and provides the long term benefits in healing.

It has long been thought that cold therapy (with moderate cold exposure in cold water rather than ice packs) could be used to increase local blood flow and thus have a direct effect on tissue healing, but this idea is now challenged by more recent research. The idea had its foundation in some very old research by Lewis in 1930 who observed that finger temperature rose and remained elevated for some time with immersion in cold water, after an initial period of vasoconstriction[91]. Later research by Lewis with more prolonged cold immersion showed that there was oscillation of increases and decreases in finger temperature. The hypothesis which arose from these findings was that the body triggers a reactive vasodilation (dilation of the local blood vessels and capillaries) to increase blood flow and protect the body part from cold injury. This reaction was called the 'hunting response'. It was accepted for many years, before research led by Knight and others questioned the existence of the response and the methodology of the original research which had several flaws in design and presentation of the data[64].

When the experiments were repeated, it emerged that similar results could only be reproduced when the fingers were cold to start with (due to a cold room temperature in the lab). The vasodilation response was not seen in fingers which were initially warm; the oscillations of finger temperatures from prolonged cold immersion did not produce greater temperatures than the pre-treatment temperature. Rather, there was a marked decrease in finger temperature followed by comparatively small oscillations which remained depressed below the pre-treatment finger temperature. Moreover, it was observed that the oscillations in temperature may be due to the build up of a temperature gradient in the water around the immersed limb. The limb warms the surrounding water, but when it is moved, tissue temperature falls rapidly, resulting in oscillation of temperature as the treatment progresses.

These findings may be confusing to many climbers who have used cold water immersion to treat finger pulley injuries with apparent success. Firstly, the treatment gives pain relief and there are many anecdotal reports of more rapid progress of healing. Secondly, the immersed hand turns red and feels warmer following the treatment. How are these findings explained?

It is likely that the immediate pain relief is due to a direct effect on pain sensing nerve endings in the area, reducing their sensitivity by 'closing the gate' to pain (see section 2). It may be that any improved healing effect arises from the more rapid exercise loading progression facilitated by the pain relief. This extra loading could come from more vigorous climbing or simply being less guarded with the injured area during activities of daily life. The redness of the skin could theoretically be caused by lowered tissue metabolism resulting from the lower temperature.

The available research does not satisfactorily confirm or refute the idea of increased blood flow during this treatment. What has not been extensively studied is the effect of multiple treatments. Many climbers, including myself, who have experimented with hand immersion for pulley injuries have noted that the initial week of daily 30 minute cold water immersion produces only a feeling of painful cold and little beneficial effect. However during subsequent weeks of treatment, the reaction to the treatment changes dramatically. The water in the basin warms up significantly faster than in week one of the treatment, in my own experience. I often start with four

ice cubes in a large pot of cold tap water. During week one, these take 15-20 minutes to melt. Even once the ice has melted, the water remains uncomfortably cold for the remaining 10-15 minutes. In subsequent weeks, I need to progress to 5-7 ice cubes and often need to replace them halfway through the treatment as they melt after 10 minutes. Moreover, the feeling of warmth and relief of pain feels progressively better and longer lasting.

Perhaps there is an adaptation to repeated exposure to cold, either in the response of the local blood vessels, or even in capillary growth? Further research is needed to investigate this idea. However, with the current available knowledge, it appears more likely that the benefits of cold treatment are more likely to be related to simple pain relief rather than a direct effect on healing. Thus, if climbers use this treatment, they should take care to use it in conjunction with progressive, appropriate loading of the injured tissue to take full advantage of the treatment. In the opinion of Knight[14], cold treatment performed in the absence of therapeutic exercise may actually delay healing by reducing tissue metabolism.

'Contrast baths' of alternating heat and cold are also commonly used by athletes. There are various theories for how this treatment may be beneficial, including increased blood flow, decreased pain sensitivity or a 'pumping action' stimulating drainage of swelling. Most of these hypotheses have little scientific basis[92]. For instance, swelling cannot be removed by the vascular system (blood circulation) as mentioned previously. Rather it is removed by lymphatic vessels and this is achieved by mechanical compression and pumping by movement and muscle contraction, or external compression. Due to the lack of evidence for their effectiveness compared to either cold or heat application on their own, the idea is falling out of favour in sports medicine.

In summary, the available research and clinical knowledge suggests the following rules for therapeutic heat/cold application:

- Heat application should only be used once the initial inflammatory period after an acute injury has passed. Before this, cold application should be used instead, to reduce swelling accumulation and reduce pain. However, once there is existing swelling, compression and activity are needed to reduce it.

- Heat application is especially useful where stretching of tight, contracted scar tissue is needed, such as following immobilisation. Heat or cold application can both be used for assisting with stretching muscle tissue, although cold may be more useful for damaged muscle due to its inhibition of spasm and muscle stretch reflex.

- Cold or heat application both provide pain relief which promotes increased and earlier progression of therapeutic exercise. The choice may come down to individual preference of the athlete or therapist. There is little scientific data to construct a rationale to choose either in specific situations.

- Pain is reduced by direct effects on pain sensing nerve endings. Blood flow increases may be useful but are insignificant compared to that caused by exercise, even at moderate intensity. Therefore, to promote progression of healing, heat or cold application may not be useful on its own.

Cryotherapy protocol

Using ice to prepare the area for stretching or exercise can be done with the following protocol:

- Immersion of the area in iced water is the most effective method, but is not practical with certain body areas. Ice packs folded in a towel or ice water in a plastic bag is a good substitute. For areas such as the upper back, ice massage is often used with a large ice cube made in a paper cup (you can place a stick in it to make an 'ice lolly' style handle).

- Ice the area for 10-20 minutes. Sensation in the treatment area should progress through painful cold, to a warming sensation, then tingling and finally numbness. It takes a bit of motivation to get through the initial stage of painful cold.

- Perform the therapeutic exercises for the injury, reapplying the ice as needed every few minutes to

keep the area numb.

- Great care must be taken to plan the intensity of the exercises before undertaking them so that the pain relief from cryotherapy does not lead to over-zealous exercise. It is much safer if the therapy is planned and performed under the supervision of a physiotherapist.

The above protocol is commonly applied for ankle sprains and sprains to other joints where the ligaments around the joint are tight and sore, and the remaining swelling from the acute stage is still settling. This protocol could also be used for exercising common acute injuries that climbers get such as pulley tears, or acute tendon or muscle strains such as biceps, brachioradialis or the shoulder and upper back. However, as mentioned above, I and other climbers have had good results with a 30 minute, twice daily immersion in moderately cold water, especially for pulley injuries. There is no research available to support the rationale for this treatment. Until this area becomes better researched, I would encourage climbers to experiment with alternating periods (perhaps a week) of numbing cold and physio exercises, moderate cold immersion after physiotherapy, and a control condition of no ice, and compare rates of progress during these periods.

Ultrasound

Therapeutic ultrasound is the application of sound waves of a frequency faster than can be heard by the human ear. In medicine, very intense ultrasound can be used to destroy tissue. Low intensities are used for diagnostic scanning. Ultrasound of moderate intensities has been used by therapists for several decades with the purpose of accelerating healing. The possible mechanisms of benefit of the therapy are not well understood. However, the proposed benefits fall into two categories; thermal and non-thermal effects.

The transfer of energy to the tissue under the ultrasound applicator gives moderate heating of collagen rich tissues. The tissue is heated by a few degrees, stimulating blood flow and metabolism, and temporarily increasing the elasticity of the tissue. Its advantage over superficial heat application (warm water or hot packs) is that deeper tissues can be much more effectively heated. There are several proposed non-thermal effects on cells and cellular chemicals that may promote healing. Ultrasound also seems to be an effective analgesic, although the mechanism for this effect is not understood.

Although ultrasound continues to be a popular treatment of physiotherapists, scientific evidence that demonstrates positive effects on healing is still extremely limited despite repeated attempts. However, much of the research on humans has been of poor quality. Thus, the treatment is still controversial from a scientific point of view, despite the ample anecdotal reports of improved healing.

There is good evidence in animal studies that ultrasound can improve ligament, tendon, bone, nerve and other tissue healing. However, repeated attempts to reproduce these effects in human studies have given conflicting or disappointing results[93]. There is some good evidence that ultrasound can speed human bone healing, particularly where there is delayed or non-union in healing fractures. The failure to consistently reproduce good results in human soft tissue healing could be down to the complex variables involved: wave frequency, intensity, duration of the therapy and total number of treatment sessions. This poor understanding of the appropriate treatment method for different situations casts doubt on the rationale for parting with hard earned cash or time for repeated treatments. In spite of this, ultrasound continues to be a popular treatment with physiotherapists. It may be that in future the research will demonstrate irrefutable support for this treatment, together with much clearer guidelines for application in injuries of different depths and different treatment goals.

In the meantime, if you are considering ultrasound treatment, two concerns stand out which may influence your decision. Firstly, if you are able to perform even moderate exercise loading with the injured area, it may be possible to achieve the thermal and blood flow increases more regularly without the need for expensive meetings with therapists, and also gain all the other benefits that come with exercise therapy. Secondly, ultrasound may be particularly useful to help stretch stiff, scarred tissue

and if you are seeing a therapist regularly for guidance on therapeutic exercise, they may be able to perform ultrasound treatment during the appointment. In other words, if the treatment is there for the taking, it makes sense to take advantage of this. However, given that the treatment protocols used differ from therapist to therapist, it would be prudent to research which protocol is appropriate for the specific injury and discuss this with the therapist. For more detail on ultrasound protocols, readers are referred to the excellent book *Therapeutic Modalities* by Kenneth Knight and David Draper[64] which contains detailed notes on choosing the appropriate protocol based on scientific principles.

A final concern is the number of treatments recommended. Knight and Draper suggest that a course of 14 treatments is currently recommended before taking a break from the treatment (due to possible negative effects on blood cells). However, since the research literature has not even managed to prove that ultrasound works, there is no good data on how many treatments are appropriate. Current accepted practice seems to be simply to continue treatments as long as improvements are observed. If improvements are not noticed after the initial four or five treatments, alternative treatments should be tried.

Other electrotherapeutic modalities

There are numerous other electrotherapeutic modalities which are commonly used with varying popularity across the world[63]. The one thing they have in common is a lack of good scientific evidence supporting their use in sports injuries. In view of the lack of evidence, I have described them only briefly here. It seems logical that climbers should consider their use only where cheaper and more reliably effective treatments such as exercise therapy are not possible. There is also the issue of availability of treatments. For instance, many more physiotherapists are likely to have ultrasound machines than diathermy machines. If time and expense are not an issue, as may be the case for some professional athletes in other sports, adding electrotherapeutic modalities to the rehab treatment picture are, at least, unlikely to do any harm. The case for their use is harder to justify when time and money are limited and many of the other treatments described in this book are much better supported by scientific evidence.

Future research may help us clarify which of these treatments, if any, are worth doing. In the meantime, if your physiotherapist offers the treatment as part of a wider picture of therapies during your sessions with them, it is worth discussing whether they might be appropriate for the specific injury. Some of the available electrotherapeutic modalities are described below:

- Diathermy - Shortwave diathermy is the application of electromagnetic waves similar to radio waves to the tissue. The effects are similar to ultrasound with a gentle heating of the tissue and various proposed non-thermal effects at the cellular level that may promote healing. The therapy may be a better alternative to ultrasound for deeper tissues or especially if a larger area needs to be heated. The scientific evidence for its effectiveness is inconclusive at best.

- Magnetic therapy - Magnetic therapy has been used for centuries but remains a controversial treatment. There are plenty of anecdotal reports of it providing good pain relief from various injuries. There is also some weak scientific evidence that the therapy may have some positive effects, but the studies are of poor quality so no conclusions can be drawn. Magnetic therapy is thought to be most useful in bone healing and chronic pain conditions such as osteoarthritis. But there is not enough evidence to recommend its use in musculoskeletal injuries.

- TENS therapy - Transcutaneous electrical nerve stimulation (TENS) is the application of electrical currents through the skin to stimulate the local nerve fibres. The goal of the treatment is to reduce the sensations of pain from an injury by altering the way pain signals are transmitted. The treatment reportedly causes a temporary change in pain threshold. Again, evidence for its effectiveness, both in modulating pain and in improving the speed of rehabilitation from sports injuries, is weak at best. Despite several studies failing to show

significantly better effects than placebo, it remains a fairly popular treatment. Anecdotally, some patients report good pain relief from TENS therapy, but both therapists and the researchers agree that responses seem to be variable between individuals, with some reporting no effects.

- Laser therapy - The use of mid powered lasers (also known as cold or soft lasers) has been used to attempt to promote healing in various injuries. Once again, research evidence for its effectiveness is extremely limited and there are more studies demonstrating no benefits than otherwise[75]. Moreover, the possible mechanisms of action of laser therapy are poorly understood. A significant problem with laser therapy is the penetration depth of the beam. At best, penetration of around 5mm is possible, meaning that only superficial tissues will be affected and the reach of the beam into the tissues will be further limited by the thickness of subcutaneous fat.

In summary, therapeutic modalities have a small but potentially important role in rehabilitation from sports injuries affecting bone, muscle, ligament and tendon tissue. This role is best described as an adjunct or facilitator to the central foundation treatment of therapeutic exercise. Cold and massage therapies arguably have the strongest evidence base for pain relief and potentially other important effects which promote healing. However, it is vital that sportspeople don't learn to lean on the short term pain relief in order to mask symptoms and carry on sports participation, instead of completing the rehabilitation program. The result of this is likely to be injury recurrence.

Surgery

Even surgeons are reluctant to advise their patients to undergo surgery on sports injuries. Despite ever advancing techniques and technologies, surgery still carries with it an inherent risk of damage to healthy tissue when accessing and repairing the damaged area, and the risk of serious complications such as accidental damage to nerve branches or deep wound infection. Moreover, conservative (non-invasive) physiotherapy has also advanced and is better understood to give equivalent or better results in the long term than surgery for some injuries. In certain cases, surgery still has an essential role for serious injuries or those which fail to respond to physiotherapy.

The goal of surgery on sports injuries is generally to remove, reconstruct or realign damaged tissue and to promote a healing response. Each tendon or ligament in the body has its own set of variables in how it responds to standard treatments and surgical techniques. For instance, it is now thought by many hand surgeons that the vast majority of finger pulley injuries and elbow tendinosis can be dealt with successfully with a well designed, conservative treatment protocol. Conversely, advanced cases of rotator cuff impingement in the shoulder may require surgery in a higher proportion of cases since the thickened, frayed rotator cuff tendon causes progressive worsening of the condition with further activity.

Common surgical procedures for specific injuries and situations are outlined in the later parts of this book. For some tendon or ligament injuries, surgery is performed only when at least six months of conservative treatment with optimum compliance from the athlete has failed to produce improvement. However, in the case of complete ruptures in professional athletes, early surgery is sometimes the better option.

Surgery is more readily used in cartilage injuries since articular cartilage does not have the capacity to heal in adults. Even in this case, the decision to have surgery or not depends on the extent and nature of the damage and the individual athlete. Moreover, recent research continues to cast doubt on the effectiveness of surgery for cartilage injuries such as meniscal tears of the knee when compared to a 'sham' placebo procedure[94]. Certain procedures to repair joint cartilage work well in teenagers but not in adult athletes.

Repair within joint capsules such as the rotator cuff in the shoulder is increasingly done using arthroscopic (keyhole surgery) techniques. The arthroscope is inserted through one very small incision to view the area of interest, while the surgical instruments are inserted via a second portal. Arthroscopy carries a much smaller rate of complications than open surgery, and generally offers more rapid post-operative return to activity. However, for some procedures, a better repair can be performed with open surgery. The most important risk is still deep infection via the wound site, so hygiene in the immediate post operative period and careful monitoring for signs of infection are critical.

Both acute tissue tears and chronic overuse injuries outside joint capsules are often treated with open surgery. In the case of chronic tendon injuries, the damaged tissue is often excised by making a longitudinal incision in the tendon without releasing it (cutting it free from its origin on the bone). Where tissue has been lost to necrosis, the ligament or tendon may be reconstructed using a graft of similar tissue from another ligament. Where scarred, bulky tissue is causing a nerve entrapment, such as in the elbow, the scarred tissue is scraped away and the nerve is moved away from the compression site. New minimally invasive scraping techniques are also now showing promise in tendinosis, which remove the nerve ingrowths from the surface of painful tendons[95].

If you have an injury which you have established will require surgery, there are a number of things you can do to improve the outcome of the operation and the chances of long term success. Perhaps the most important is to have the surgery carried out by the best surgeon available. Highly experienced surgeons who have acquired a good reputation are really worth seeking out at all costs. One of the biggest problems with surgery is that the procedure itself has to cause tissue damage to gain access to the injury site. A good surgeon will be likely to cause less trauma to healthy tissue. Surgeons often develop an interest in particular joints or surgical procedures and become very highly skilled in those areas. Your task is to find out who they are and whether you can be treated by them.

Your search for the best surgeon available should have several lines of enquiry:

- Have high profile, professional climbers or other professional athletes had similar surgery? Can you find out who their surgeon was?

- Is there a recognised expert in this injury who has written books, research papers, articles or has a lecturing role a major university? If seeing them involves travelling overseas, just do it if you possibly can - it is far more important than any climbing trip you'll ever go on.

- Ask your doctor if they are aware of nationally recognised surgeons specialising in this field.

- Speak to local sports medicine clinics who are used to treating high profile athletes across different sports; they are a good source of contacts for locally based surgeons who have the highest levels of expertise and are chosen by professional athletes.

Even if the the surgeon of choice is not based locally, you may be able to be referred to them through the NHS due to their specialist expertise. If NHS referral is not possible, then a private appointment must be considered due to the importance of accessing their expertise. Of course, for some, this will be out of the question and the best bet will be a persistent approach to persuade your doctor to refer you under the NHS. For many climbers, a simple cost-benefit comparison should establish that it is money well spend instead of doing something else. At the very least, you should get a quote for a consultation, any scanning required and for the surgery. The actual cost may not be what you expected (in either direction!). If you can afford to access better surgical skills instead of a climbing trip or other consumer items, you should at least consider this. If you take your long term sporting health seriously, it may be a 'no brainer' in some cases.

Following surgery, post operative care, either through the NHS or privately, may not be as good as it could be. Yet the quality of post operative rehabilitation is just as important as the surgery itself. In meeting with the surgeon immediately after the operation, have your questions ready and try to get as much detail as you can on the appropriate activities and progression recommended. You may not be in an alert state following the surgery so it is best to have a family member with you who is briefed to enquire for you. Similar arguments apply for seeking out the best possible physiotherapy advice. Under the NHS, the initial physiotherapy appointment can sometimes be delayed and generally does not offer the level of detail appropriate for an athlete. Seeking out a consultation, even if it is only one or two sessions privately at a local sports medicine clinic, could be critical to success. The progression in the initial days and weeks is very important for determining subsequent progress, so your initial physiotherapy appointment is an urgent matter.

The content of post-operative rehabilitation depends on the procedure performed and the individual case. Generally speaking, the goal is to get the area moving and then onto light resistance training as early as possible. With some procedures, unresisted movement can begin immediately. For others, a period of immobilisation is essential to let tissue knit together. In the initial few days, great care must be taken to avoid infection in the area. Compliance with the hygiene regime recommended by the surgeon is critical. If infection spreads from the skin wound into a joint or bone, the consequences are severe. Supervision and guidance from a good physiotherapist is critical because it can be difficult for individuals to judge acceptable levels of discomfort during early mobilisation and to recognise signs of under- or over-doing it.

Drug and other emerging treatments

Since soft tissue injuries were traditionally thought to be inflammatory in nature, two classes of anti-inflammatory drugs, steroid injections and non-steroidal anti-inflammatory drugs (NSAIDs), have been a mainstay of treatment until recent years. Today, both are becoming increasingly controversial and although they are still regularly prescribed by GPs and some physiotherapists, their use in sports medicine is becoming increasingly limited. There are some novel drug treatments which show some promise for tendon healing and while these may not yet be readily available or desirable, their use is discussed below.

Corticosteroid injections

Local injections of cortisone to reduce inflammation and pain were a popular treatment for ligament and tendon injuries until recently. The loss of favour for steroid injections to treat both acute and slow onset tendon injuries has been one of the major developments in sports medicine over recent years. One of the primary reasons for this is the evidence that many soft tissue injuries do not involve the classic inflammatory process. Moreover, it now seems uncertain whether steroids have favourable effects on the strength of the tissue itself. Steroid injections tend to cause rapid relief from tendon pain although the actual physiological effects on tendon tissue (and hence longer term outcome) are not fully understood. The available research suggests the long term benefits of steroid injections are poor[96]. It may be that the strong analgesic effect of steroid injections merely acts as a catalyst for tissue strengthening by allowing the sufferer to commence exercise therapy sooner.

Although pain is reduced and functional capacity is rapidly restored compared to other treatments, injury recurrence rates are high - much higher than with therapeutic exercises alone. An even more worrying finding has been repeated reports of subsequent ruptures in tendons that have been treated with multiple steroid injections. Increasingly, steroid injections are avoided in sports medicine and are viewed as damaging in chronic tendinopathy cases. There may be a case for early use when their effects of reducing tendon swelling would be important, such as in impingement of the supraspinatus tendon in the shoulder or trigger finger. However, some GPs still routinely treat painful tendons at the outset with injections, perhaps because of poor awareness of recent research developments or because of their appealing short term effects on pain. If this is offered at your first GP consultation when first presenting with a new injury, it may well be prudent to seek a more specialist opinion before accepting the injection. It is also critical that good injection technique is used. The steroid should be injected onto the surface of the tendon and not into the tendon itself as this has been shown to cause degeneration and weakening of tendons. For this reason, it is important that the injections are performed by a specialist. Imaging techniques such as ultrasound will often be used to guide the needle to the appropriate site to prevent the severe side effects of inadvertent injection into the tendon substance.

Due to the risks of injury recurrence, tendon damage or even rupture in the long term, steroid injections should be considered with great caution, as a last resort and only under the advice of a sports medicine specialist. If you do choose this course of treatment, limiting the number of injections may help to reduce the risk of poor long term outcome. For less serious cases of tendinopathy or ligament tears, a well designed program of physiotherapy may well be just as effective in the short and medium term, but with much better results in the long term.

Non-steroidal anti-inflammatory drugs (NSAIDs)

NSAIDs have been routinely recommended to control pain and inflammation in soft tissue injuries for decades[75]. They are still often prescribed by GPs and are regularly taken by athletes. Ibuprofen, one of the most popular NSAIDs is nicknamed 'Vitamin I' because of its liberal use among sportspeople to control pain from injuries and even from normal training and performance.

The emerging understanding that slow onset, soft tissue injuries do not involve a classic inflammatory response, and a clearer delineation between the objectives of controlling short term pain and long term tissue healing, have undermined the rationale for their use. Today, the picture from the available research is inconclusive and rather complex[66].

The first aspect to consider is that NSAIDs are not one type of drug but a whole class of drugs that fall into different categories with several different individual drugs in each. The two main categories are non-selective and selective COX-2 inhibitors. The primary mechanism of their action on inflammation is thought to be the inhibition of production of inflammatory mediators called prostaglandins. Inflammation plays a crucial role in triggering the later stages of healing, so it has been suggested that reducing inflammation may delay or blunt healing after injury. Although slow onset tendinosis has been classed as 'non-inflammatory' by some researchers since it doesn't follow the classic inflammatory response of swelling, heat and redness, there is some evidence of certain inflammatory chemicals that may be important in its healing[67]. There may also be Inflammation of the surrounding area such as tendon sheaths due to adhesions or friction from the swollen and disrupted tendon as it moves. Effects on this inflammation may be important in the analgesic effects of NSAIDs in tendinosis.

There is now some evidence, albeit conflicting, that NSAIDs do significantly interfere with bone healing and possibly should be avoided after fractures[97]. Studies into the effects of NSAIDs on ligament and tendon healing have been even more conflicting. Different studies have used different individual drugs and some have investigated their effects in acutely cut soft tissue in animals, while others have measured pain and time-course of return to sport in humans. Both research methodologies are inadequate for making firm conclusions about their effects. Animal studies on artificially cut tendons do not reflect what happens in the slow onset tendinosis of many sports injuries. In the human studies, it is not clear if effects of NSAIDs on recovery times are due to positive effects on tissue, or indirectly, through effects on pain. Hypothetically, if pain is reduced by NSAIDs, earlier and more vigorous physiotherapy may be possible and this might facilitate healing. However, this effect could be offset if there are direct negative effects of the drugs on tissue healing.

Given the widespread habitual use of NSAIDs among sportspeople, it is also important to mention their serious side effects. NSAIDs are toxic to the gastrointestinal tract and their prolonged use precedes many cases of gastric ulcers. The US spends $1.6 billion per year on treating gastric bleeding from NSAID use[65]. Heartburn, dyspepsia and gastritis may occur first. Of the conventional, non-selective NSAIDs, Ibuprofen has the lowest rate of gastric side effects. Selective COX-2 inhibitors, known as

'coxibs' have much lower rates of gastric side effects, but carry other serious cardiac risks[65]. Renal toxicity is also an important concern and although kidney problems in athletes are rare, there are examples of kidney failure in athletes regularly using NSAIDs for sport injuries.

The overall finding of recent reviews on NSAIDs and soft tissue healing is that there is no reliable evidence either for or against their use in soft tissue injuries[68]. Where they are used, the best strategy may be to limit this to a short course during the initial few days following an acute injury[12, 75]. Pain can be controlled in other ways to facilitate early progression of therapeutic exercise. Moreover, reduction of pain is not generally the priority of the injured athlete. Pain from sports injuries is usually moderate and is an essential feedback mechanism for the fine tuning of exercise intensity and prevention of further damage. The masking of pain via drug use to allow sportspeople to underestimate the need to back off, or to go into a state of denial and act as if the injury has disappeared, is a major problem for self-coached athletes like climbers. Using pain relief to ignore symptoms may well be an important cause of progression from early symptoms to much more serious chronic tendinopathy. Increasingly, the opinion of reviewers seems to be that blunting the body's inflammatory response in acute injuries is, on the whole, undesirable. In injuries where there is significant acute trauma; bleeding, swelling and compete loss of function, there may be an argument for blunting this response in the initial period (2-7 days) to allow faster progression to mobilisation and exercise and prevent damage to healthy tissue surrounding the traumatised area from the bleeding. However, where this excessive acute inflammation is absent, such as in most tendinopathies, there is no good evidence that supports the use of NSAIDs.

Glyceryl trinitrate (GTN)

Glyceryl trinitrate patches are normally used in medicine as a vasodilator for angina patients. The patches donate nitric oxide, a free radical, through the skin. Nitric oxide is toxic in high doses, but in small quantities it is used by the body as a messenger molecule. It has been established that it is important in promoting tendon healing and so several trials were performed to examine whether nitric oxide donation with glyceryl trinitrate patches could be used to treat tendinosis. The results of these have been promising with sufferers of various tendinopathies experiencing significant improvements in their symptoms, compared to a control group[98, 99]. The well designed nature of the studies makes this appear to be an exciting development. However, there are some problems. Firstly, the studies were done in non-athletes. Only when studies have been done in athletes will we be able to tell if nitric oxide donation will be important for this population. It is the opinion of researchers I have spoken to that they appear to be ineffective in athletes.

Taking the available research to show my GP, I managed to obtain a prescription to try GTN patches on my own golfer's elbow. Although it is impossible to isolate the effects of the treatment from the training and physiotherapy I was doing at the time, I didn't notice any improvement in my condition during the weeks of the treatment. What I definitely did notice though were the side effects. Severe headaches are the common side effect and I experienced immediate severe headache which made compliance with the treatment extremely challenging. In the published trials on GTN therapy, the dropout rate due to headaches was low and dose related, although the bulk of the treatment group did suffer headaches[100]. I also experienced a painful rash under the patch site, which necessitated rotating the position of patch placement on subsequent days. Rashes also caused dropouts in the published trials. Overall, my own experience was that this treatment was ineffective compared to standard physiotherapy for golfer's elbow (eccentrics). A more recent study with a five year follow up failed to show any benefits to GTN therapy and physiotherapy compared to physiotherapy alone[101].

In the early published trials, dosing of GTN was 1.25mg per 24 hours. Patches often contain 5mg so the patch is cut into four quarters and the 1.25mg segment is applied to the skin over the site of maximum tenderness. A later study which trialled the effects of different doses found that a lower dose (0.72mg/24 hours) was most effective, although there was not a clear dose-response relationship[100]. The lower dose is appealing because the associated headaches are dependent on dose, so compliance might be easier. The dosing study was not done in conjunction with physiotherapy, which may have yielded clearer results.

So, like many emerging treatments, the picture coming from the research to date is unclear. More research is needed to establish any positive effects in athletes, optimal dosing and the best combinations of therapies. There is simply not enough evidence to recommend its use at present.

Extra-corporeal shock wave therapy (ESWT)

A promising new treatment over the past ten years has been has been the use of shock wave therapy on chronic soft tissue injuries. Although there has been some quite good evidence that it promotes tendon healing, the results have been conflicting and opinions differ on its value[66, 75]. The mechanism of its effects are not fully understood either. Theories include increases in tendon cell activity, blood flow and growth factors, together with inhibition of pain sensing nerve endings. The results of ESWT have differed when studied in different tendons. Recent work showed good results in the Achilles tendon when used in conjunction with eccentric exercise therapy. However, various studies have shown no benefits when treating other tendons[66]. Of course the treatment requires regular sessions with a therapist but availability of therapists with the wave generator machines necessary for ESWT may be limited and the treatment is expensive. There is not enough evidence to recommend it for tendon injuries at the moment[75]. Having said that, if you have access to the treatment via your therapist, it could be worth considering.

Autologus blood injections

Injections of autologus (from the patient) whole blood or blood extract (platelet-rich plasma) have been tried in tendinopathy[66]. The platelet-rich plasma is extracted from whole blood using a centrifuge and then injected around the injured tendon. The rationale is that the injected blood induces a healing response via the action of growth factors which are abundant in the plasma preparation. This is still an emerging treatment although there is some limited evidence that it promotes healing[102, 103]. There have only been a few studies in humans so far and these have been small, with some conflicting results[104]. The latest review (2014) suggests the treatment is probably ineffective and not worth recommending, although other researchers argue it is too early to abandon it before more research is done[105, 106].

Sclerosing injections

Tendinosis causes new blood vessels to form ('neovascularisation') in degenerating tendons. It has been thought that obliterating these new vessels with a sclerosing injection would relieve pain and help restore more normal tendon structure. Sclerosing injections of polidocanol are usually used to treat varicose veins. When injected into chronically painful tendons, they obliterate the neovessels and in the process appear to eradicate the pain sensing nerve endings that are present in abundance in these vessels. Although the treatment gives pain relief, it is not understood how it might improve the tendon tissue itself. New theories of tendinopathy to point to observations that tendon pain may persist in chronic cases, despite improvements in the health of the tendon substance. The extent to which neovessels are the source of tendon pain is still not clear. Some research demonstrates good short term results used in combination with eccentric exercise for tendinosis. However, more research is needed to form a clearer picture of how the effectiveness stacks up against other available treatments[102]. A recent review proposed its use only after a program of eccentric exercise, GTN patches, ESWT and steroid injections have failed to improve symptoms[71]. Research is ongoing and the treatment continues to be tried by the leading experts in tendon pathology, at least as an adjunct to exercise therapy[95]. Based on the current evidence, sclerosing injections may be among the best adjunct treatments currently on offer for slow onset tendinopathy.

Botulinum toxin injections

Botulinum toxin, is normally used to treat muscle tone disorders, as well as cosmetic treatments. Some researchers have experimented with it as a last-resort alternative to surgery for tennis elbow. The toxin is injected into the wrist extensor (extensor carpi radialis brevis) and this paralyses the muscle. The muscle gradually recovers from the paralysis and regains functional capacity over 2-6 months. The theory behind the treatment is that complete rest of the muscle allows the tendon a chance to recover. The few research trials have shown conflicting results. One study compared the effectiveness of botulinum toxin to surgery and found both to have good but comparable results. The argument for its use is that it is less invasive than surgery. However, some studies have shown no advantage of botulinum toxin treatment compared to a placebo control group. For severe cases of tendinosis which have been resistant to physiotherapy over time, botulinum toxin may be an alternative to surgery, although it is expensive. It seems very unlikely at the moment that the treatment will catch on among the sporting community.

Gene or stem cell therapy

Therapies which produce altered expression of important genes in tendon or ligament healing are currently being developed, but are not yet an approved technique. They show considerable promise for the future of sports medicine. Genes for important chemicals such as growth factors can be introduced to injured tendons in a few different ways. One method is to implant the relevant DNA into a virus which is allowed to infect the target cells in the injury site and begin expressing the desired gene. Another is to remove cells from the injury, add the required DNA in the laboratory and then re-implant the cells. Trials in laboratories and animal studies have shown good results with the ability to stimulate growth of normal tendon tissue[71].

The main hurdle is safety of applying the technique in humans. There is a theoretical risk of malignancy of the altered cells and uncontrolled expression of the newly implanted genes. If these problems can be overcome it seems likely this treatment will become important in years to come. Some clinics are already offering stem cell therapy using various techniques, with promising case studies and clinical trials ongoing.

In summary, convincing evidence for taking drugs to recover from soft tissue injuries is lacking across the board. In the case of NSAIDs and steroid injections, this is because research gives conflicting results that have undermined the rationale for their use. In the case of emerging treatments, this is because not enough research has been done to establish the best way to use the treatments and get a clear picture of how effective they are. Availability is another issue; NSAIDs and cortisone are arguably overused despite their poor effectiveness, while accessing some of the newer treatments, in the UK at least, may be difficult and expensive. Most of the treatments described above should be explored only once physiotherapy and correction of causes have been tried repeatedly. Focusing on drug treatments at an early stage risks distracting from physiotherapy and cause-correction which are likely to form the backbone of any positive effects. The opinion of the most qualified expert you can find will be invaluable in choosing drug treatments for injuries.

When to stop rehab?

The short answer to the question "when are you ready to stop rehab?" is "never". Even if you have achieved full return to normal climbing and no longer need to perform rehab exercises, two aspects of your rehab work must continue indefinitely: monitoring and ongoing prevention.

The risk of a given injury may be much higher if you have had that injury before. Complete removal of underlying susceptibility is very much a best case scenario, and even if it can be achieved, existing damage to tissue may remain. So athletes who experience an injury must usually make permanent changes in one or more aspects of their technique or their training regime.

The extent to which you must do this depends very much on the injury suffered. Finger pulley injuries heal well and allow climbers to carry on crimping hard for decades beyond. However, even here there must normally be a permanent change in the ratio of crimp/openhand grip used to prevent accumulation of stress on the pulleys. In the case of elbow tendinosis, eccentric exercises may be necessary on a permanent basis to prevent re-injury. Similarly for many shoulder injuries, rehab exercises

which corrected alignment and movement may need to be continued indefinitely to prevent the same injury process recurring.

Many injured athletes long to get back to a place where they can forget about the looming possibility of further injury. Unfortunately, the reality is that experiencing an injury forces athletes to mature and realise that they must be constantly vigilant and incorporate preventative work into their routine, even in a healthy state. Once you accept this, it is not such a big deal. In fact, as you get older and see more and more of your peers affected by sports injuries, it is likely you will be grateful that your approach matured when it did and is keeping you climbing hard year after year where others have struggled and failed to solve their injury problems.

Summary

No single treatment stands out as being the most effective for dealing with tendon or ligament injuries. The available research is far from complete, so comparing the available treatments is difficult at present. However, exercise therapy appears to demonstrate the most consistent results and lowest rates of recurrence of the injury. Be aware that choices between the available treatments, even by professionals in sports medicine, may relate to what has historically been used rather than the current state of thinking among scientific researchers. Moreover, focusing on one treatment which is held in high regard by the professional or peer who recommends it does not mean that other treatments should not also be tried.

What is absent from the current research is an investigation into combinations of several therapies simultaneously. Outside of research, in 'real life' injuries which are treated with or without the supervision of a professional, a combination of therapies is often undertaken by the athlete with good results. It can be extremely difficult to guess which is responsible for success or failure of the rehab process. Seeking the multiple sources of advice, together with diligent application of multiple therapies, may be the best way to approach the art and science of treating a soft tissue injury.

Never despair, but if you do, work on in despair.

Edmund Burke

Psychology of injuries: dealing with the anguish of injury

Face it: it really is that bad!

The experience of getting an injury that is going to affect your climbing is, inevitably, a psychologically painful experience. Climbers can be shocked by just how badly they feel. Inability to participate in the activity you think about or do every day of your life can make you realise for the first time how important it is to you. The depth of this negative experience is the unavoidable opposite of the 'highs' you experience when climbing goes well. There are two aspects of the injury process that are particularly unpleasant: the moment you realise you have a serious injury, and the experience, during rehab, of seeing no discernible progress towards recovery despite rest and/or rehab interventions. Perhaps the strongest of minds and temperaments could deal with these setbacks without feeling frustrated, but most of us definitely will be deeply affected by the experience of a serious sports injury.

There is no simple solution to make the negative feelings after getting injured vanish; the injury is a reality. However, those negative feelings during a period of injury are a good thing because you are going to need them. With the right approach, this frustration with your predicament can be transformed from a torment into an essential tool that drives your journey back to health. This section will explore the ways you can achieve this.

Humans are amazingly good at adapting to adversity. Psychological studies into the effects of traumatic life events on happiness convincingly shows that following a short period of unhappiness, people rapidly return to a 'normal' state of happiness despite having to adjust to the most awful of circumstances[107]. We do adjust. There are of course some exceptions to this. Situations where there is unnecessary injustice, unfairness or constant pain are examples of circumstances which are extremely hard to adjust to. Generally speaking, adversities we can best absorb are those in which we can do something, however small, to influence our situation and improve things. The vast majority of injuries that climbers commonly get fall into this category.

Yet in many cases (possibly a majority), climbers fail to achieve this adjustment, fail to get over the feelings of frustration, anger or apathy and get on with their recovery with a positive mindset. There are two main reasons for this. Firstly, climbers maintain a state of denial about the injury they have, and as a result fail to start implementing a rehab program or even make the injury worse by ignoring pain and continuing to overload damaged tissue. Secondly, they simply don't realise how effective a good rehab response can be and therefore feel powerless to do anything except wait and hope the injury heals.

Avoiding a prolonged state of denial about a new injury is critical to saving you from much of the psychological pain of an injury, and resultant upset of your normal routine of climbing. Ignoring or playing down the injury in your mind has only one outcome: a prolonged recovery and even more painful acceptance of the new situation down the line. So the more quickly you get a solid diagnosis and have a clear discussion with yourself about what this means for your climbing over the coming weeks and months, the better. Climbers often take a 'wait and see' approach instead of getting a diagnosis, with the rationale that it might turn out to be a very minor and transient injury. This might be a safe way forward for very experienced and knowledgeable climbers (usually with past experience of injuries), even then only for a few days. For everyone else, it's asking for trouble. It is better to swallow the bitter pill and accept that it really is that bad, in order to start making it better as quickly as possible.

As soon as a cycle of denial sets in, it can be hard to break. Here are some of the signs of a denial approach:

- Simply ignoring or underplaying pain.

- Using pain medication to mask symptoms. At first, their use is with a 'just this time' justification, which then becomes a habit lasting several sessions or even longer.

- Using the fact that pain partially or wholly disappears after a thorough warm-up as a reason to pretend the injury isn't there or isn't serious.

- Taping an injured finger very heavily and thinking that since pain is reduced, so is tissue damage. Pain may in fact be reduced via the heating or 'counter irritant' effects of the tightness of the tape via the gate control mechanism (see section 2).

- Short term thinking: "I'm going on a trip next week, so I can't be injured!"

As soon as the climber realises that one or a mix of these strategies allows him to keep going as if the injury hasn't happened, it becomes very difficult to later find the discipline to step back and accept the injury. What usually forces this to happen is that the injury is made significantly worse over the course of a few sessions. In the case of slower onset injuries such as golfer's elbow or impingement syndrome in the shoulder, this process can go on for months.

The risks ought to be made clear. This approach is likely to make partial finger pulley tears rupture completely, transient and mild golfer's elbow become chronic over several years and shoulder impingement bad enough to require surgery and extended lay-off from climbing.

What's more, the adjustment you need to make to avoid worsening an injury might not need to be that big; avoiding the campus board or fingerboard for a few weeks, a change of scenery from the same venue or route, or just climbing some less crimpy terrain for a while. You might be risking a lot for the sake of a small and temporary adjustment.

Acceptance that your injury will require a change in your climbing habits, and a challenge to your discipline seems like an unpleasant prospect. However, once the switch is flicked and you accept that you are in 'rehab mode' and changed your short and medium term goals accordingly, it feels like a relief. At least you have avoided making it any worse.

Even in the case of injuries which are very difficult or impossible to resolve, and the interventions to be made involve working around rather than rehabilitating them, it is possible to respond by absorbing and dealing with the new reality, without carrying any negativity about what has happened in the long term. However, the recovery from the psychological challenge might fail if there is a feeling of unfairness. Studies into the happiness of people living in chaotic societies with either violent conflict or a high crime rate are often just as happy or happier than those in much more stable societies. The reason the troubles faced don't seem to affect them negatively in the long term appears to come down to a sense of what is normal. If everyone else suffers the same risks or negative experiences, then they appear to be much easier to absorb. Athletes who express the deepest and longest lasting frustration with their injuries are those who compare themselves only to a false image of their peers. It is easy to forget that all athletes get injured. Furthermore, most athletes will suffer numerous serious injuries during a career that will force them to change their routine. And even if we don't suffer injuries that cause permanent loss of function, we all share the risk of that happening. In other words, we are all human and all in the same boat. Comparing yourself to peers who are healthy (as far as you know, anyway) while you are injured is a surefire way to make the experience deeply frustrating. It is easy not to take note of the injuries your peers suffer. We tend to notice and remember good performances in sport, not depressed performance. Moreover, you probably tend to see less of climbing acquaintances while they recover from their injuries because they aren't training at the same venues.

The more aggressively you reassess your goals for training and performance given the new situation, the shorter and less psychologically painful your recovery is likely to be. Quite apart from minimising the negative psychological effects of injury, there are positive effects to take advantage of, too. A new injury in an athletic career brings with it the opportunity to thoroughly take stock, refresh and rethink all aspects of your game. In the longer term and in a best case scenario, your injury may actually propel your improvement rather than delay it. Athletes who stay injury free for a long period often fall short of their potential due to stagnation of one sort or another. This can be caused by things like failure to sort out aspects of their life outside of climbing (lifestyle, routine, career, finances, etc.) and these become a brake on progress that goes unnoticed. They get bogged down in what's urgent: the next session or route goal, and miss out on the important (the deeper weaknesses they really ought to address). With an injury, such short term thinking goes out of the window. If you take this unique time in your career to go back to basics, look hard at your routine and sort out not only the causes of your injury but the causes of failing to meet your potential that are just easier to miss when healthy, you can end up coming back from the injury a much better climber than before. Clearly, if you can put yourself on this path, the recovery time from the injury will become a lot more rewarding and pass a lot more quickly than if you just sat at home and did the physio exercises for the painful tendon. The next section explains some ideas for how to go about this.

Take heart

Live your life so that whenever you lose, you are ahead.
Will Rogers

If you have become injured and are going to have to suspend your short term climbing goals for a while, there is lots to get on with! And that applies whether you are able to keep climbing in some form during rehab, or will be taking a complete break from climbing for a spell. The only climbing goals left are longer term ones. To start making progress towards them, there are a whole different set of short term goals on which to get moving.

The first task is to figure out what they are. The combination of the time you have for stepping back and thinking clearly, and the psychological mindset of the frustrated injured climber, creates the perfect environment to do this. You have distance from your normal routine and are unable to act out unconscious habits, so those habits become clearer to see and easier to break than at any other time. Moreover, your frustrated mindset puts you in the right mood to break free from habits and make bold decisions.

Simply thinking carefully about the underlying causes of both your injury and the factors that may have been holding your climbing progress back might be enough to figure out what to do. However, your family and climbing partners are vital counsel to observe the patterns in your

climbing objectively over time. Make sure to ask them what they think of your climbing. Ask them what they think you could do differently in your routine to improve your climbing. If the sports medic or physiotherapist you see about diagnosing and treating your injury has specific knowledge of climbing, he might be able to offer more advice. A climbing coach you have seen before you were injured might provide additional help. If you haven't used a climbing coach before, now might be a good time for a session. Even if the climbing you can currently do is limited, a discussion with a good coach about your routine might provide valuable insight into the weak areas of your performance and your risk factors for injury. It is important to use all of these sources of advice, because between them, they will help you see the patterns and make insights into almost all aspects of what you do.

Once you have some ideas, use the time away from immediate climbing goals to clock up the hours addressing those weaknesses. You may well be aware that if you were climbing 'normally' and injury free, you would never be able to discipline yourself to work on these things so diligently. So take advantage!

The later sections of the book deal with addressing underlying susceptibilities which are specific to particular injuries. Below are some examples of more general things which climbers ought to do but often don't do enough of:

1.   Change of scenery

This is possibly the most important thing you can do for your climbing routine. The expression "a change is as good as a rest" doesn't begin to cover the importance of doing something different. It is not just a rest that is provided by a change of scenery, it is an opportunity to go back to basics, either metaphorically or practically, by going back to climbing on physically easy terrain.

A really good thing to do if you can still climb during rehab is to spend the recovery time going to completely new places, possibly climbing with new people and getting on routes that you just wouldn't do if you weren't limited to easier grades by the injury. Because the focus is not on always trying to push your limit and create a personal best performance every session, there is room to notice things.

For those involved in trad climbing, visit the big, scary or out of the way adventure crags and get on them, but on routes that are easy for you. Enjoy being there. Climb in the dark, climb in the rain. Climb chimneys, cracks, ice climbs. Taking to one side the obvious point that you'll have a great time, the other important point is that you will start to see weaknesses in your climbing technique and tactics that you would never have noticed if you had been on your usual terrain. This will happen even if the drop in grade is huge.

This effect was the single biggest revelation about injury rehabilitation in my own climbing career. At age 18, after two years of suffering a string of finger pulley injuries with lay-off times of up to four months, I had yet another pulley tear and couldn't crimp anything without aggravating it. At the time, I was climbing 8a redpoint and E4 onsight and had just spent several months trying to break into onsighting E5 without success. After the injury I decided to try not stopping climbing and to simply drop my grade to whatever I could climb without making my injury more tender and painful. That was the grade VS.

I could normally do VS in my trainers and would quite happily solo up or down that grade. So where could I find challenge? I looked through my guidebooks for all the VSs I could find that were either very long multipitch, or very loose, or rarely climbed, or if I knew they were dirty or had a reputation for being a full-on experience for the grade. Then I systematically targeted and worked through them. The first crag I went to was called The Whangie, a basalt outcrop near Glasgow which is notoriously loose and badly protected. Some of the routes were top-roped or protected by pegs which are no longer there.

If you had suggested going there for a day's climbing before that I'd probably have looked at you like you'd gone mad. But for this situation, it was perfect. And I had lots of fun there. What's more, many the VSs I chose were hard! I knew they would be hard and that's why I would have otherwise avoided them, like everyone else.

They were scarily loose and poorly protected. On every route I learned more about reading the rock, judging the solidity of holds, finding inventive protection placements and downclimbing to rest or to maintain an escape route should I come up against an impasse higher up.

I quickly found it easy to carry on with this policy of seeking out routes that would be challenging in every way apart from crimping on small holds. I could feel that it was making me a better climber. One of the first things I noticed was that there were no 'excuse days'. Whatever the weather, we climbed something. In fact, I was amazed how many metres of rock I climbed in a given week. I lost weight and felt fitter. By the time I had worked through most of the VSs on my hit list, my finger was improved enough for HVS. Over the subsequent three months, I repeated the same process through the grades, climbing both the big classic E1s and E2s as well as the nasty, scary ones I'd otherwise avoid. By the time I worked back up to E4, my finger was not 100% better but I could crimp most holds without any pain and every aspect of my climbing was better. Shortly afterwards I onsighted the first E5 I tried, and the following season around 30 E5s and E6s and a few E7s. I am totally convinced that those three months of serving a proper apprenticeship in all the aspects of climbing I would otherwise have avoided are still benefitting my climbing to this day. Plus, it was one of the most fun and memorable periods of my 20 years of climbing.

A counter-argument for doing this might be "well that's nice, but I'm just not interested in doing that sort of thing - it doesn't sound appealing". That is fair enough, but it remains that the alternative is simply doing your rehab exercises or other activities outside of the sport. Even if you can't find a way to enjoy the experience of some easy but different climbing, it might be enough to see it as the lesser of two evils: 'either do this or lay-off completely'. Moreover, the feeling of building a stronger performance base to build your long term performance level ought to be a good motivator.

Another concern might be that your climbing level is not very high to start with, so even at very low grades you notice the injury becoming aggravated. It doesn't really matter how low an intensity you have to go, the effects are still worth it. Even mountain scrambles, ice climbing, technical mountaineering or parkour are close enough to rock climbing to help develop your movement, strength, fitness and confidence in a way that will be beneficial for your climbing.

Although a change of scenery which involves climbing is good for your performance, non-climbing activities can also be good, in an indirect way, as the next point explores.

2. Improve lifestyle and routine

All sorts of ridiculous things get in the way of climbing. People get stuck in jobs that just don't fit with climbing and are not the only option available. They never take the time to figure out a good routine to fit in all the regular tasks of life in the most efficient way. They let themselves be slaves to other people's deadlines. More often than not, there is no magic bullet for the innumerable problems that suck up time and opportunity to get climbing, or get good at it. The solution might be clever workarounds. So what do most of these problems have in common?

They usually involve an investment of time and effort to 'make the move' and tackle the problem directly enough to actually get it solved. The analogy that is of getting over a hill. It is easy to get an opportunity to make small runs at it. But only a sustained effort gets you over and only then can you move on.

A break from short term thinking in your climbing thanks to an injury is the perfect time to get all those things sorted out once and for all, with a concerted effort. What a shame if these things were still in your way by the time you recover and want to spend your time getting out and getting your goal climbs done. Some examples of things that are good to get done while you wait for a tendon to heal:

- Pass a university or college course.
- Move house to an area with some nearby crags or climbing walls.
- Change jobs to one that gives you better conditions for climbing.
- Sit down with your boss and give a persuasive

argument to change your working practice.
- Build a climbing wall in your house.
- Get your driving license.
- Go on a non-climbing holiday (to a beach or something scary like that!).
- Work extra hours to save for a long climbing trip.
- Do some aerobic training to lose weight if you are over your ideal weight.
- Experiment with different weekly routines of work and chores to find something better.

There are many possible ways for you to use this time to set yourself up for a better climbing routine than you had before. However, it can be hard for some to figure out what they could be doing differently in their routine. Part of this can be down to the mistaken belief that you are powerless to change some specifics of your routine. An objective source of advice such as a partner, good friend or coach is invaluable in helping with this problem. Ask them to be brutally honest; what would they do if they were you? One way to start the process is to imagine your perfect life routine, in which you were able to fulfill all of your work and family commitments as well as pursue your climbing freely. What would a weekly routine look like? Write it down, then compare it to a few written diaries of your current weekly routine. The aspects that are causing the biggest differential between 'actual' and 'ideal' should start to show themselves clearly. Even if you can improve only the biggest limitation or awkward demand on your resources of time and energy, it might be enough to drastically improve your performance in all aspects of your work and sport.

3. Address postural/biomechanical weaknesses

If you have responded sensibly to a new injury by seeking out diagnosis and advice from the best professional you can possibly find, together with becoming an expert on it yourself through diligent research and reading, you will probably have uncovered some postural/biomechanical risk factors that may have contributed to the injury. Just doing sufficient research to make sure you clearly understand the postural faults or weaknesses uncovered by your physiotherapist takes a fair bit of time. Once you have settled on an appropriate selection of exercises to improve these faults, the challenge is to actually complete them!

It is no surprise that non-compliance with therapeutic exercises during rehab is a major contributor to re-injury upon return to sport. The problem is less significant in professional athletes. For one, they tend to take more seriously the relationship between their postural faults and the injuries they suffer. But perhaps more significantly they are often supervised during their rehab exercises. The research into the effectiveness of rehab exercises clearly shows that both compliance and successful recovery are more consistent if the injured athlete performs the exercises with a physiotherapist rather than being left to complete them in their own time[108].

Don't make this mistake. Of course, part of this comes down to taking responsibility for your own rehab outcome. However, you can also increase your chances by making life easier on yourself. The big problem with many rehab exercises is that they are as dull as hell, monotonous, and you need to do a lot of them. How can you make it easier for yourself to get them done?

- Some people are more likely to complete the exercises if they have made the effort to travel to a gym to do them. If you do them after work, try to do it before you go home. It is much easier to find a reason not to once you are in the comfort of your sofa.

- Others will find it easier to comply with an rehab exercise program if they do it in front of the TV at home. It will probably help if you link the rehab program to a daily routine such as a regular show you like to watch or listen to. A well stocked iPod is another very useful compliance tool.

- Linking up with a training partner always helps. Be inventive and seek out partners to meet up with to complete your workouts. If it is a regular date in the diary, it's harder to back out of.

- Avoid scheduling your rehab workouts when you are likely to be tired, rushed or distracted and make sure the environment is warm and comfortable.

Even details like choosing your training clothes carefully and making sure they are clean and ready for the next session can make sure you avoid that dreaded decision to skip the session 'just this time'.

- If you do skip sessions, as everyone has to do occasionally, don't beat yourself up and feed yourself the message that you don't have the discipline to keep going. Just forget about it and get right back on the horse.

- If you are having trouble with regularly skipping sessions, step back and have a fresh think about how you could schedule them differently. Don't just keep hoping that next week things will be easier. Habit replacement and self-discipline go hand in hand.

The overall goal is to do everything you can to make your rehab exercise time enjoyable, useful or even relaxing. By the time your elbow is better, you might have learned a new language via your iPod, not missed a single episode of your favourite TV show, spent regular chatting time with a good friend, or simply relaxed and not thought about anything at all for 30 minutes every day.

4.   Improve flexibility

If you have suffered from an elbow or especially shoulder injury it is pretty likely that your physiotherapist will have compiled a program of exercises to stretch short muscles around these joints and re-balance the strength of antagonists. If you are going to be spending some time working on these exercises, it makes sense to make the most of the opportunity and address inflexibility in other areas of the body too.

Most climbers, especially the men, could do with more hip flexibility for climbing, but never find the time to do anything about this. When you see your physio about your injury, make sure to ask them to make a quick assessment of flexibility in your hip adductors, glutes and hamstrings, and to describe some of the very simple stretches for them. A few minutes per day performing these targeted stretches will increase your range of motion significantly after a few weeks and months.

Moreover, performing regular flexibility training during rehab, and getting some results because of your sustained effort, might motivate you to keep doing it once you re-enter your normal climbing routine beyond your rehab period.

Finding motivation

No matter how you look at it, successful rehabilitation from many climbing injuries revolves around clocking up the reps of some fairly mind-numbing exercises. Although the points above should help to mitigate the boredom of having these exercises forced upon you where once you did uninterrupted climbing, there is more you can do to help you complete your rehab program and to enjoy it.

The overarching mindset you adopt in response to your injury will ultimately determine whether the experience is a painful one full of setbacks, or a successful return to your sport at a higher level than before.

Motivation is always easy to find if you can find some meaning in what you are doing. Injury can often fill you with feelings that you have been burdened with meaningless bad luck or unfairness. We saw in the first part of the book that your injury may be alerting you to a weak area of your performance that you must change in order to progress. This, at least, may restore the sense of fairness in what has happened, even if with hindsight you could have seen the injury coming with better monitoring.

However, a greater meaning can be found if you decide to use the injury as a chance to step back and make a bottom-to-top reassessment of every aspect of your climbing game, with the goal of coming back stronger than before. In many cases it is an achievable goal. The experience of athletes is that, provided it has been possible to identify and mitigate the underlying susceptibilities to injury, the time to reflect and sort everything out can propel your progress faster than if you had stayed uninjured, just carrying on as you were.

The reasons for this are, no doubt, complex. The direct effects of addressing all the weaknesses in your performance are one positive aspect. Another may be the time away from the sport you love, which can restore the 'hunger' for it that sometimes wanes a little during times of health. The rest for body and mind from the constant demand to push to higher and higher levels of training and performance must not be underestimated either. This is true whether you are an elite athlete focused on just one thing, or whether your life has full-on demands from all corners - career, family and sport.

My own experience has been that post-injury periods have consistently brought the most significant jumps in progress in my climbing. Obviously, these have not been the result of uninterrupted training, but rather by making game-changing alterations to my routine or approach, together with re-igniting the hunger to push myself further. During my rehab periods I adopted a 'purgatory' mentality in which I saw the dullness of rehab exercises as the fair consequence of failure to pay enough attention to messages from my body and educate myself to the possible sources of error (whether that was a true assessment or not). I saw it as my clear challenge to go right back to basics and question everything I did, how it impacted my climbing and how it could be done differently, as well as diligently completing my exercises without fail. I saw that my reward, if I could complete this, would be a jump in performance greater than if I had just done my normal, healthy training. This has worked every time for me.

The subtleties of attitude and approach to a challenge like injury rehab are dependent on individual personality and it is up to you to find the necessary way to frame the challenge in a way that you think will work. It is important to remember that if you find your strategy isn't working and you are failing to see the positive sides of your injury and resultant rehab program, go back and build it again from square one rather than allow motivation to falter.

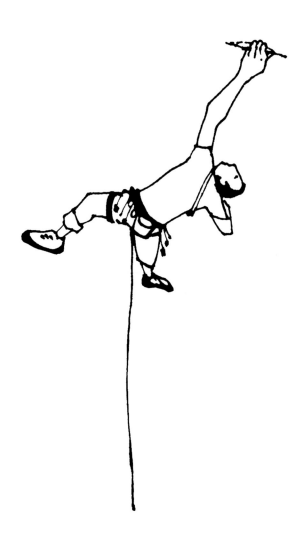

Young climbers

What young climbers should know

Young climbers suffer many of the same injuries as older climbers. However, there are some significant differences in the types of injuries that youngsters get because of the structure of their growing bodies. In addition, there are some important points that young climbers must learn as early as possible, to avoid the inevitable injuries frequently caused by inappropriate climbing activities.

Climbing, generally speaking, is a healthy activity for youngsters to be involved in compared to plenty of other sports[109]. Although it is partially weight dependent, it lacks the strong culture of aggressive weight manipulation that causes severe health implications and short careers for young competitive gymnasts. Fractures from falls are relatively uncommon compared to other mountain sports such as biking. It also has a healthy mix of competitive and non-competitive arenas and fairly healthy prevailing attitudes toward training and performance. However, excessive stress on growing fingers is a particular cause of concern for young climbers. If training is applied too early and aggressively, these injuries can and do end young climbers' careers before they have really begun. Although the available research is far from complete, it is fair to say we know enough to make recommendations that ought to make this sort of scenario avoidable. However, lack of knowledge is not the real issue, it is getting youngsters to change their habits before it is too late.

When it comes to injuries, the vast majority of sportspeople, whether adolescent or adult, learn the hard way. They learn how to take care of their bodies by getting repeatedly injured and cursing their misfortune until sheer frustration prompts them to look more closely at what is going on, and realise there is something they can do about it.

For youngsters, it is even harder. They don't have the awareness and aren't as experienced in thinking strategically and anticipating problems as real athletes do. They just go at it, training as keenly as they like until something starts to hurt.

A critical concept for young climbers to understand is that injuries are the result of a gradual process. Their climbing, resting and eating habits today are the cause of the injuries they will suffer in months or years to come. Having the motivation to act now on the threat of future injuries is hard to do. The smartest thing youngsters can do to find the motivation is to look upon their older (but not much older!) peers who are already suffering injuries and realise that those climbers were doing exactly the same activities as they are now. If they can see the frustration of their peers and see that they can do something to avoid having to go through the same process, it will be easier to make changes.

At a basic level, there are two main problems facing young climbers. Firstly, it takes tendons and ligaments a long time to adapt and become able to cope with high volumes of intense climbing. Secondly, the growing skeleton creates periods of imbalance in strength of different types of tissue, creating additional vulnerability to injury.

At face value, this seems like a frustrating aspect of sport for youngsters; they feel that they must hold back despite impatience to progress in climbing. Fortunately, when we look in more detail at the requirements of climbing, this is not the case. In fact, injury prevention and optimum progression of climbing performance in the young add up to the same thing. The reason for this is that climbing is first and foremost a technical sport. As I argued in my book *9 out of 10 Climbers Make the Same Mistakes*, climbers often feel that it is strength that holds them back. Strong fingers are only a performance advantage in the presence of good technique. Good technique remains the most important aspect of training for climbing, and is the aspect that takes the longest to develop.

Although training gains do occur in young athletes, physical strength and endurance develop best from the late teens onwards, when the body's hormonal state has developed to allow training to stimulate muscle tissue growth[110]. Meanwhile, technique is developed faster during childhood and adolescence than any other time in life. Therefore, the best climber is likely the one who focuses most on clocking up large volumes of technique training until the late teens and then shifts focus slightly to add physical strength gains on top of this.

Unfortunately, young climbers commonly focus too much on making early strength gains, and it shows[111, 112]. When coaching youth climbing teams, an overwhelmingly common finding is strong young climbers who have large holes in their technique repertoire, yet are unaware of this. They fall off competition routes because they are unable to spot sequences. The strongest young climbers are often the most unhappy with their performances. Because strength is more measurable, they know they are the strongest, but don't understand why they are not the best.

Opinion from sports medics and climbing coaches around the world is increasingly clear that climbers below the ages of 16-18 should focus on learning technique and gain strength and endurance simply through their climbing activities. Climbers who do this are likely not only to progress to higher levels of performance in the long term, but to suffer fewer injuries.

The following section explores in detail the kinds of injuries young climbers risk by premature or over-zealous training, and specific ways to minimise the risks.

Too much, too young: a warning

Since youngsters often have large amounts of time and freedom to climb regularly, increasing the load on ligaments and tendons too quickly is an easy mistake to make. As a consequence they suffer the common climbing injuries such as finger pulley or ligament tears, elbow tendinopathy and acute shoulder injuries. A likely contributing cause in at least some of these injuries is poor planning and discipline during climbing sessions[110]. Warm-up routines are often inconsistent and the climbing session may be dictated more by what peers are doing than anything else. A classic example is near the end of the session when climbers are tired and focus is waning. Someone suggests a dyno competition. Everyone joins in even though some or even all of the climbers are aware that fatigue is causing both their technique and strength to wane. The risk of damage to

fingers or shoulders is easy to see in hindsight.

It is fine for young climbers to be flexible about their climbing routine. However, a little awareness of the importance of warm-up, and of potentially dangerous choices about what to climb during the session, goes a long way. Young climbers could probably get away with more total climbing volume for a given level of injury risk if they had a more careful warm-up and were more disciplined about what kind of climbing they did late in their sessions, when fatigued. They should also take care to build the volume of their climbing up slowly and steadily over the longer term. Sudden increases in volume such as when a school term ends or a new season of club meets begins should be 'smoothed' with some preparatory sessions.

Fingers

Like adults, the incidence of finger pulley injuries would probably be dramatically reduced if young climbers used an openhanded grip more often and crimped less. Again, this is something that usually has to be learned the hard way after several pulley tears have happened, necessitating many months of climbing lost. Observations from coaches suggest that even using a 'half-crimp' grip without the thumb is significantly safer than full crimping. The predisposing factors of poor footwork and anticipation of slips is arguably even more significant for youngsters. Their bodies become much heavier due to rapid increases in bone mass during the adolescent growth spurt. Cutting loose due to sloppy footwork is less likely to cause a youngster with a light pre-pubescent body to fall off, so young climbers are accustomed to letting it happen. Unfortunately the extra loading caused by cutting loose as their bodies become heavier is hard on the pulleys.

Perhaps the most serious risk that young climbers should be aware of relates to the physiology of growth interacting with high loads on the fingers[113]. Fingers stop growing at around age 16.5 years (with considerable individual variation). It seems that rigorous climbing before this age can cause significant bone and cartilage injuries in the fingers[114]. Growth plates (epiphyseal plates) at the ends of growing bones are vulnerable to injury from repeated high loads. During growth spurts, the growth plates are much weaker than the surrounding tissue and training with high loads can cause fractures at the epiphysis (Fig. 6.1). Epiphyseal fractures are serious because they affect the subsequent growth of the affected bone, with the possibility for lifelong deformity or loss of function. There is evidence of epiphyseal fractures in the fingers of young climbers and these are associated with finger strength training, especially basic strength work such as campus boarding. It appears that this injury is becoming progressively more common in young climbers. More research is needed to get a clearer picture on exactly how these injuries develop. For instance, it is not clear whether a training program consisting of just route climbing or bouldering is significantly safer than adding basic strength work such as fingerboard or campus boarding. However, there is evidence that these injuries are linked to overuse of crimping, so there is room to further reduce the risk even if the young climber sticks to purely climbing by limiting use of crimping. The fractures which have been documented tend to have been caused by repeated micro-trauma. In other words, they are caused by overloading over time, rather than a sudden trauma. Given the available information, if I were an adolescent climber I would choose to stick to route and boulder climbing until at least 16.5 years of age. After this, I would carefully supplement with a little fingerboard work and only use the campus board at 18-20 years old, if at all.

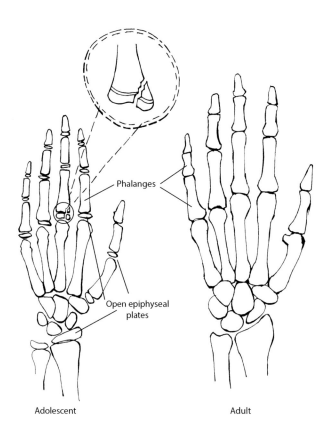

Phalanges

Open epiphyseal plates

Adolescent

Adult

Fig. 6.1 Growth plate fractures in the fingers.

Even following this protocol, safety is not guaranteed, and some risk of damage to growth plates or avulsion fractures must still be expected from climbing. Apart from avoiding aggressive finger strength training and progressing slowly and steadily with training, the most important thing young climbers can do is be vigilant, and report painful fingers to a qualified sports medic immediately. Permanent loss of function can be avoided with prompt treatment[114]. Ignoring symptoms and making injuries much worse is unfortunately very common and has resulted in permanent drop-out from climbing at a young age. The seriousness of this final point cannot be underestimated. Ignoring symptoms or medical advice may not only lead to a permanent exit from the sport, but severely deformed fingers which remain swollen, painful and unable to bend for life.

Young climbers who report finger pain to a doctor, even an experienced sports medic, should be careful to ensure the utmost rigour is used in diagnosis. Growth plate fractures of the fingers can be initially misdiagnosed as pulley or tendon injuries[115]. Growth plate fractures often do not show up on x-rays. Moreover, this is a very unusual injury which is highly specific to adolescent climbers and was only first described in the medical literature very recently. Therefore even experienced sports medics or orthopedic surgeons may be unaware of the risk of this injury in young climbers. If at all possible, an MRI scan should be performed to exclude growth plate fractures. To ensure that correct diagnostic procedure is adhered to, young climbers would be advised to print the paper 'Finger pain in rock climbers: reaching the right differential diagnosis and therapy' by Schöffl[115] and take it with you when you see your doctor. This is important because the consequences of misdiagnosis are so severe. If a growth plate injury is diagnosed, the finger will probably be immobilised for 4-6 weeks in a splint or cast, followed by a very gradual return to climbing. If the fracture becomes displaced, surgery is required.

Height, weight and body fat

High impact training such as the repetitive jumping activities of gymnasts are known to cause stunted growth compared to athletes in other sports[113]. Although there have been no investigations, it seems possible that repeated jumping or falling from bouldering walls could affect lower limb growth in pre-pubescent youngsters in a similar way, although this has never been studied. Modern dedicated bouldering centres are increasingly high and the theoretical risk this presents is certainly something to be aware of.

The energy restriction practiced by young gymnasts and dancers to reduce body fat levels also stunts growth and carries several other significant risks such as eating disorders and osteoporosis. Stunted growth from negative energy balance can be at least partially reversed if training load is reduced and normal eating is resumed. Thankfully, to a large extent, climbing does not share the unhealthy dietary practices of these sports. However, during adolescent growth, there is increased risk of climbers adopting unhealthy eating patterns in order to reduce their weight. Bone mass doubles during the years 13-17, which may explain some of the remarkable climbing performances achieved by children who are very much lighter than their adult counterparts. There are reports from competitive youth team coaches that the standard of young climbers can stop increasing or even fall as adolescence progresses, and bone and muscle mass increase sharply. During this period, attempting to offset body mass increases by reducing body fat percentage is unlikely to be performance positive, since it interferes with growth and reduces the capacity to maintain training.

Young climbers who reach a high standard at an early age must be realistic that their weight advantage will change and this may well affect their standard compared to their peers. The best thing adolescent climbers can do to optimise their progress is to continue to focus on their climbing technique and tactics. The changes in the body are dramatic and rapid, and it takes time to learn to climb well in their 'new' adult body. A period of poor balance and awkward movement following growth spurts is well documented in other sports. Young climbers should also keep in mind that their peers or competitors are going through the same process, or will be very soon. By focusing on good technique, which is one of the strongest components of long term success in climbing, they have the opportunity to gain an advantage over others who may resort to short term tactics of weight control or dangerous strength training practices.

Overall, the pressures on young climbers adapting to body changes during adolescence are probably much worse for those focused on indoor and competitive climbing. Real rock offers much more variability in how a move can be done, and tends to flatten out advantages or disadvantages of different body shapes. Those who take part in a variety of climbing disciplines and climb outside may be less likely to feel pressure to adopt short term thinking which increases their risk of injury.

Parents and coaches of young climbers can do a lot to influence the risk of youngsters developing injuries, and can act to mitigate the damage once injuries appear. The section below outlines the details of this. If you are a young climber who has neither an experienced coach nor parents who are able to offer informed advice, guidance or influence on good climbing practice, it is up to you to take responsibility for educating yourself and acting accordingly. It is ironic that young climbers can show such keenness for working at their climbing but can be willing to neglect injury avoidance measures, even though injuries may be more likely than anything else to determine their long term success in the sport.

What parents and coaches should do

Someone has to take charge of looking after the young athlete's body. The young climber themselves has the best, most direct feedback from their own bodies about how it is absorbing the stresses placed on it. And after all, they are the ones who will manage themselves in adulthood. The sooner they awaken an awareness of injury and its prevention, the better.

Where this attitude and breadth of physiological knowledge has yet to develop, parents must educate themselves to guide their children toward safe practice in climbing. However, even where the youngster shows good awareness of the risks and how to manage them, parents should still ask their children regularly about their climbing practices to check that they are applying

the principles rigorously, and to encourage critical thinking and review of their practices as they progress. How to approach this without seeming dictatorial is no easy task. Pressure or interference from parents or coaches are among the top reasons why youngsters give up organised sport. An emphasis on the positive - that injury prevention is one of the most important factors in climbing success - may be more effective than pointing out the threat of the negatives of injury.

An increasingly common aspect of the youth climbing scene today is the involvement of climbing coaches through climbing walls and youth clubs. Climbing coaching is still in the very early stages of development, so the extent of coaches' involvement and the standard of their work is still extremely variable. This presents a growing problem.

Being coached a little is sometimes worse than not being coached at all. The youngster relies on the coach to keep them on track and progressing, sometimes at the expense of thinking critically and strategically for themselves. That's fine if the coach is taking care of everything, but often the coaching only tackles one small aspect of the sport skills, such as the technique or training exercises, which is possibly at the expense of the recovery, nutrition and injury avoidance/management.

If a climbing coach only sees them occasionally, there is likely to be only time to focus on the climbing activities, with little time to discuss development and risk factors for injury with each individual in the group. The coach should recognise this limitation and encourage the parents to start thinking and acting like coaches, and realise that training for sport is a 24/7 activity that comprises training and recovery, and that both are just as important.

This is further complicated if youngsters do more than one sport. This can involve multiple training programs and multiple coaches all working independently, not always with an eye on the total training load and how it is changing over time, or where possible sites of stress on a joint or tendon might be becoming excessive. In my own early climbing, was lucky in a way to have no coach rather than partial coaching. With my first finger and elbow injuries at age 16 I realised that no one but me was going to get me back to climbing. So I discovered that university book stores were good places to find sports medicine books, and I huddled in their corners reading everything I could to while away the many hours and days of my lay-off.

Even if a climbing coach has limited expertise in climbing injuries or limited time with their climbers, he can still play a pivotal role in limiting injuries. Quickly asking climbers if they have any niggles or pain developing can prevent problems remaining hidden until they become more serious. If a discussion reveals a report of pain, the climber can be encouraged to seek further advice and, in the case of adolescent climbers, reminded of the risks of not getting this advice. Coaches should make themselves aware of local and national contacts of sports medical expertise to pass to their climbers if necessary. In youth climbing clubs and teams, a fund to support private consultations would be of great benefit where possible. A good relationship between climbing clubs and local sports medical clinics would be a great asset. It may be of benefit for parents or coaches to regularly record height changes in their young climbers so they are aware when the climber is entering the higher risk period during adolescent growth spurts or spot a downward trend in growth indices[113].

Where coaching time and expertise are limited, a coach who recognises his or her limitations, and has regular open discussions with the young climber and parents is the best situation. Supplementary consultations with sports medics or physiotherapists should be grabbed with both hands wherever possible. A great Christmas present for a keen young climber would be a consultation for general screening and discussion of injury prevention with a sports medic or physiotherapist with an interest in climbing.

Summary points for young climbers

- Focusing on technique through large volumes of climbing is the best way to progress at a young age since technique cannot be learned so quickly in adulthood.

- Large volumes of basic strength training before the late teens is less effective as the body does not yet have the right hormonal balance to turn the training into large strength gains.

- Basic strength training before the late teens using fingerboards, and especially campus boards, carries a risk of serious growth plate fractures. If left untreated these can cause permanent exit from the sport and lifelong loss of function.

- Develop your use of openhand and half-crimp grips as early as possible to avoid having to do it after having had an injured pulley.

- Through childhood and adolescence, a gradual progression from climbing volume to harder bouldering moves and eventually basic strength work at age 18-20 is the safest progression.

- Careful warm-up for every session is critical.

- Avoid climbing hard moves when tiredness compromises technique.

- Build up volume slowly - sudden increases in weekly climbing at different times in the year is likely to cause injuries.

- Listen to your body and report pain immediately to parents, coaches and mentors, and ask them to help you get in contact with a professional sports medic. Ignoring symptoms or medical advice is simply stupid and you'll definitely regret it.

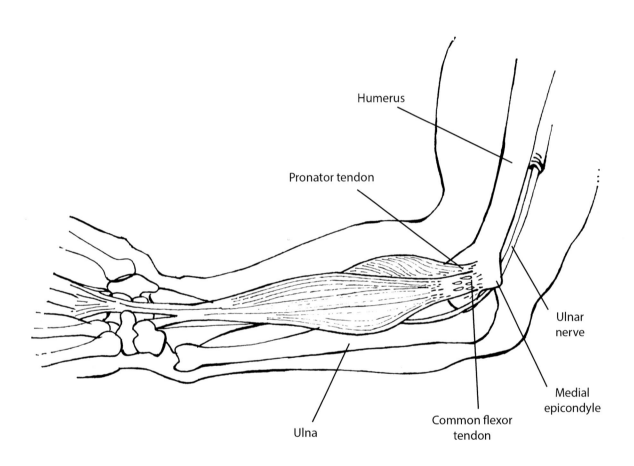

Humerus

Pronator tendon

Ulnar nerve

Medial epicondyle

Common flexor tendon

Ulna

The elbow

Section 7

Climbing is very hard on the elbow joint and it is very likely you will suffer some sort of elbow pain from climbing at some point. Golfer's elbow is undoubtedly the most common elbow injury suffered by climbers and is one of the most serious of all the common climbing injuries since complete recovery can be very difficult to achieve. Climbing obviously involves repetitive flexing of the elbow under high loads. But probably more significant is that the elbow is loaded frequently at the extremes of its range of motion (with outstretched arms or fully locked-off). Moreover, this loading is often eccentric (lengthening under load) such as when we absorb the backswing after catching a hold. Less obvious aspects of climbing may also be important, such as sudden unloading when we slip or 'explode' off a hold while pulling hard creates shear forces within tendons which cause microscopic tearing.

Generally speaking, the best way to take care of your elbows as a climber is to optimise your training progression, develop balanced strength across the elbow, avoid repetitive deep lock-offs by using dynamic movement instead, and to ensure that your general climbing technique is as good as possible.

Golfer's and tennis elbow

Golfer's elbow, affecting the tendon attaching to the 'inside' or medial aspect of the elbow is arguably the nastiest injury risk facing climbers, especially those who have been climbing for over a decade. Unfortunately, it is common among climbers and extremely difficult to cure completely. However, recent developments in its treatment have now reached the stage where most sufferers ought to be able to achieve long term relief. Discovering symptoms, or more likely, discovering how reluctant they are to respond to rest or treatment is a depressing experience for climbers. It may not be of much consolation that a significant proportion of climbers in their 30s or even younger will get the condition. Among those climbers who do not take advantage of recent advances in exercise treatments, it still regularly causes climbers to give up the sport. Fortunately, even when

symptoms have persisted for several years, the condition tends to be responsive to a rigorously applied regime of physiotherapy[36, 86].

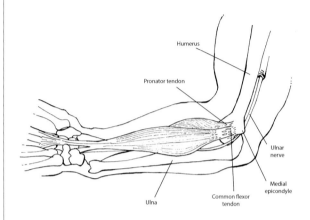

Fig. 7.1 The wrist flexors and golfer's elbow.

Golfer's elbow affects a tendon known as the common flexor origin (Fig. 7.1). The muscles which flex the wrist, pronate the forearm (rotate to a palm down position) and flex the fingers all attach to this tendon. However, it is the portions of the tendon attaching to the wrist flexors 'flexor carpi radialis', 'flexor carpi ulnaris', or the forearm pronator 'pronator teres' which are usually affected. The common flexor origin attaches to the bony lump on the inside of the elbow called the medial epicondyle. The condition is also called medial epicondylitis.

Its sister condition, tennis elbow or lateral epicondylitis, affects the equivalent tendon on the outside of the elbow, the common extensor origin. It is the wrist extensor muscle 'extensor carpi radialis brevis' which is normally affected. The common extensor origin is one of the most frequently injured tendons in the body and it is a very common injury in a whole host of sports and manual work activities. Hammering or other work with tools, backhand tennis strokes and even excessive use of a computer mouse or typing are all recognised causes. Outside of climbing, tennis elbow is roughly five times more common than golfer's elbow. However, there is anecdotal evidence that golfer's elbow is much more common among climbers. This makes sense since the wrist needs to be forcefully flexed and pronated to press the fingers into the holds. It seems likely that when climbers get tennis elbow, the underlying cause is some non-climbing activity, but the condition is prolonged or worsened by climbing. Excessive keyboard and mouse use without the wrist supported could be the most common cause[86]. Repetitive manual work with machinery or tools, or even hauling ropes could place an overload on the wrist extensors. Tennis elbow is most likely to be aggravated by moves on undercuts, gastons or pinches, especially when reaching them with a straight arm.

Simply participating in climbing is the likely cause of golfer's elbow, with many details within the climbing routine that increase the risk of the injury occurring. Here is a list of possible contributors, based on my own experience with the condition and coaching other sufferers:

- Crimping activates the wrist flexors more forcefully than openhanding. Overuse of a crimp grip aggravates the condition markedly, and may be an important cause.

- Deep lock-offs seem to be the most aggravating position. It seems logical that climbers who rely heavily on static lock-offs or who do a lot of training involving this position such as lock-off training, pull-ups or campus boarding will be more at risk. Even seemingly less intense activities such as trad climbing can be aggravating for golfer's elbow since it involves locking off for sustained periods to place gear and search for holds. Climbers may try a period of route climbing instead of bouldering in an attempt to reduce the stress on the injury only to find this has the opposite effect. Bouldering on steep walls involves a lot of time with the elbows moving through the mid-range of flexion which seems to be least aggravating for the condition. In my own case, I have never had to reduce the intensity of bouldering on steep boards even when the condition was bad enough to provoke symptoms during comparatively less intense sport or trad

routes. Ice and mixed climbing is also often well tolerated, possibly because the forearm is held in a neutral, rather than pronated position, while climbing with ice tools.

- Poor posture has been suggested, but not proven, as a cause of epicondylitis[32, 86]. Rounded shoulders and associated internal rotation of the humerus may affect the load on the wrist flexors during movement. There may also be an effect of compression of both nerve branches and blood vessels supplying the forearm with poor posture higher up the chain. If blood supply and neural activation are compromised, it seems logical that this will affect the ability of the elbow tendons to absorb training load over years and decades.

- It may be that the wrist flexor/extensor muscles fail to develop strength at the same rate as the fingers with a given climbing routine, leaving a strength deficit that contributes to tendon damage. Alternatively, imbalances of strength across the elbow musculature may be important. Strengthening of the wrist flexor/extensor muscles has been recommended both for prevention and treatment of epicondylitis[26].

- Inadequate strength further up the kinetic chain may be a related contributor. Development of momentum during movement from the core outwards reduces the work done by the distal muscles in the forearm. There is evidence that weakness of core and shoulder muscles in tennis players is associated with tennis elbow. No scientific work has been done to explore how core and upper body strength may affect epicondylitis in climbing, so this cause remains theoretical at present.

- Individual differences in finger length could, in theory, affect the angle adopted by the wrist during different grips in climbing. If a certain wrist angle affects the length at which the the wrist flexors/extensors must work, this could add to the risk of overload. The hypothesis has never been explored scientifically.

- As well as these specific, possible contributors, epicondylitis is of course subject to the usual general predisposing factors for injury risk discussed earlier in the book.

The reasons why the elbow epicondyles seem to be particularly vulnerable to tendinopathy, and why the tendon fails to adapt to the load placed upon it, are not understood by sports medicine. In fact, only recently has the nature of the damage to the tendon and healing response been elucidated. It appears that the tendon fails to complete a healing response to microtrauma that occurs with all sports activity. Interestingly, the injury is relatively common across all ranges of ability and level of training load. This may suggest that the tendon fails to respond quickly enough to sudden increases in training volume regardless of the athlete's level. The recreational climber who climbs intermittently through the year and takes large gaps from climbing which result in loss of tendon strength may be just as at-risk as the serious climbing athlete who maximises training volume year in and year out, but builds up to this level slowly. The initial damage may not reach symptomatic level, but set off the chronic degenerative process of tendinosis which reaches the level of pain some months or even years later.

Epicondylitis is a misnomer. The 'itis' part of its name suggests a classic inflammatory condition, but this idea was abandoned by researchers (and should have been by therapists) in the 1990s[67]. Recent research has shown that the condition is much more complex, with some inflammatory mediators, but not others. For this reason, the RICE protocol to deal with acute injuries is not usually required unless a particular incident has rapidly worsened the condition.

Diagnosis can usually be made without scanning, by reproducing pain on resisted contraction of the affected muscle near or over the epicondyle, together with tenderness when a thumb is pressed into the affected part of the tendon (See photos 7.1 - 7.5).

Photo 7.1 Resisted contraction of the wrist flexors to diagnose golfer's elbow. Press downwards, trying to flex the wrist.

Photo 7.2 Pressing on the medial epicondyle. Tenderness near or on the epicondyle indicates golfer's elbow.

Photo 7.3 Resisted contraction of the wrist extensors to diagnose tennis elbow.

Photo 7.4 Pressing on the lateral epicondyle. Tenderness near or on the epicondyle indicates tennis elbow.

Photo 7.5 Testing for involvement of pronator teres in golfer's elbow. Attempt to pronate the forearm with resistance from a partner. Pain in the medial epicondyle indicates damage.

Photo 7.6 Tinel's test for ulnar nerve irritation with golfer's elbow. If the ulnar nerve is involved, there will be pain, tingling or parasthesia in the little finger and ring finger.

For tennis elbow, hold your arm out straight and attempt to extend the wrist (or alternatively the middle finger) with resistance from a wall or from the doctor's hand (Photo 7.3). For golfer's elbow, three tests must be performed to establish whether the wrist flexors, pronator teres, or both are involved. To test the wrist flexors, hold your arm out straight and perform resisted wrist flexion (Photo 7.1). Pain in the medial epicondyle is a positive result. Testing pronation is best done in a handshake with your doctor with your arm outstretched. Attempt to turn the doctor's hand by pronating your forearm (Photo 7.5). Pain in the medial epicondyle is positive. Tenderness will be apparent by pressing a thumb into the affected tendon. A further test must be performed to establish if the ulnar nerve is being compressed by the scarred degenerating tendon. The ulnar nerve passes in a groove between the medial epicondyle and the olecranon bursa and then very close to the common flexor tendon. The bulky scar tissue that forms in golfer's elbow can press on the nerve causing pain that mirrors the tendon pain itself. Ulnar nerve compression is thought to be involved in as many as 50% of golfer's elbow cases[66]. The clue that the ulnar nerve is affected is called 'Tinel's sign'. Tinel's test involves flexing the elbow and tapping on the ulnar nerve along its length as it passes the common flexor tendon (Photo 7.6). If damaged, the tapping will cause pain or tingling and parasthesia in the little finger and ring finger. It is important that the test is done by a professional, as false positive results can be obtained by improper testing technique. Professional diagnosis, taking into account a full history and the diagnostic test responses, is critical to rule out other more serious conditions which can masquerade as epicondylitis.

Treatment

Occasionally, epicondylitis can be brought on by an acute overload, such as a weekend using a screwdriver, or a particularly intense bout of training. If the tendon has been otherwise healthy beforehand, symptoms might resolve with a week of rest and a careful return to training. If sufficient rest is not applied, the damage can easily progress to chronic tendinosis.

In the past, recommended treatment for slow-onset, chronic golfer's and tennis elbow consisted of rest, ice, anti-inflammatory medication, stretching and large volumes of low intensity strengthening exercises. The effectiveness of these treatments was poor and the rate of recurrence was high, especially where steroid injections were used.

Today, eccentric exercises are the mainstay of treatment and the effectiveness of this new treatment has greatly improved prospects of recovery for athletes. However, it is critical to remove the underlying causes to avoid recurrence[71]. An important task following diagnosis is to have your physiotherapist assess necessary postural correction and strengthening of weak areas from your core outwards. A therapist who is also a climber is a great advantage. Perhaps more importantly, seek the advice of an experienced coach with a good understanding of the biomechanics involved to assess your climbing technique, your strength in different muscle groups, and your training regime to identify predisposing factors. This may be a difficult step for many climbers as there are few suitably experienced coaches around at present. Climbers should keep in mind that there is probably more than one predisposing factor at work. Even if movement errors, strength deficits or training errors can be identified, a change of scenery is a good precaution as the monotony of climbing on the same holds or venues is an important cause of any overuse injury.

Current opinion is that new cases of golfer's or tennis elbow should be treated with at least three months of eccentric exercise therapy before undertaking further treatments, and up to one year before considering surgery. Lack of compliance or ongoing adjustment of the eccentric exercise regime are likely to be the main reasons for failure to recover[71, 86, 108]. Healing is unlikely to take place on its own, even with prolonged rest, although some cases do spontaneously resolve. There are reports from climbers of unchanged or even worsened symptoms after a year of lay-off with no climbing or physiotherapy. Continual adjustment of the exercise protocol is required to ensure the damaged area of the tendon is being stimulated by the exercises. This is a challenging task requiring careful attention to feedback from the tendon as the exercise program progresses over weeks and months.

A full discussion of current opinion on the volume of exercise is detailed in section 5. The best consensus available at present is that either 90 or 180 reps per day, performed in sets of 15 and split into morning and evening sessions is best. For some cases this may be too much and may make the condition worse, hence the need for a tailored program monitored by a professional[116]. The loading should be heavy enough to elicit moderate pain.

For golfer's elbow, the exercises involve starting with the wrist flexed and lengthening the wrist flexor muscles slowly under load, through the whole range of motion (Photos 7.7 - 7.12). This can be done using a dumbell, or by simply pressing on the edge of a table with enough force to provoke moderate pain. The obvious advantage of this is that no additional equipment is required, so there are even fewer excuses for non-compliance. If using a dumbell, make sure you use your other hand to lift the dumbell back to the starting position. It may also be important to keep your thumb on the same side of the bar as your fingers. Using a traditional wrap-around grip with a heavy dumbell sometimes causes De Quervain's tenosynovitis (described in section 9). It is only the eccentric portion of the movement that should be performed under load. Most climbers use a dumbell between 6 and 12kgs. The angle of the elbow during the exercises appears to be important in influencing the success of the program. There is no universal recommendation for the optimal angle since this seems to depend on the exact location and severity of the damage in the tendon. In my own experience, I had good

Photo 7.7 Eccentric exercises for golfer's elbow - starting position. With an outstretched arm, place three outstretched fingers on the edge with your wrist pointing down (so the wrist flexor muscles are shortened). Press downwards and maintaining a firm pressure, allow your wrist to drop, lengthening the wrist flexor through its whole range of motion.

Photo 7.8 End position. You should be able to provoke some pain in the tendon near your inner elbow (medial epicondyle) as your wrist extends. Once you reach the end position, bring your wrist back up to the start position under no load and repeat in sets of 15. Reduce the force you apply if the pain gets significantly worse as you work through sets. But for injured tendons, tolerance of some mild pain may be necessary to stimulate healing. These exercises can also be performed seated at a desk.

Photo 7.7

Photo 7.8

Photo 7.9 Eccentric exercises for golfer's elbow using a dumbell - starting position.

Photo 7.10 End position. Use your other hand to lift the dumbell back to the starting position.

Photo 7.11 Eccentric exercises for golfer's elbow using your other hand - starting position.

Photo 7.12 End position.

Photo 7.13 Eccentric exercises for pronator teres - starting position.

Photo 7.14 End position. Use your other hand to lift the dumbell back to the starting position.

results using a completely straight arm with elbows locked. However, during a later flare-up a few years later which was much worse and with the pain closer to the tendon insertion onto the bone, I found that straight elbows were too aggravating and I had better results with my elbow held at 90°. Julian Saunders recommends keeping the elbow angle between 90° and 135°[86]. If pronator teres is contributing to the pain, exercise this using a weight on the end of a bar such as a dumbell with the weight only on one end. Allow the weight to rotate outwards to eccentrically exercise the pronator (Photos 7.13, 7.14).

For tennis elbow, the exercises are performed by placing the forearm pronated (palm down) on a surface such as a table and the wrist extended. Allow the dumbell to drop, flexing the wrist and eccentrically loading the wrist extensor on the outside of the forearm. Climbers usually have much weaker wrist extensors than flexors so a much lighter weight may be required. If you don't have a suitably light dumbell, a bag, heavy book, or even simply resistance from your other hand are good alternatives (Photos 7.15, 7.16). See the photos for details of how to perform the exercises for each condition.

Photo 7.15 Eccentric exercises for tennis elbow - starting position. With outstretched arms, extend your wrist upwards and place the other hand on top.

Photo 7.16 End position. Press the affected hand downwards, flexing the wrist by applying pressure with your other hand. You should feel moderate pain near the lateral epicondyle on the outer elbow.

Managing the intensity of the exercises is a careful balancing act. The tendon must be aggravated to provoke a healing response. Slight worsening of pain during activity for the first few weeks is acceptable. However, symptoms should start to improve in subsequent weeks providing the exercise positioning is optimal to stimulate the damaged portion of the tendon. It seems to be unnecessary to lay-off from climbing during the rehabilitation period in most cases. However, it is unknown whether progress with the eccentrics would be quicker if the additional load of climbing were reduced or eliminated. In my own case, I kept climbing at medium volume and medium intensity during rehab from both golfer's and tennis elbow. However, I felt that basic strength work such as fingerboarding and other strenuous manual tasks such as chopping wood or manual work with hand tools tended to slow progress so I kept these to a minimum. Using this routine, I experienced slightly worse but stable levels of pain for around 4 weeks, followed by steady improvement. However, this was only achieved after much adjustment and experimentation with the exercise position. In other words, I failed several rounds of treatment before finding a successful mix of the treatment parameters for my individual case. I also never let the condition get very bad. Where the sufferer ignores the pain until basic daily activities provoke pain, lay-off from climbing until the eccentrics have significantly improved the strength of the tendon is probably inevitable. With golfer's elbow, basic activities that might give pain include washing your hair or a handshake. With tennis elbow, opening jars, lifting kettles or even computer use may cause pain. Swapping the hand I use to control my computer mouse corresponded with the period I started to experience recovery from from tennis elbow. If you notice the condition during these activities, some modification of your climbing routine while you undertake the rehab program is probably necessary. If there is pain at rest, or pain that wakens you in the night, it is probably advisable to lay-off from all activities except the rehab exercises. It can be easy for sufferers to get to this stage by using NSAIDs or other pain relieving modalities to prolong a state of denial about the condition.

Photo 7.17 Golfer's elbow 'yoga' stretch. There are anecdotal reports of this stretch causing rapid relief from symptoms. It may be that this stretch is effective in stretching the pronator muscle which is often very well developed and shortened in climbers. This photo demonstrates the position of the arms for the stretch.

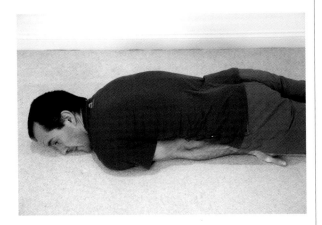

Photo 7.18 Using this position for the arms, lie on your front and slowly arch your back so your hips apply direct pressure onto the back of your forearms. Lifting one leg off the ground at a time can apply further pressure if necessary.

Photo 7.19 Modified upward plank stretch for golfer's elbow. There are some anecdotal reports that these specific stretches to target the damaged area of tendon in golfer's elbow may be a useful adjunct to eccentric exercises. However, there is no available research evidence to substantiate this.

If a course of eccentrics has failed to result in progress after 6 weeks despite compliance, the next move would be to alter the exercise positioning. If subsequent rounds of modified eccentrics with full compliance fail, other treatments should then be considered to augment the eccentrics. These would be sclerosing injections, modalities such as ultrasound and friction massage, extra-corporeal shock wave therapy (ESWT) and blood injections. All of these treatments are discussed in detail in section 5. Sclerosing injections may be used for tennis elbow, but not golfer's, due to the proximity of the ulnar nerve. There are also a couple of stretches which have good anecdotal support among climbers (Photos 7.17 - 7.19) although there is no research available to suggest why these might help relieve symptoms. If all of this

fails, some sports medics would still consider a steroid injection at this point, although this is highly controversial. Many researchers consider the use of steroid injections to be a path to a much poorer long term outcome and recommend they are avoided altogether. It may be much safer in the long run to go back and attempt another round of individually tailored exercise therapy, or look at the newer surgical options which are being developed (see below).

Wearing elbow braces or using tape has been recommended by some sources, but research on the efficacy of this is conflicting. Sufferers who use braces or tape report symptoms being reduced. However, it is unclear whether the brace simply adds a subjective feeling of security (placebo) rather than actually reducing the forces applied through the tendon. Studies have failed to show improvements in strength using a brace with tennis elbow sufferers[117]. The rationale for use of a brace is to alter the biomechanics of force transfer, to reduce force on the affected tendon. Given the more recent theory of stress shielding as a potential cause of tendinosis in the epicondyles, use of a brace or tape to alter force transfer could hypothetically contribute to stress shielding. On the other hand, if bracing reduces inhibition during use, it could promote greater use of the affected tendon. A further problem with elbow braces is that they constrict the forearm which may cause limitation of forearm blood flow during pumpy endurance climbing. It is fair to say that the opinion of the majority of researchers in elbow tendinopathy is that using a brace is unnecessary and has little effect on healing[117].

Surgery

The last resort is surgical repair. This is only considered appropriate if the condition is serious and has failed all of the above treatments. Current opinion is that only a tiny minority of sufferers will require surgery. The objective of traditional surgery is usually to remove the degenerative scar or even calcified tissue within the tendon, or to free compressed nerve fibres. If your doctor has recommended surgery, a paramount concern is to choose a highly regarded surgeon with a special interest in the elbow. This may involve a longer wait on the NHS or resorting to private treatment. Progressively worsening neuritis of the ulnar nerve requires surgery regardless of progress of non-operative therapy. However, this situation is usually experienced by throwing athletes, another group of sportspeople who are bad to their elbows. Return to sport after surgery usually takes 4-6 months. For tennis elbow, reported success rates of surgery range from 90-97%. The remaining percentage only experience pain with particularly aggressive training. For golfer's elbow, the success rate is very high (over 90%) for sufferers with mild or no neural symptoms. Where there is neuropathy present, the success rate is thought to be 50%. The main reason for surgical failure is premature return to sport or overly aggressive progression of therapy. However, there are some other complications which can arise in a small number of cases. Climbers who have had elbow injuries which may require surgery are directed to the excellent book *Operative treatment of elbow injuries* by Champ Baker and Kevin Plancher[118].

An interesting new development in the field comes from Hakan Alfredson and others who have developed a minimally invasive scraping technique. The neovessels which form around the surface of the painful tendon are scraped away using an arthroscopic technique, guided by scanning ultrasound. Since the procedure is not very traumatic, return to sport is very rapid and results are excellent in both the Achilles and patellar tendon[95], with trials ongoing in elbow tendinosis. Interestingly, when patients with bilateral Achilles tendonosis are treated on only one side with this technique, both tendons show improvements, highlighting the complex nature of pain in tendinopathy and the involvement of the central nervous system in tendon pain[119]. The technique can also be performed with a needle, guided by scanning ultrasound to scrape the neovessels on the tendon surface.

Brachioradialis/brachialis strain

Pain in the brachioradialis or brachialis muscles or tendons is the second most common elbow complaint among climbers. The brachioradialis is the long, stringy muscle that runs up the top of your forearm and crosses the elbow joint. Its job is to flex the elbow with the forearm in a neutral or pronated position (biceps does the bulk of the work only when the forearm is supinated such as when holding undercuts). Pain usually takes the form of an annoying, but not debilitating dull ache which is poorly centred around the top of the elbow. If you let it get really bad, it feels more nauseating and persists even once you have stopped the climbing session.

Brachialis is an important elbow flexor when the forearm is pronated, as in many climbing moves, and may be the source of diffuse elbow pain. This muscle is not well seen since it is a deeper muscle, mostly hidden by the biceps muscle. Where brachialis is involved, the pain may be centred more on the inside of the elbow, just above the

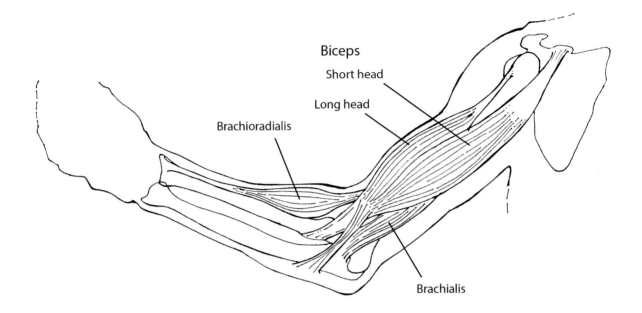

Biceps

Short head

Long head

Brachioradialis

Brachialis

Fig. 7.2 The brachioradialis and brachialis muscles.

elbow crease[120]. It is often mistaken for biceps tendon pain.

There are two main probable causes. Firstly, an overly rapid increase in the overall load of climbing or training you do can bring on the condition. Basic strength training on fingerboards or campus boards are particularly good at annoying this muscle. Secondly, moves that involve compression (bear-hugging rounded arêtes) or big slopers seem to be a particular cause. Indeed, the condition is referred to by some climbers as 'Font elbow' as many cases are brought on during bouldering trips to the sloper-ridden boulders of Fontainebleau in France.

Not much is known about the condition, although most cases in climbers seem to follow a consistent pattern. The pain seems to be located in the muscle belly or at the muscle-tendon junction[121], although I have also

experienced sharper pain in the brachioradialis tendon where it attaches to the upper arm bone during heavy fingerboard work. If it comes on quickly, a short rest and avoidance of the type of move that brought it on often brings resolution in a few days. If the aggravation is a little worse, a reduction in training, or change of emphasis to less aggressive training for a few weeks usually resolves the pain (i.e. dropping hard bouldering and doing routes instead).

Some climbers experience a pattern of constant recurrence with any intense climbing or training, pointing to an underlying susceptibility that may be difficult to pinpoint. Even a good physiotherapist may have difficulty finding the source of the problem since this appears to be a rare injury outside climbing and the exact site of the damage may be impossible to palpate on examination. Thus, climbers may have the best chance of

Photo 7.20 Compression moves and climbing on slopey terrain is a common cause of brachioradialis/brachialis strain.

Photo 7.21 Brachioradialis stretch.

recovery by trying a range of treatments. None have yet have been scientifically tested or reported in physiotherapy practice, so there is no evidence base at present on which to recommend one treatment over another.

- Stretching the brachioradialis daily, together with manual therapy such as deep tissue massage appears to be very helpful in the short term. Deep tissue pressure over the painful area in the muscle belly may provide relief.

- Assessment of strength of all the elbow muscles should be performed by a physiotherapist to identify any obvious weakness which is causing the brachioradialis to be overstressed. Many climbers, including myself, have seen fairly rapid improvement with a program of daily press-ups (at least 5 x 10 reps daily with strict form). However, strengthening with brachioradialis or brachialis curls may also be useful.

- If there is damage to the brachioradialis tendon, it may be possible to find the tender spot while it is aggravated during a climbing session. Use the fingers to locate the humerus on the outer side of the arm. The brachioradialis has a broad attachment here, starting just above the elbow. If the pain is coming from the tendon itself, an eccentric exercise therapy program may be useful although there are no reports of this in the literature.

- It is also possible that the pain is caused by something else - damage inside the elbow joint capsule itself or nerve compression[121]. If it fails to respond to the above treatments, go back to your sports medic for further diagnostic tests.

Other elbow injuries

There are many possible injuries to tendons, ligaments and nerve fibres crossing the elbow, as well as injury to the joint itself. Throwing athletes suffer many of these, especially ligament and joint damage, but these injuries seem to be absent in climbers.

Below are some elbow injuries which do occur in climbers, albeit much more rarely than epicondylitis.

Nerve compression

Climbers should be careful that nerve compression symptoms are not missed in diagnosis of elbow injuries. Injured tendons and ligaments in the elbow form bulky scar tissue which can compress the ulnar, radial and occasionally median nerve branches which pass through narrow spaces in the elbow[121]. Nerve compression can also be a secondary complication of a broken arm, especially the radial head. Symptoms can sometimes mimic the pain of more common injuries and so go undiagnosed. However, as well as local pain, most nerve compression syndromes at the elbow cause sensory symptoms which can be used to differentiate them from pain coming from a tendon or ligament. There is often altered sensation in the forearm and hand including tingling, numbness and parasthesia. Assessment of nerve function must be carried out by a professional and may include simple but very specific tapping tests or more involved nerve conduction tests. The cause of sensory

symptoms in the forearm and hand may actually result from compression further up the nerve, in the shoulder or neck (see section 10, thoracic outlet syndrome). Mild cases of nerve compression in the elbow can be resolved with friction massage to break up adhesions and bulky scarring in adjacent healing soft tissue, or by steroid injection. However, more serious cases must be treated with prompt surgery to be successful. The rare occurrence of tumors must also be excluded during diagnosis.

Biceps tendon pain/rupture

There are some reports of tendinosis and sudden rupture of the biceps tendon at the elbow in climbers. Powerful undercut moves or crack climbing may be particularly risky for injuring this tendon. Where there is chronic tendinosis, the tendon should respond to eccentric bicep curls using a similar loading protocol to that used for golfer's elbow (section 5). Complete ruptures do occur without any previous history of pain. Outside of climbing, biceps ruptures are more common in athletes with well developed biceps. So it seems plausible that excessive or poorly planned elbow flexor training activities such as pull-ups, lock-offs or dry tooling would introduce a risk of this injury. However, it is very uncommon in climbers. Complete ruptures are always treated with surgical repair, followed by four months of physiotherapy and then gradual return to sport.

Triceps tendon pain/rupture

As with biceps, tendinosis or rupture of the triceps tendon is rare but does occasionally occur. Gout (rheumatoid arthritis affecting a single joint) should be excluded during diagnosis. There may be a predisposing factor peripheral to climbing that contributes or causes the injury such as manual work with tools or weight training. Even the repetitive, cyclical loading of using walking poles may be important in climbers. Ruptures are treated surgically, whereas chronic tendinosis is treated with an eccentric exercise therapy program (section 5).

Elbow dislocation

Elbow dislocation usually occurs from falling and although there aren't data available about occurrence rates in climbing, it seems likely this injury will occur with uncontrolled falls in bouldering. Dislocation can result in chronic elbow instability in severe cases. It is important the dislocation is reduced (pulled back into place) as quickly as possible. However, given the risk of nerve damage, reduction should not be attempted at the site. Assessment of forearm pulse should be performed, as loss of blood supply to the forearm and hand is a major complication of elbow dislocation. If pulse is absent, reduction is urgent. Following reduction, careful assessment of the collateral ligaments of the elbow is required and X-rays are needed to rule out bony damage. Some cases require surgery. The rehabilitation depends on the type of dislocation and extent of damage. Simple dislocations do not need a long spell away from sport, but loss of range of motion, especially extension, is common, but can be prevented by early mobilisation. If full extension is lost and the athlete cannot 'lock' the elbows, triceps need to be extensively strengthened to stabilise the arm.

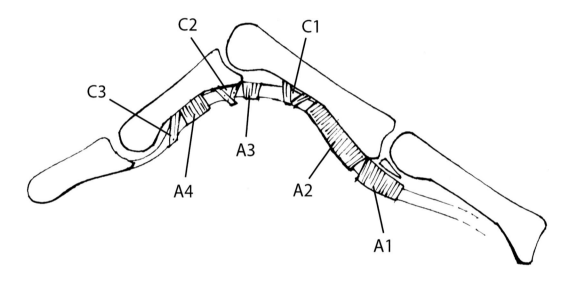

The fingers

Section 8

The fingers of climbers have been shown to adapt considerably to the loads placed on them by a life of climbing[21, 111, 112]. Increases in the thickness of the collateral ligaments of the fingers, the finger joints themselves and up to 50% thickening of the finger flexor tendons have all been reported. It is no surprise that there is a high likelihood of suffering an injury to the fingers over the course of your climbing career. Nearly half of all injuries in climbing involve the fingers, and of these, pulley tears are the most common. Although the risks of getting a finger injury are high, most finger injuries heal well if treated properly, and there is much that climbers can do to reduce their occurrence.

Different grips in climbing and their consequences for injuries

Broadly speaking, there are four main ways for the fingers to grip holds (see section 3). Each bring their own profile of benefits for climbing and risks for particular injuries. Both casual observation and research evidence clearly show that crimping carries the highest risk of injury, which is often a pulley tear. Although it is probably fair to say that a fully openhanded pocket grip is the safest of all grip styles, injuries can happen with this grip too. This especially true if fewer fingers are used, such as in two-finger or mono pockets.

As we saw earlier in section 3, varying the grip type rather than becoming dependent on any particular grip is a critical strategy to reduce finger injury risk, as well as to improve your climbing standard. Dependence on one grip type means that wear and tear is more likely to build up from overuse. Meanwhile, the underused grips become weaker and prone to sudden tearing when used *in extremis*. Crimping is normally overused on small holds, even by climbers at a fairly high performance level. However, I have seen some climbers at a high level who overuse the openhand grip and are left weaker on crimps.

The idea of varying the grip type seems counterintuitive

at first. Why shouldn't you use whichever grip feels strongest for a given hold? You should. The way to approach the problem is to do some basic strength training so that your weaker grip styles are strong enough for you to naturally utilise them more in your everyday climbing. The most efficient way to achieve this is by doing some fingerboard work. Some climbers can be so weak with an openhanded grip that climbing with this grip is just not realistic without some basic training first. Fingerboarding with assistance from the feet (on a chair) is essential to get off the starting blocks before the grip type can be incorporated into your climbing repertoire. Dedicated work on the fingerboard to address grip strength imbalance may also be necessary if you are climbing at a fairly high standard. Simply using your weaker grips in normal climbing might not provide a strong enough stimulus to achieve real strength gains. However, if you are climbing at an intermediate standard, then simply doing some boulder problems or routes that force you to use your weaker grips will help improve your strength and get you more accustomed to using those grips. For example, those weak on openhanded grips will benefit from some climbing on pockets.

Changes in the climbing terrain or style also dictate different patterns of grip style or loading pattern. If you don't habitually pull on one-finger pockets, attempting to do so can feel so painful, dangerous and just plain 'wrong' that you wonder how others can seem so comfortable with it. Yet, after a trip to an area relying on small pockets such as the Frankenjura in Germany, or a sustained progression of careful deadhangs on monos is enough to make them feel pain free and much more stable. Similarly, if you have been doing long, steep sport routes or mountain trad for a season, and start bouldering on small crimps for the first time in months, your finger joints are likely to become swollen and very painful. Yet, if you progress gently into the new regime for the bouldering season, this should subside within days as the body adapts to the new demands. It is critical to develop an awareness that different climbing styles, no matter how subtle, can represent a significant change in the loading pattern for the finger tendons and joints. Make any changes in your climbing regime as smooth transitions or progressions, rather than sudden changes. Be prepared to back off a little during transitions to new climbing areas, rock types, climbing walls, or disciplines.

The following sections discuss the common finger injuries climbers suffer and how they can be best prevented and treated.

Pulley injuries

The tendons that flex the fingers are rarely injured in climbers. However, the flexor tendon sheaths are heavily stressed by climbing and are the most commonly injured structure among climbers. The flexor tendon sheath in our fingers has two main functions. Firstly, it nourishes and lubricates the tendons and allows them to run freely. Secondly, it holds them in place against the bones of the finger so they do not 'bowstring' when we bend our fingers. This reinforcement is provided by thickened areas along the sheath, known as the annular pulley system (Fig. 8.1).

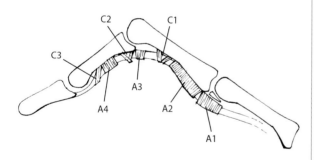

Fig. 8.1 The annular pulley system and how it comes under tension in crimping.

The pulley system in each finger consists of 5 annular pulleys (A1-A5) and three weaker cruciate pulleys (C1-C3). The cruciate pulleys do occasionally tear, but this is quite rare. Despite impressively high breaking strength for their tiny size, the annular pulleys are regularly pushed close to their limits in climbing[122]. Partial tears, complete ruptures of a single pulley, or multiple ruptures along the length of the pulley system are all possible. The A2 pulley is the most commonly damaged pulley, while

A1 and A5 injuries do not seem to occur.

The pulleys are under maximum stress while crimping, and comparatively unloaded with an openhanded pocket grip. Pulley tears tend to occur when making a rapid movement while pulling maximally on a crimp, or when a foot slips off while crimping hard. When the fingers open slightly while loaded in a crimp position, extra friction is created between the flexor tendons and the pulleys, which assists in generating maximal crimp strength. In fact, this tendon locking mechanism, more developed in bats and birds, helps them to dangle for long periods without using muscular energy. Although more force can be developed with this eccentric opening of the fingers, it is also when the pulleys are most heavily loaded and likely to tear[123]. The fact that the ring finger can rotate laterally while maximally loaded, if the little finger is dropped may explain why this finger is particularly vulnerable to pulley tears[4]. Some climbers allow their fingers to move, or open, quite noticeably while crimping small holds. This may be a risky practice.

Photo 8.1 Lateral rotation of the fingers while crimping. Note the gaps between the fingers.

Other common injury situations occur performing the same move repeatedly, such as while working a very intense crimping move or campusing. Although openhanding is generally much safer for the fingers, pulley injuries do also occur while trying to grab one or two finger pockets dynamically, probably because the finger does not have time to settle into a true openhanded grip before it is suddenly loaded. Crimping on mono or two-finger pockets instead of openhanding is particularly dangerous.

Prevention of pulley injuries:

- Balanced grip type strength and utilisation, less reliance on crimping.
- Avoid crimping small pockets where possible.
- Anticipate foot slips and be ready to react.
- Moderate your volume of very repetitive moves on the same holds during training.
- In warm conditions try to keep the fingertips dry with chalk to reduce the chance of a single finger slipping under load on a hold.
- Where possible, allow the fingers to 'settle' into the final position before pulling maximally, to avoid any movement under maximal load.
- Be ready to let go if the grip feels dangerous.
- Warm up progressively and re-warm up if body temperature drops too much.
- Train your fingers for a large part of the year and take extra care after a break in training or reduced intensity periods (e.g. summer trad). Build up again with a steady progression that is appropriate for the length of the break.

Partial tears of a single pulley may or may not be noticed at the moment of injury, depending on severity. You may be concentrating so much on the move that a minor pain goes unnoticed and the problem only becomes apparent in subsequent days or even weeks. Thus, you may be able to complete the climbing session with only minor or no pain. More severe injuries may be heard as an audible tearing noise and immediate pain, sometimes with a little swelling. Further climbing will be impossible. Complete ruptures are generally accompanied by a pop or crack sound that can be heard readily, even by others in the vicinity. Some reports describe "the sound of a gun going off".

Diagnosis and treatment

Although it is not advisable, many climbers routinely manage pulley injuries, both partial and complete ruptures, without ever going to see a doctor. This at least partially reflects the fact that many medical and physiotherapy professionals are unaware of the injury or how to treat it and that it takes a bit of effort and possibly expense to track down someone who is. Thus, it is useful to know some diagnostic clues that can increase suspicion of a pulley injury. However, it remains a risk for climbers not to seek specialist medical help to eliminate the possibility of other injuries which may be causing the symptoms or have occurred in addition to the pulley tear.

Fractures, stress fractures, or in young climbers growth plate fractures, may have occurred and so an injured finger should be X-rayed to rule this out. Moreover, multiple pulley ruptures or more complex damage to the flexor tendon sheath may benefit from surgery to heal properly. MRI scanning can detect pulley injuries by measuring the amount of bowstringing of the flexor tendons away from the bone. However, this is obviously expensive and hard to justify depending on your health care provision. In recent years, ultrasound scanning has proven to be a cheap and effective way to diagnose pulley injuries and assess whether more serious injuries require surgery[124]. If you are referred to see a hand surgeon, ultrasound may well be the tool of choice for diagnosis[125].

Partial tears

Pain will be felt on the base of the finger, fairly localised to the damaged area. Having said this, pain can sometimes be poorly localised for several days before finally centering on a consistent spot. If A2 is torn, the pain will likely be between the base of the finger and the PIP joint. Sometimes it can be centred more on one side of the finger. If A3 or A4 are damaged, the painful spot will be between the PIP and DIP joints. As well as provoking pain, the damaged area can be located by pressing the thumb of the opposite hand into the affected finger. The level of tenderness provoked by this is a very useful measure of the status of the injury throughout the rehabilitation process.

After allowing a few days for the initial inflammation to settle down a bit, some manual testing can provide a clue to the nature of the damage. Pulling on a crimp grip will provoke pain from pulley damage, whereas a completely openhanded pocket grip may produce no pain at all, or at least markedly less pain. If pain is present with an openhanded grip alone, the damage may be a flexor unit strain (see below). If there is pain with both openhanded and crimp grips, both types of injury may have occurred. However, it must be stressed that this is a very rough and ready diagnostic test which may be prone to a false result. Inflammation in an acutely injured finger may be sensitive to almost any type of loading. If a clear result is produced (e.g. sharp pain with crimping, no pain with openhanding), then it may be useful in getting closer to a diagnosis. If not, the need for scanning and examination by a specialist to achieve a sound diagnosis is underlined.

Partial tears can often bear climbing without causing pain if there is strict adherence to a true openhanded pocket grip. For the disciplined, this also forms the main treatment for the injury. Continued climbing helps to maintain the strength of all the relevant structures in the finger and provides the opportunity for regular progressive loading of the pulley on holds it can tolerate as healing progresses. This technique comes with a stark warning: one momentary lapse of concentration is enough to turn a healing partial tear into a complete rupture, needing a much longer period of rehabilitation. It is extremely difficult to maintain complete use of openhanding throughout the recovery period, especially if it is only with one hand. One method to make this less prone to a disastrous error is to splint the PIP joint with tape[25]. This way crimping will be impossible even if you forget to maintain the openhanded grip.

Judging the rate of progression in volume and intensity of climbing to undertake while a partial tear recovers is a difficult balancing act. Pain, both upon loading and in tenderness measured with thumb palpation, provides the feedback you need. A basic algorithm is that any hold or move that causes pain during loading should not be tolerated. All moves should be pain free. However, a modest increase in palpable tenderness during and after climbing sessions may be acceptable. Often, the injury will feel more tender during the warm-up, but this will subside a little during the session, only to increase again towards the end of the session. As this tenderness increases, this is a signal that the pulley is reaching the maximum it can tolerate and it is time to stop. What is

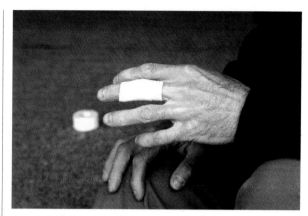

Photo 8.2 Taping to splint the PIP joint to ensure a fully openhanded grip.

an acceptable level of tenderness is extremely difficult to judge, since it is affected by individual threshold and perception of pain. Perhaps all we have to help us is development of a 'feel' for how the tenderness changes from session to session. Try to develop a record, either in memory or better still by writing it down, of how the tenderness changes from day to day. This way, you might be able to judge when you are overdoing it, or when it is safe to nudge the loading up a little. Often, there will be a battle between your desire to climb more or harder, and a voice in your head that is telling you "you're overdoing it" as the finger is becoming more tender. The consequences of this are simply that healing is slowed, possibly by a large amount. However, if you continue to ignore worsening symptoms, the weak healing tissue may rupture altogether.

The time course of healing is extremely variable, depending on the severity of the damage and the discipline applied to rehabilitation. The most minor of tears may not require any time off crimping but only a small reduction in training for a few weeks. A3 and A4 tears appear to heal faster than A2 tears. Partial tears can take between six weeks and six months to heal, with three months being the often-quoted time frame. Some can take longer than six months, but this may be because either there was an undiagnosed complete rupture, a complex rupture creating lots of scar tissue and ongoing irritation of the flexor tendon sheath, or because errors in rehabilitation prolonged the healing process.

Adjunct treatments

There is little hard evidence in support of adjunct treatments alongside carefully progressed loading for pulley injuries. Hypothetically, deep transverse friction massage (DTFM, section 4) may be useful for breaking up bulky scar tissue or adhesions that do seem to occur in at least some pulley injuries. There are some anecdotal reports of climbers reporting improvements in symptoms, but it is unclear if improvements were the direct result of DTFM. Would I use it? Probably only if I had lingering pain or bulky scar tissue following pulley damage in the area. I've successfully recovered from numerous pulley tears and have never used DTFM for this injury.

Stretching the affected finger is also commonly performed, with the rationale that this stimulates healing in the pulleys. Again, there is little evidence to support its use. It is possible that regular stretching helps to minimise adhesions of scar tissue affecting the area and the movement of the flexor tendons helps to nourish them. However, the pulleys themselves are best stretched by controlled loading through functional exercises and then progressive climbing.

Photo 8.3 Cold water treatment for pulley injuries.

A third adjunct treatment that has become popular is cold water treatment. The hand is immersed in cold water with the aim of stimulating reactive hyperaemia (dilatation of blood vessels). The efficacy of this treatment is still controversial. The treatment protocol and the debate over its efficacy is discussed in section 4. However, although the research evidence for its use is still conflicting, there are many reports of improved symptoms among climbers. It may be that the effect is purely analgesic from the cold, allowing more rapid progression of loading to occur, rather than a direct effect on blood flow and healing. Regardless, until more research is done to strengthen or undermine the case for this treatment, it appears to be a useful adjunct to exercise therapy for this injury. I would encourage climbers to experiment with it and record whether they notice decreases in pain and recovery time of the injury between rehab or climbing sessions, or increases in the climbing they can tolerate.

Complete and multiple ruptures

If you heard a pop or had immediate pain, swelling, and an inability to use the finger after the moment of injury, don't mess around - track down a specialist hand surgeon immediately. Proper examination and scanning are essential to establish exactly how many pulleys have ruptured and whether surgery is necessary. An audible snapping noise is usually heard (75% of cases), but not always[126]. If more than one pulley has ruptured and surgery is needed, it should be done without delay to avoid problems with flexion contracture.

Since pulley tears are a rare injury outside of climbing and hence few surgeons are regularly treating them, opinion on how to deal with ruptures is still not completely settled[127]. However, thanks largely to the prolific research of German climber and hand surgeon Volker Schoffl, a treatment algorithm has emerged[125]. Simple ruptures of a single pulley, without additional damage to nearby structures, are generally treated without surgery with good results[128-130]. Multiple ruptures or additional damage to the flexor sheath or finger joint ligaments may benefit from surgery, although this is still controversial; there are many examples of climbers with multiple ruptures who have successfully recovered without surgery[131]. Surgery also seems to have good results even if conservative therapy is tried and fails to produce a satisfactory result after several months, although flexion contracture resulting from delayed treatment may affect the outcome[127, 132, 133]. Surgery may also be necessary when the bulky scar of a ruptured pulley which has retracted rubs on the flexor tendons, causing synovitis[134]. There are various surgical techniques available to repair multiple ruptures, which involve tissue grafts used to reconstruct a new pulley system rather than reattach the ruptured pulleys. These techniques are evolving rapidly at the moment and a good discussion of current opinion was published in 2012 by Volker Schöffl and colleagues in the *Journal of Hand Surgery*[133].

Ruptures of a single pulley are usually immobilised for up to two weeks before therapeutic movement and loading can begin[4]. Four weeks of basic movement and loading at home precedes a return to easy climbing and a slow progression of climbing level for at least three months. Postoperative progression after surgical repair of multiple ruptures is similar, although the commencement of easy climbing activities may not be started for several months, and progression of loading towards normal may last more than a year. The outlook for even multiple ruptures is good, with many examples of climbers returning to high level climbing and training, except in cases of over-zealous return to climbing or lack of discipline with therapeutic exercises.

Tenosynovitis

Another related injury to pulley tears is tenosynovitis (also known as tenovaginitis). This condition is an irritation of the flexor tendon sheaths that lubricate and nourish the tendons of the fingers. Excessive friction and impact on the tendons causes the sheaths to become inflamed and produce excessive synovial fluid. The result is a painful, sensitive and swollen finger on the palmar side which will be further irritated by more crimping.

Along the length of the pulley system, the greatest friction between the tendons and their sheaths is at the greatest changes in angle. During crimping, this is at the edges of the A2 and A3 pulleys. It follows that these are the most affected locations. Tenosynovitis can be caused rapidly such as by repeatedly performing a hard move, or on a particularly sharp hold. It can also have a slow onset caused by excessive training or over-zealous transition or progression to a new training load. Scar tissue from a previously ruptured pulley, which rubs on the flexor

tendons as they move can also be a cause[132, 134].

I've included it in this book alongside pulley tears because the symptoms of both conditions are similar and excluding either condition while trying to make a diagnosis can be difficult, certainly without professional help from a hand surgeon experienced in treating climbers. The pain can present itself as a dull ache and tenderness similar to a partial pulley tear, in the same location. Perhaps the best diagnostic clue is the history of onset. Pulley injuries can often be traced back to a particular moment of injury, even if this was insignificant at the time. One minor pulley injury I had went unnoticed until days after it had happened. Thinking back through my previous sessions, I recalled feeling a slight pain in the affected finger, while hanging from a sharp-edged resting jug. At the time I just attributed it to the sharpness of the jug. But later I realised that the pulley tear must have occurred on a fingery crux just a few moves before. It was a hard, bold trad route and I may not have noticed it as I was concentrating on staying alive at the time.

If you can't point to a moment of injury, tenosynovitis may be suspected. Severe cases may also have a 'grinding' sensation in the tendon when moving the finger, and redness on the skin over the painful area.

Where tenosynovitis has appeared rapidly due to a particularly aggressive training session or a nasty hold, it may settle after some days of rest and the standard RICE protocol. Anti-inflammatory medication (NSAIDs) is also still recommended to help calm down acute inflammation. More chronic cases that have a slow onset and have persisted for weeks or months need to be taken more seriously and recovery can be challenging. Immobilisation in a splint for 1-2 weeks may be necessary, followed by a further two weeks lay-off from climbing. Failure to adequately rest appears to cause long-standing symptoms that can last for years. The worst cases can be treated with steroid injections, but as we saw in section 4, this treatment comes with its own problems for tendons. So little is known about the condition that it is hard to offer a reliable treatment algorithm. If you suspect your finger pain could be tenosynovitis and not a pulley tear, the most appropriate protocol may be to first of all try resting with ice and NSAIDs to calm it down and then proceed at a level that does not provoke any worsening of the condition. If it proves difficult to start making progress despite sticking to this, I'd seek out an expert hand surgeon with experience of the condition for further advice.

When and how to tape the fingers

Tape is still commonly used by climbers, mainly to support the pulleys while they heal. However, its use is still controversial in the research field despite attempts to clarify whether it is able to relieve the pulley of some of its loading. Although tape has been used by many who have successfully recovered from pulley tears, until recently researchers have failed to demonstrate how it unloads the pulleys and concluded that tape is neither strong enough nor can it be applied tightly enough to have any effect without cutting off the finger's blood supply. Two studies published in 2000 tested taping on un-injured pulleys. One measured the distance between the flexor tendons and bones of the fingers in a crimp position, with and without tape. Only minimal support was gained from wearing tape, and this diminished the more the fingers were loaded in a crimp position[135]. The other study measured differences in the maximum breaking strength of pulleys in cadavers with and without tape[136]. Again, there were no significant differences and both studies concluded that tape was not effective in protecting healthy pulleys against injury.

Schoffl and colleagues published a useful study in the *Journal of Biomechanics* in 2007[137], investigating whether tape could help reduce bone-tendon distance in injured pulleys using a new taping method, called 'H-taping'. H-taping was proposed as a potentially effective taping method because it was observed that the greatest tendon-bone distance along the length of the finger is where the tendons cross the PIP joint, between the A2 and A3 pulleys. This area is impractical to tape using the traditional circumferential taping method since it would prevent flexing the PIP joint. The H-taping method allows the flexor tendon to be supported across the joint,

without restricting bending of the finger. They found that this taping method did indeed reduce the tendon-bone distance, thus providing some effective support for the injured pulley system. Moreover, the reduction in tendon bone distance afforded by the H-taping method meant that the injured finger was a little stronger than with no tape. Importantly, they found that although other taping methods such as the standard circumferential taping method or a figure-of-eight method did reduce tendon-bone distance slightly, their effects were insignificant. Their study also reaffirmed the previous studies finding that taping offered no benefits to un-injured fingers.

Although these studies are limited, the available picture from the research tells us that taping your fingers to prevent pulley injuries may be of no benefit. However, injured pulleys may benefit from the H-taping method to protect them during climbing while they recover. Hypothetically, the decreased angle change of the tendons at the edge of the A2 and A3 pulleys from this taping method could be useful for relieving tenosynovitis, too. However, this has not been tested. Note also that this research evidence does not mean that taping decreases the recovery time from a pulley injury. There is, as yet, no evidence for that. It may be that it simply allows you to climb at a slightly higher level during the rehabilitation.

The real world of body and mind interacting with sport and training is far more nuanced than that recreated in the research laboratory, and research findings have to be interpreted with this in mind. For one thing, even the researchers acknowledge that some or all of the strength benefits to injured fingers from taping may be psychological. Climbers may simply be less inhibited by their pulley injury when wearing tape, and its use may simply tempt you further down the road towards more aggressive climbing that could create the circumstances for reinjury[25]. Secondly, the research results were gathered from very short loading bouts with freshly applied tape. The researchers themselves point out that in a real climbing situation, unless fresh tape is applied after every route, it is possible, if not likely, that it will stretch to the point that all benefits are lost.

There are also practical problems with tape application. All tape application in sport requires skill and practice to apply optimally with the correct amount of tightness. The H-taping method requires skill just to cut the tape in the correct way before even applying it. There are some reports of climbers finding this difficult to achieve with the commonly used zinc oxide tape. Some have tried using Kinesio tape instead and been pleased with the results. However, this tape has never been tested scientifically on fingers and it seems implausible that it could be effective given that it has more stretch capacity.

In my own experience, I've tested taping my own injured pulleys using all the available methods over the years and never been able to detect any benefit. If I have a pulley injury, I don't use tape and I feel the rate of recovery is just as fast. My own opinion is that the rapid stretching of tape seems likely to negate any benefits of applying it. Moreover, the benefits of taping, whether mechanical or purely psychological, in allowing you to climb at a slightly higher level during rehabilitation, is not worth the effort of constantly re-applying fresh tape.

If you do choose to use tape, be careful that it doesn't become a psychological mask to forget you have the injury, and climb as normal. If you want to be on the safe side, my advice would be to only use tape to splint the PIP joint (Photo 8.2) thus forcing you to climb openhanded.

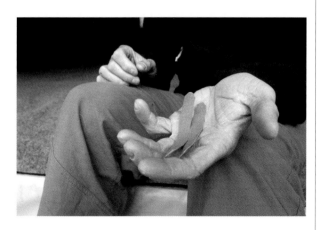

Photo 8.4 Preparing tape for H-taping.

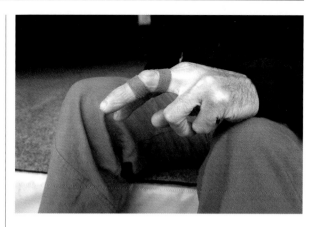

Photo 8.5 H-taping to support an injured pulley.

H-Taping: the method

- Cut a 10cm length of 1.5cm wide tape.
- Cut the tape in half longitudinally from both ends, leaving a 1cm long bridge in the middle.
- Wrap the proximal straps around the finger, just proximal to the PIP joint.
- Flex your PIP joint and then wrap the remaining straps around the finger just distal to the joint so the bridge is over the PIP joint.
- Replace the tape as often as you can during your session since any physiological effects are likely to be lost very quickly as the tape stretches.

Painful finger joints

Impressive adaptations of the finger joints have been shown in X-rays of climbers' hands, even at a young age[111, 112]. The ends of the phalanges (finger bones) become thickened at the edge of the finger joints, and calcification of the finger joint capsule has also been shown. Hence it is often possible to spot a rock climber outside of their sporting environment just by looking at their hands with unnaturally swollen finger joints. So far, there isn't evidence that a life of hard climbing directly causes early onset of osteoarthritis in the finger joints.

However, the combination of some other pre-disposition to arthritis (genetics, untreated injury, poor training practices, etc.) and a life of climbing could hypothetically result in arthritis of the fingers later in life. This would fit with the findings from other joints of the body and other sports. Distance running, for example, is not directly associated with knee, hip or ankle arthritis, except for cases where an injury or biomechanical problem changes joint mechanics.

There have yet to be any long term studies following climbers through to later life to look for evidence of increased osteoarthritis risk. So, it is perhaps surprising that the main group of climbers who should really worry about arthritic changes in their finger joints are youngsters[111]. Epiphyseal fractures, described in section 6, are a very real concern for the new generation of young climbers growing up with climbing walls, training and competition from a young age.

There are a few other finger joint problems that are commonly suffered by climbers. Acute injury to the finger joint capsules or the cruciate ligaments that stabilise them are one concern. This usually happens when a move goes wrong such as getting a finger stuck in a small pocket as you try to slap to the next hold. The finger gets 'wrenched' the wrong way and the joint capsule or ligaments are torn. If an acute injury such as this is accompanied by a large swelling, an X-ray is essential as the ligament may have avulsed (pulled off a piece of bone) and may have to be immobilised to heal properly. Once any necessary immobilisation is complete, the ligamentous tissue should respond to a similar treatment protocol for pulley injuries described above. Buddy taping to an adjacent finger may help to support the weak healing joint for a few weeks until it is resistant to further injury during climbing.

It has been noted that the bone spurs near the finger joints in climbers can become so large that the extensor tendons can become irritated as they have to rub back and forth over the bony protuberance, especially during crimping[138]. How this is best treated probably depends on the severity of the problem. Mild cases will respond to the treatment protocol described below for synovitis, although severe cases benefit from surgery to remove large or detached bone spurs.

The most common finger joint problem suffered by climbers is joint synovitis. Essentially, synovitis is 'acute arthritis'. It usually lasts days if it is properly managed, although if left untreated it can develop into a chronic condition. You will most commonly notice it after a break from training, especially a long seasonal break such as for doing summer trad climbing. But it can also be caused by a change of climbing wall or type of hold.

You have your first session indoors after the summer, or first day of your climbing trip and everything is fine. But the next morning you wake up and your finger joints (usually PIP joints) are stiff, tender and swollen. In severe cases, knocking them off a hard surface like a table is exquisitely painful. The sudden unexpected load on the joint has produced a synovial reaction. Excessive amounts of synovial (joint lubricating) fluid are produced in the hours after the session and this results in increased pressure and swelling in the joint. The increased pressure itself causes the tenderness and increased sensitivity.

When you try to climb again within the next day or two, this time the fingers feel stiff and sore when crimping, although the sensation may diminish at least a little after warming up. Given a couple of days rest followed by a week or two of more gentle loading, either with shorter sessions or extra rest days, it clears up quickly for most climbers. Indeed, many carry on regardless and simply tolerate any pain and stiffness until the finger joints finally adjust.

However, this may be dangerous. A chronic cycle of synovial inflammation appears to persist in some climbers if left unmanaged by rest and careful training transitions. In chronic cases, a small cortisone injection is sometimes used to break the cycle of synovitis. Climbers should be careful to look after the health of their finger joints to prevent the condition getting to a chronic stage. Smooth transitions from one season and type of climbing to another, and extra care when starting a lot of crimpy climbing after some time doing something else will help with prevention. Sudden stiffness in all the fingers may indicate that an over-zealous change in training is to blame for an acute bout of synovitis. Conversely, swelling and pain in just one finger is more concerning and may indicate that some more serious damage has occurred. There are also many other forms of arthritis which although rare, may interact with climbing activity to cause symptoms in climbers' fingers. If the problem fails to respond to rest and sensible training, an orthopedic specialist should be able to help you start to look for other potential causes of the joint pain, which may be treatable.

Loss of accessory movements in the finger joints has been hypothesised as a contributor to synovitis[139]. Accessory movements of a joint can be described as 'play' in the joint to be able to make small movements in different directions from its normal axis of motion. Loss of accessory movement occurs in many joints with age or after injury when the joint stiffens up, and is suspected as a cause of osteoarthritis. In the case of the fingers, these accessory movements are side bending and twisting of the fingers. Of course, the fingers are not designed to have much laxity in these directions, but it seems that having a little more than none is critical for the health of the joint. Thus, regular stretching of the fingers with side bending and twisting may help to alleviate the susceptibility to PIP joint synovitis. Attempting to aggressively stretch the fingers during a flare up of synovitis may not achieve much more than further irritating the joint. If you are prone to synovitis, stretch the fingers as an ongoing preventative measure to maintain mobility of the finger joints.

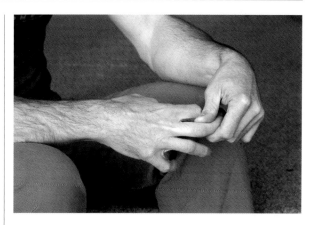

Photo 8.7 Stretching the proximal interphalangeal joint.

Flexor unit strains

Soft tissue injuries of the finger flexor structures as they run into the palm and forearm are common in rock climbers, but barely described in the scientific literature since they are rare in other activities. A blanket term for the injury climbers suffer has emerged, called a 'flexor unit strain' (FUS). Although this name has been organically ascribed to the condition, it is not a specific diagnosis since it doesn't refer to a particular anatomical site. So what exactly is this injury?

Flexor unit strains are the 'Achilles' heel' of the otherwise very safe openhanded grip style. It seems to be much more common in the ring finger than other fingers and usually occurs when pulling hard with a fully openhanded grip with the pinky dropped and curled into a flexed position. It occurs in the ring finger with a three finger or middle-two fingered grip although it also occurs in the middle finger when using mono pockets. It tends to be an acute (sudden) onset injury although it can develop over time if you start climbing or training a lot on small finger pockets without appropriate progression.

The likely scenario for acute onset is during a hard pull on a pocket or stretching to a hold at the limit of your reach. If a foot slips, or the fingers slip a little, or the forearm moves while pulling maximally or the little finger moves

Photo 8.6 Stretching the distal interphalangeal joint.

or 'pings' off the hold, a flexor unit strain can occur.

Moderate cases will elicit pain in the palm in line with the ring finger, at the base of the finger, and often along the full length of the finger tendon into the forearm as well. A confirming test is fairly straightforward. Pull on a hold with a four finger openhanded or crimp grip. Little or no pain should be felt. Now 'drop' the pinky and while pulling with an openhanded grip, pain should appear along the length of the ring finger tendon. Moving the

pinky up and down while pulling with the other fingers may reproduce the symptoms even more strongly. If you have injured the middle finger from a mono-pocket, simply pulling on a mono should reproduce symptoms where using a three finger grip is pain free.

It is unclear which structures become injured in the condition, but there are three possible areas of damage and all may be involved simultaneously (Fig. 8.2). The first is the junction between the individual finger

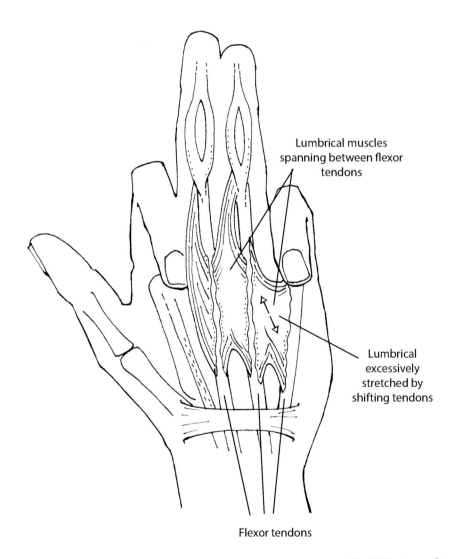

Lumbrical muscles spanning between flexor tendons

Lumbrical excessively stretched by shifting tendons

Flexor tendons

Fig. 8.2 Structures affected in a flexor unit strain.

tendons where they fuse with the muscle belly in the forearm. Imagine how the muscle and tendon fibres of the pinky are relaxed and shortened while those of the neighbouring ring finger are lengthened and under maximal tension. There is obvious potential for high shearing forces between the two tendon structures.

The second area likely to be affected is at the tiny lumbrical muscles in the palm itself. These muscles flex straightened fingers at the MCP joint at the base of the fingers. Rather than attaching to bone, the lumbricals are unusual in that they attach to the flexor tendons of the fingers (a moving structure) in the palm. Thus, when the ring finger is held in extension on a hold while the pinky is highly flexed, the lumbrical muscle connecting the two tendons becomes stretched and can be torn. Injury to the lumbricals in this way has been called 'lumbrical shift syndrome'. Finally, the flexor tendons themselves or their sheaths may be damaged, giving pain along their length,

Although successful treatments for this injury are, so far, solely down to the experiments of affected climbers rather than research, the prescription is relatively simple: climb without provoking the symptoms and the injury seems to heal well, if slowly in bad cases. It is usually best to keep climbing but completely avoid dropping the pinky at all times. Simply make sure you hold on with all four fingers, whether with a four finger openhanded grip or crimp. For two finger pockets, you will probably be forced to either use the 'front two' (index and middle fingers) or refuse to use them at all. Unless your climbing resource is dominated by pocketed limestone, this should be achievable. Stretching the affected finger also seems to soothe immediate symptoms, but whether it speeds healing is unknown. Very moderate strains may clear up in a month or two and may cause little or no limitation in your climbing after a careful warm-up. Bad cases can be reluctant to heal completely, but usually do resolve eventually after as much as one year. Even when pain is largely gone, you will feel a tendency for unpleasant 'twanging' sensations in the affected finger and will justifiably suffer a lack of confidence to jump for pockets. The best option is simply to shift the focus of your climbing goals and training away from pockety terrain until you have been symptom-free for some time.

Dupuytren's contracture

Dupuytren's is a disease affecting the hands, with a genetic predisposition that normally appears in later life in those with manual jobs, or with alcohol dependency or smoking. It has emerged in recent decades that Dupuytren's can appear in much younger people, from the stress on the hands caused by climbing. Because Dupuytren's is so rare in the young, climbers have been misdiagnosed with tumors of the hand.

The disease involves gradual formation of fibrous nodules and then cords in the palmar fascia and sometimes into the fingers. In non-climbers, these generally appear between the ages of 40-60 and gradually get worse, pulling the fingers into an increasingly contracted position. The genetic disposition is originally of Viking origin and is carried by various populations descended from the Vikings. The prevalence is about 19% in the UK as a whole, but is as low as 5% in the south of England and as high as 39% in north-east Scotland. There is now strong evidence that climbing causes much earlier onset of contracture among carriers[140].

The main problematic symptom of Dupuytren's is the of loss of extension of the affected fingers (usually the ring and little fingers). The fingers curl progressively into flexion as the disease progresses, until any movement is impossible in severe cases. The nodules of fibrous scar tissue do also become painful, especially to direct pressure. In a small proportion of cases, the progression of scarring stops and some cases even spontaneously resolve. However, most continue to progress to the point where the affected hand becomes useless. Various treatments such as cortisone, ultrasound and massage have been tried in the past with with no success. Surgery can reverse the problem, but it is reportedly a difficult operation and recurrence is very common[141].

It appears that the variety of available treatments has moved on quite a bit in the past decade, with some promising treatments now available, albeit privately and at considerable cost:

- Radiotherapy. Irradiation of the affected area with X-rays has been shown to be effective in slowing or stopping the progression of the disease altogether. It appears to be most effective if the treatment is applied as soon as the disease is first noticed, when the diseased cells dividing to form the small nodules are most active. Thus, if you have just noticed unusual growth appearing on your palm, it may prevent the disease becoming a lifelong nuisance if you get an early diagnosis and treatment with radiotherapy. It is not currently widely available on the NHS at the moment and private treatment may be expensive, but money well spent.

- Collagenase. Another promising emerging treatment is the injection of the enzyme collagenase (in the form of the drug Xiaflex/Xiapex) into the fibrous cords to dissolve them. The treatment gives relief for up to several years. However, the skill of the injecting surgeon is critical since accidental contact of the collagenase with surrounding structures such as the finger tendons or pulleys would cause their destruction too. The risk of this is reportedly low.

- Needle aponeurotomy. The fibrous cords are repeatedly punctured with a large needle under local anaesthetic until they are weakened enough to be broken up by extending the fingers. It is simpler, quicker and much less invasive than surgery and although recurrence is still likely, the treatment is safe and can be repeated.

Ganglions

Ganglion cysts are synovial fluid-filled lumps that bulge out from the finger joints or tendon sheaths. They are visible as a lump under the skin. They may or may not be painful, but often 'catch' on the rock while climbing and provide a nuisance. Their size is influenced by your recent climbing activities. They will become bigger after a climbing session, since this stimulates production of more synovial fluid, but they often reduce after rest days. Affected climbers often 'work' the ganglion down by massaging the fluid out of it, or even bashing it off a hard surface to break it[139]. But they soon reform. Ganglions are caused by a weak area of joint capsule or flexor sheath. They also commonly form on the back of the wrist. There is no good conservative treatment to permanently reduce ganglions. They may subside over months or years spontaneously. If rest days and ice to reduce the finger's synovial stress reaction are insufficient to manage it successfully, surgical removal may be necessary, with a reasonably good success rate[139].

Other finger injuries

Various other finger injuries are more rarely suffered by climbers:

- Trigger finger occurs when a knot-like thickening forms on the flexor tendon of one finger. It becomes trapped in the tight tendon sheath and suddenly 'snaps' when it is forcefully released. Aggressive massage is often used in an attempt to break down the knot, but this is not thought to be effective. Some cases resolve gradually over time without intervention. Cortisone can be injected onto the tendon sheath (not the tendon) to widen it and if this fails then surgical splitting of the A1 pulley is a last resort but may be effective.

- Fractures are mostly caused by rockfall or by falling with the fingers jammed in a pocket or crack. Stress fractures are also possible in adults as well as the increasingly common epiphyseal fractures in adolescents (described in section 6). Minor fractures can sometimes be misdiagnosed as a pulley injury. If a pulley rupture is suspected or the injury fails to respond as expected in pulley rehabilitation, an X-ray should be performed.

- Digital nerve irritation sometimes occurs from small pockets, sharp edged holds or particularly violent moves such as 'exploding' off a hold after trying to grab it at the end of a dyno. The symptoms of pain or numbness tend to settle in a few days for mild cases or up to several months with more serious damage.

- Finger amputation or severe traumatic injury to fingers sometimes occurs when climbers fall while clipping the rope or while grabbing a quickdraw by getting their fingers caught in the karabiner gate. Attempting to hold on to a bolt when unable to clip in extremis has also caused severe traumatic injuries to the fingers. Urgent reattachment sometimes has a successful outcome. Amputation also occurs with rockfall and a surprising number of cases of home improvement accidents. Climbers, take care with those fingers when using sharp tools.

- Hyperhydrosis. This condition causes excessive sweating, often affecting the hands. Sufferers have considerable problems with rock climbing for obvious reasons. A new treatment protocol using iontophoresis seems to be very effective for limiting the condition, and there are reports of climbers having transformed their experience of climbing using it. It involves placing the hands in a basin of water ionised by the iontophoresis machine for around 30 minutes. It is painless, unless you have cuts in your fingers. Why iontophoresis works is still not understood, but it is thought that it blocks the sweat glands in some way. A proportion of sufferers do not seem to respond to the treatment. For the effects to be maintained, iontophoresis needs to be repeated every couple of weeks or so. It is offered on the NHS although availability may be patchy. Regular private treatment would become expensive if done regularly, so it may be a better option for sufferers to buy their own iontophoresis machine and treat themselves at home. Machines cost around £400.

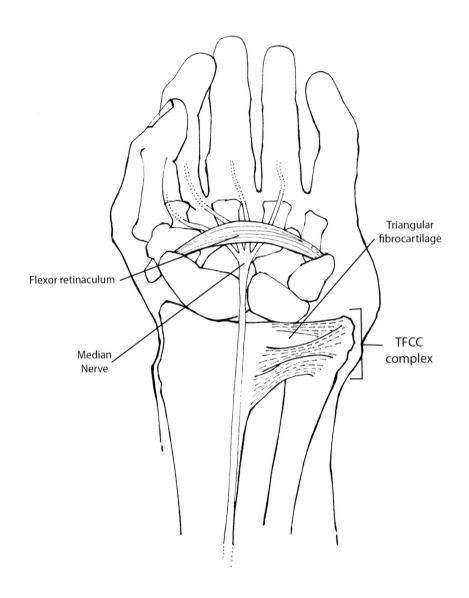

Triangular
fibrocartilage

Flexor retinaculum

Median
Nerve

TFCC
complex

The wrist

Section 9

Injuries of the wrist joint can be a serious challenge to diagnose and treat. The variety of things that can go wrong is huge and far too diverse to fit into this book. Attempting to try to self-diagnose and manage a wrist injury is a huge gamble for climbers. Just see a professional. Apart from uncontrolled falls in bouldering, climbers tend to injure their wrists on big slopers, where the whole hand is used to grasp the hold. Also, other manual activities at work or things like weight lifting tend to cause wrist injuries which are then maintained or aggravated by climbing. There are three injuries which are particularly common among climbers and I have described them below.

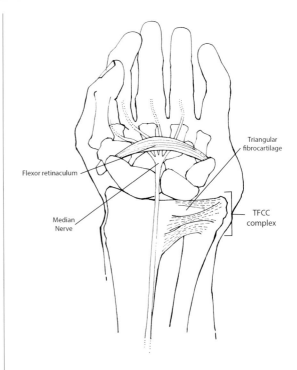

Fig 9.1 The TFCC complex and carpal tunnel of the wrist.

Triangular fibrocartilage injury

The triangular fibrocartilage complex (TFCC) is a small disc of cartilage that forms part of the wrist joint (Fig. 9.1). It lies between the end of the ulna and the carpal bones of the hand, on the pinky side of the wrist. It is commonly injured in sport, usually from compression such as diving onto an outstretched hand. In climbing, it is normally injured by a distraction force at the wrist (pulling the forearm and hand apart). Large, flat slopers where the whole of the hand is placed on the hold are a common scenario for this injury, especially when an unusual move such as this is done repeatedly in a session. The injury will cause use of certain hold shapes and orientations to feel painful and you may feel the wrist making a 'clunk' as it is loaded. The pain usually comes on slowly over weeks or months. A common diagnostic test is to attempt to raise your body weight from a chair with outstretched arms on the sides of the chair. This compresses the TFCC and causes pain if it is damaged.

The best thing climbers can do is to respond before the injury progresses, and avoid the types of holds that aggravate it before it becomes more serious[142]. Indoor boulderers who spend a lot of time on big, poor slopers are probably most at risk, and most likely to be able to change the types of holds they climb on for a while.

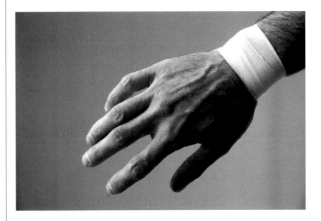

Photo 9.1 Taping the wrist to support a TFCC injury.

The tear can be in the cartilage disc itself, or the ligaments that hold it in place. Treatments include several weeks of rest, followed by strengthening of the wrist flexors and extensors so the wrist is more stable on big slopers. Crimping is usually painless and allows continued, careful climbing even when the condition is quite bad. Circumferential taping of the wrist may also be useful to offload the TFCC while it heals. Effective taping of the wrist is notoriously difficult to learn by yourself. Get a good physiotherapist to show you how. Apart from not helping the TFCC problem, poorly applied tape on the wrist can cause other wrist conditions. To prevent recurrence, you will have to control the amount of big sloper problems in your climbing routine. Most climbers who train for outdoor climbing do far too much climbing on big slopers anyway.

Carpal tunnel syndrome

Numbness, parasthesia or burning pains in the wrist are all symptoms of carpal tunnel syndrome. Experiencing the symptoms at night is a classic pattern. Some climbers report that their climbing is unaffected by the condition. However, disturbed sleep may have significant indirect effects on your climbing.

The carpal tunnel is the tight space in the wrist through which nine tendons and the median nerve pass, hemmed in on one side by the carpal bones and a thick band of connective tissue (the flexor retinaculum) on the other (Fig. 9.1). It doesn't take much for the median nerve to become compressed and painful. Any inflammation or tightness within the tunnel can impinge on the median nerve. Professional diagnosis is important because the nerve can also be compressed further up the arm and neck and this must be excluded by manual or nerve conduction tests. Tinel's test, which involves tapping on the median nerve at the wrist, will produce tingling and altered sensation where nerve compression is present. There are a host of medical causes too, which your doctor can exclude, everything from pregnancy to diabetes mellitus. It appears that some people simply have a genetic tendency for a narrow carpal tunnel, predisposing them to the condition.

The most persistent cases require surgery to decompress

the nerve. However, a combination of several conservative treatments usually resolves milder cases:

- Initial splinting with the wrist in a neutral position to relieve pressure on the carpal tunnel, especially during sleep.
- Mobilisation exercises for the carpal bones.
- Short term NSAIDs to reduce inflammation.
- Stretching the flexor retinaculum.
- Vitamin B6 supplementation[143].
- Removal of aggravating factors - get an ergonomic mouse and keyboard.

Photo 9.2 Stretching the flexor retinaculum for carpal tunnel syndrome.

De Quervain's tenosynovitis

De Quervain's is an inflammation of the synovial tendon sheath of the muscles that extend the thumb. The sheath becomes inflamed at the point where the tendons cross the wrist at the the radial styloid. Pain is felt with resisted extension and abduction of the thumb. Finkelstein's test for diagnosis of the condition involves fully flexing the thumb and then ulnar deviating the wrist to stretch the tendon and sheath, which will be painful if the condition is present.

Rock climbing isn't usually a direct cause, but can aggravate it if you already have the condition. The real cause is usually some sort of repetitive manual activity, either something you do all the time (i.e. for work) or something unaccustomed such as starting a program of wrist exercises with dumbells using poor form.

Photo 9.3 Finkelstein's test for De Quervain's tenosynovitis.

In all cases, identifying then removing or modifying the activity that caused you to get it is the main treatment. A recent review of other treatments observed that rest and NSAIDs didn't appear to be beneficial. In mild cases, simply removing the cause should allow the condition to clear up in a week or two. It also seems to respond well to DTFM and ice over the affected area. The next line of treatment, if recovery fails to progress in a few weeks, is a small cortisone injection into the sheath to reduce bulky scarring that causes the irritation. Splinting is also used but its utility seems to be controversial. Rare, chronic cases require surgery.

Modification of the aggravating activity usually comes down to better form while using tools or doing other heavy manual work. Excessive use of keyboard and mouse may also be a cause. In climbing, the most aggravating activity is pinching at different angles. Climbers suffering from the condition often try to hold the thumb out of the way to relieve stress on the thumb. Unfortunately this usually has the opposite effect.

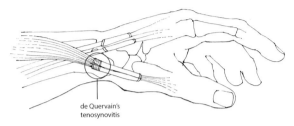

de Quervain's
tenosynovitis

Fig. 9.2 De Quervain's tenosynovitis

Other wrist injuries

- Carpal dislocation. Falls or a history of instability in the wrist may allow one of the many bones of the wrist to partially dislocate (known as subluxation) as it moves. Subluxation differs from true dislocation in that the bone may pop in and out of place regularly, perhaps even every time it is moved. This may be relatively painless in some situations. But I have noted climbers with a painful 'clunking' accompanied by a loss of power as they weight holds at certain angles. Treatment is usually a short period of splinting followed by a physiotherapist guided program of wrist strengthening. True dislocation of one of the wrist bones, especially if it follows from a ligament tear, sometimes needs surgical repair.

- Handlebar palsy. Plenty of climbers do a fair bit of cycling. The repeated shock loading of the wrist in a hyperextended position on handlebars can irritate the ulnar nerve as it passes across the wrist, outside the carpal tunnel. Symptoms may include numbness, tingling, pain or weakness from the wrist to the pinky and ring finger, which are innervated by the ulnar nerve. Mobilisation of the carpal bones, especially the pisiform, might help relieve the pressure, as will changing your handlebar setup. More persistent cases may be caused by a ganglion cyst in the wrist and will need professional advice.

- Scaphoid fracture. Fracture of this wrist bone is often missed and passed off as just a sprain. It occurs most often after a fall onto an outstretched arm. Pain is located near the base of the thumb, in the 'anatomical snuffbox'. If you suspect this might have happened, go back and get another opinion. Scaphoid fractures need prolonged immobilisation to heal properly, and if left untreated will give long term problems.

- Intersection syndrome (Oarsman's wrist). This injury appears to occur in those involved in very repetitive climbing activities such as rope access work or long mountain routes involving hauling and coiling. Outside of climbing it occurs in rowers, alpine skiers who do a lot of forceful work with ski poles, and manual workers who use power tools extensively. It can also occur as an acute reaction to unaccustomed use of the wrist in the situations above. It gives pain over the dorsal, radial aspect of the forearm (the top of the forearm, on the inner side). The pain occurs about 4-8cm up the forearm from the wrist, and this distinguishes it from De Quervain's tenosynovitis, described above. The treatment is similar to the protocol for De Quervain's, although splinting the wrist for a short period may also be useful to give the condition a chance to settle[144].

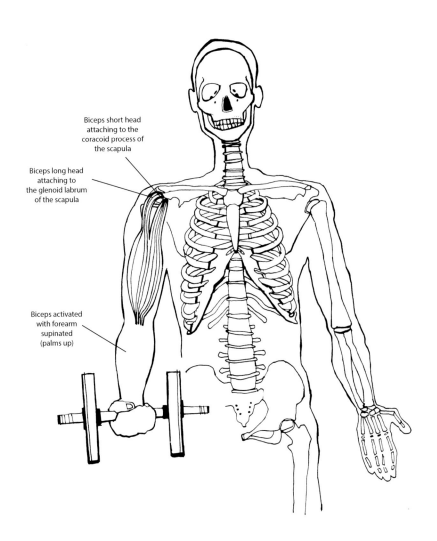

Biceps short head
attaching to the
coracoid process of
the scapula

Biceps long head
attaching to
the glenoid labrum
of the scapula

Biceps activated
with forearm
supinated
(palms up)

The shoulder

Section 10

If you are reading this section having just suffered a shoulder injury, stop. First, go and book yourself a session with the finest sports medical doctor, orthopedic surgeon or physiotherapist you can find (better all three, since at least one of them might misdiagnose you). Then, you can finish reading before you go for your diagnosis. The shoulder is the most challenging joint to diagnose and treat. And that's for the professionals. Attempting to do it yourself as an amateur is most likely to land you in even more trouble[35]. However, arming yourself with some knowledge of the conditions will have three very positive effects on your response to shoulder pain:

- You will fully understand the need to avoid messing about and to go and get professional help.
- You will be able to understand the importance of seeing more than one professional to ensure you have got the diagnosis correct.
- You will understand that ignoring prevention of shoulder problems either before they develop or as symptoms appear is really quite crazy.

The following sections detail just the most common of the myriad of ways you can destroy your shoulders through climbing and training. Of these, impingement of the rotator cuff is by far the most common, accounting for as much as 80% of all shoulder injuries. There's a lot you can do to prevent it, or nip it in the bud before it gets hard to deal with. Since so many climbers get impingement syndrome at some point, some preventative work should be done by all of us as part of our regular training activity. The commitment required is trivial, the benefits huge.

Since the shoulder is so complicated, be sure to read section 3 covering the basic anatomy of the shoulder and how it moves in order to understand the pathology of the shoulder.

Shoulder impingement/rotator cuff tears

Section 3 described the anatomy and alignment of the shoulder and how the acromion forms the 'roof' of the shoulder joint space. The head of the humerus must move freely within that space. However, poor posture and various muscle imbalances can cause narrowing of the sub-acromial space and when you reach overhead, the head of the humerus tends to bump against the acromion (Figs. 3.1-3.5). The rotator cuff, a group of four muscles that control movement of the arm, attach to the humeral head and their tendons are impinged (pinched) when the sub-acromial space becomes narrowed. In mild cases of misalignment, the impingement may be only slight and you will only notice it if you decide to paint all the ceilings in your house one day. The majority of people walking around have poor enough shoulder alignment to be potential shoulder impingement cases, but have no pain as they don't participate in repetitive overhead activities.

However, once the rotator cuff becomes impinged enough to become inflamed, a process begins that can be hard to stop unless you take some action. The squeezed rotator cuff tendons become inflamed, swollen and eventually frayed, narrowing the space even further and movements that were previously pain free become an urgent problem (Fig. 10.1).

The most significant symptomatic marker for impingement is the 'painful arc' (Fig 10.2). Abducting the arm from rest is initially painless. The mid-range of bringing the arm overhead is painful and the final part where the arm becomes vertical above your head is once again painless as the bulbous humeral head moves out of the way of the acromion. The tendon of supraspinatus is most commonly affected since it runs over the top of the humeral head. However, depending on the individual imbalances, other tendons of the rotator cuff or the head of the biceps tendon can be irritated. The repeated rubbing or squashing of the affected tendons during everyday movement of the arm causes it to become inflamed and malnourished due to the squeezing-out of its blood supply. In non-sportspeople, it can be self-limiting; i.e. people recognise there is a problem with their shoulder and avoid overhead or painful activities for long enough for the damage to be reversed without intervention. However, if sporting activities are contributing factors, then it is likely to progress to

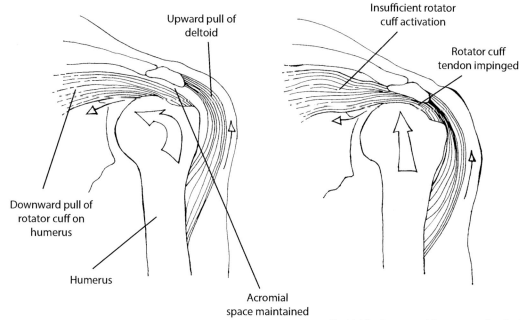

Upward pull of
deltoid

Insufficient rotator
cuff activation

Rotator cuff
tendon impinged

Downward pull of
rotator cuff on
humerus

Humerus

Acromial
space maintained

Fig. 10.1 Impingement of the rotator cuff in the shoulder.

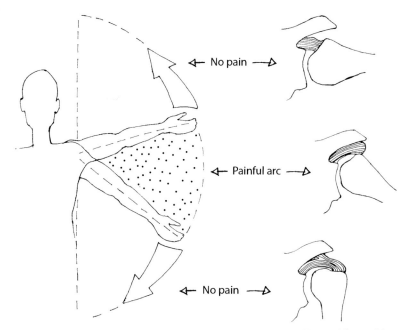

No pain

Painful arc

No pain

Fig. 10.2 The painful arc with shoulder impingement.

a more serious condition if the underlying imbalances are not addressed. In other words, you can rest until the symptoms die down, but they are likely to return when return to training at your previous level. If the affected rotator cuff tendon is allowed to become thickened and eventually frayed, the pain becomes much worse and complete ruptures are relatively common.

Common causes of slow-onset rotator cuff impingement

- Repetitive overhead activities, either climbing or non-climbing (e.g. painting your ceiling)
- Strong and shortened internal rotators (lats, pec major, pec minor, teres major)
- Weak rotator cuff muscles, especially the external rotators
- Poor posture/alignment
- Poor shoulder movement pattern
- Poor sitting position at work or driving position
- Genetic factors (hooked acromion)

Common causes of acute rotator cuff tears

- Slow onset impingement which has been ignored; weakened tendon eventually tears
- 'Shouldery' press or 'gaston' moves
- Aggressive moves performed without adequate warm-up
- Awkward lifting or overhead activities unrelated to climbing

Diagnosis of rotator cuff impingement

Accurate diagnosis of rotator cuff damage in the shoulder is recognised as being extremely difficult, even for shoulder specialists with access to scanning equipment. MRI and ultrasound scanning are reliable for diagnosis of full thickness tears of rotator cuff tendons. However, the partial tears (which are more common) are less well seen with scanning. There is a long list of manual tests that can be performed during your examination to test the integrity of the rotator cuff, but which of these tests is the most effective and reliable remains controversial. Ideally, your doctor or physiotherapist will perform several tests, the combination of which will give the best

available picture of tendon damage and any contributing muscle imbalances.

Prevention and treatment of slow onset rotator cuff pain

The time to repair the roof is when the sun is shining.
John F. Kennedy

If you have just noticed slow onset rotator cuff pain, acting quickly can reverse the symptoms quite easily in many cases. The primary intervention for shoulder impingement is to restore range of motion and proper shoulder movement[35]. More specifically, retraining the movement pattern of the scapula as you reach overhead, and retraining the weak, unresponsive rotator cuff muscles to function better during shoulder movements can rapidly remove the cause in some cases even with just a few sessions of exercises[32].

It will also be necessary to identify the muscles which have become shortened around the shoulder, and stretch these regularly. In climbers, the most common targets will be the internal rotators: lats, pec major and teres major. Stretches for these muscles are described in section 3. There will likely be associated weakness of the external rotators. Sometimes re-education of arm movement with the help of a physiotherapist will be enough to get these muscles working better and correct faulty movement patterns. But in trained climbers, the imbalance of internal versus external rotators may well be too marked and will require strengthening exercises to restore normal movement. The problem here is that jumping straight into an exercise program for a painful, irritated shoulder can exacerbate the symptoms. Guidance on progression from your physiotherapist will be essential in this event to be able to make progress. Usually all it takes is a gentle start in the early sessions, starting with re-education of arm movement before progressing to exercises with resistance.

Restoration of normal shoulder function

The following exercises are very useful to help correct the resting posture of the shoulders and ensure that the rotator cuff muscles are properly activated during movement of the arm, so that the humeral head is controlled and impingement reduced. Climbers, as well as many other sportspeople, tend to be suspicious of the simplicity of these exercises, given that they are done without resistance from external weights. Therefore, they are rarely done, hence the high occurrence of shoulder impingement.

Don't let the simplicity put you off; these are extremely valuable exercises that perform two separate and important functions. First, they retrain the correct motor pattern, or technique, of shoulder and arm movement. Our poor postural habits and muscle imbalances have taken their toll on the rotator cuff and other shoulder muscles which become lengthened, weak and inactive. Simply 'waking them up' by retraining the correct movement pattern encourages their automatic firing during everyday movements and reverses their decline.

Secondly, just because you are not lifting a heavy weight doesn't mean there is no resistance. Exercises such as wall slides are surprisingly tiring for most male climbers. This is because they are an 'inner range holding' exercise. The weak external rotators of the rotator cuff are working at their shortest length and at their limit of force development, just to counteract the pull of the much stronger and overly short lats and other internal rotators. So three beneficial effects are happening at the same time. Inner range holding tends to shorten the external rotators. It also works them hard so they become stronger and more responsive. Finally, the shortened internal rotator muscles are simultaneously stretched.

Do these from scratch by yourself if you must. But even one session with a good physiotherapist will really help you to get feedback on what the correct positioning and movement pattern of the scapula and arm feels like. Some impingement syndrome sufferers can even eliminate their pain in one session if poor movement patterns are the primary cause.

Simple abduction drill

This simplest of shoulder drills is a great place to start if you have a painful shoulder. There is little resistance and

Photo 10.1 Simple shoulder abduction drill.

the objective is to become more aware of your scapula and the correct movement pattern during arm abduction that prevents impingement. If you have impingement which is painful enough to make even this exercise difficult, getting your physiotherapist to support your arm during the movement will help. Ideally, you will quickly learn to move with better scapulo-humeral rhythm and the pain will be reduced to the point you can start to progress to the exercises below. As you raise the arm, try to notice the position of the scapulae. Try to raise and rotate the scapulae and the arm in one, synchronised movement.

Wall slides

This basic exercise to correct shoulder alignment and movement looks too easy until hunched muscular boulderers try to do it! It is an effective 'workhorse' basic exercise to stretch the lats and other muscles, and promote good activation and alignment of the external rotators and trapezius muscle.

Photo 10.2 Wall slides, starting position. Stand with your back flat against a wall, feet three inches away from the wall. Extend your arms upwards over your head and with elbows locked, try to hold your arms flat against the wall. Most females will wonder what the problem is, while male boulderers will suddenly realise how limited their movement is, thanks to their short lats. Hold your arms overhead for 10 seconds, trying to push them as close as you can to the wall, which will feel very strenuous if your alignment is poor. No cheating by barreling your chest and abs outwards.

Photo 10.3 Wall slides, end position. Then, keeping your forearms as close to the wall as possible, bring your arms down your sides until your upper arms are horizontal and forearms vertical with elbows bent. Do the exercise as often as you can daily while you are waiting for the kettle to boil, watching TV or as part of your warm up. You are unlikely to overdo this exercise, and several times per day is ideal.

Prone arm waves

This exercise re-educates and strengthens your withered and weak external rotators, long forgotten by your climbing oriented training regime. It helps to prevent over-dominant internal rotators from pulling your shoulder out of alignment during arm movements. Stop if you feel shoulder pain during the exercises. If you already have impingement pain, these exercises may aggravate it. A common mistake is to use too much external resistance. It is better to start with no resistance and progress very slowly with light weights such as a book in your hand or a bottle of water.

Photo 10.4 Prone arm waves, starting position. Lie on your front with your upper arm at shoulder height and forearm hanging down over the edge of your bed or table. Rest your shoulder and upper arm on a towel to prevent it drooping down.

Photo 10.5 Prone arm waves, end position. Turn your forearm upwards to the limit of your range of motion. Imagine you are rotating your

upper arm like an axle to achieve this and take care not to lift your arm off the towel or allow your scapula to move. Hold the end position for 5-10 seconds and slowly lower it back down. Strict form is mandatory to avoid aggravation of the shoulder.

Stretching shortened internal rotators

Photo 10.6 Stretching lats. Lats are not an easy muscle to stretch and opinions differ on the best method. One good method is to lean against a wall with arms locked overhead. Lean your trunk downwards to feel the stretch in your lats. Strong and tight lats will take a good solid lean to achieve an adequate stretch.

Photo 10.7 Stretching teres major. Lie on your bouldering mat and with one hand reach behind you to grasp the base of the mat. Use your other hand to pull the elbow towards the midline of your body. You should feel a stretch in your shoulder blade. The stretch requires a bit of practice as this muscle is not easy to stretch.

Photo 10.8 Hollow shoulders are common in climbers. Stretching pectoralis major is an important stretch for climbers to prevent shortness affecting shoulder and humerus alignment.

Pectorialis minor stretch

Hollow shoulders may also be caused by shortness of pectorialis minor. To test the length of pec minor, lie on your back with arms resting at your side and knees bent. The lateral (outer) border of the scapula should lie no more than one inch off the table[30]. A greater distance implies shortness of pec minor (Photo 10.9).

Photo 10.9 Assessment of pectorialis minor.

Pec minor is an extremely difficult muscle to stretch. In fact, some physiotherapists believe it is not possible to achieve a true stretch at all. There are two methods to try.

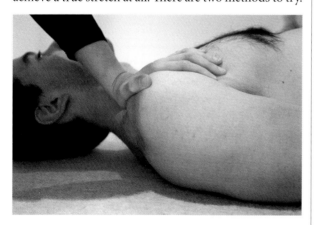

Photo 10.10 First method for pectorialis stretch. Use a partner to assist you. Lie on the floor and have your partner cup their hand over your shoulder and press the shoulder downwards. It is crucial not to let your trunk 'roll' and to maintain a level position to make the muscle stretch between the ribcage and scapula[30].

Photo 10.11 Pectorialis minor doorway stretch. Stand with one foot in front of the other in a doorway with your hands level with your shoulders. Tuck your elbows into your sides and do not let them move backwards. Shift your weight forwards and allow the chest to open[144].

Treatment of acute rotator cuff tears

Acute partial or complete tears of one of the rotator cuff tendons may either happen as a progression from chronic rotator cuff pain, or occur suddenly with no previous symptoms. An example of this would be a powerful and awkward press move. Most shoulder surgeons will recommend trying non-surgical treatment for at least 6 months before considering surgery. Non-surgical treatment has a quoted success rate between 50%-95%[8]. Exercise therapy is generally similar to that described above for slow-onset rotator cuff pain. It is vital that you see a good physiotherapist early and receive a personalised program of exercise that takes into account where the damage has occurred, your individual muscle imbalances, age and stage of athletic development.

Corticosteroid injection has been a popular treatment for rotator cuff tears and is still used by some today.

However, its use is at odds with the evidence which has failed to demonstrate that it is a worthwhile treatment. Moreover, it carries a poor long term prognosis with much higher rates of recurrence than physiotherapy. Use of NSAIDs and ultrasound therapy have a similar lack of evidence of effectiveness in treating rotator cuff tears.

A proportion of sufferers of rotator cuff tears will continue to have pain despite prolonged non-surgical treatment and will need surgery. Failure to comply with your physiotherapy program and to receive regular supervision from your physiotherapist is a good way to make this scenario more likely. Surgery is more likely if the tear has been severe, or genetic factors were a contributing cause. Today, arthroscopic surgery is favoured, although open surgery is still chosen for certain cases. Partial tears are treated by removing the bulky, damaged tissue to decompress the acromial space. Complete tears are easier to repair if the tear is fresh, and more difficult if there is a background of longstanding rotator cuff damage, previous surgery, smoking or corticosteroid injections. If you are being considered for rotator cuff surgery, chapter 12 of *Tendon Injuries, Basic Science and Clinical Medicine*[8] has a good discussion of the details of choosing the best treatment option.

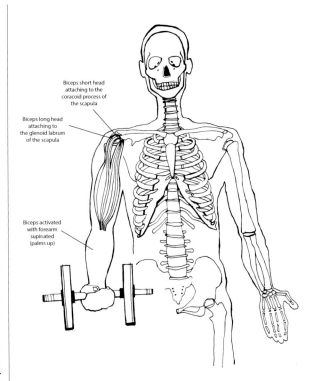

Biceps short head attaching to the coracoid process of the scapula

Biceps long head attaching to the glenoid labrum of the scapula

Biceps activated with forearm supinated (palms up)

Fig 10.3 The origin of the biceps muscle at the shoulder.

Biceps tendon injuries at the shoulder

The biceps muscle has two heads at its origin in the shoulder (Fig. 10.3). The short head runs directly to the scapula, and the long head runs through a groove in the humeral head, also attaching to the scapula. Climbing can cause various injury scenarios for this structure, which appear (from my observation) to be relatively common among climbers. Possibly the most common scenario is impingement of the long head biceps tendon at the humeral head due to poor alignment and muscle imbalance across the shoulder. Pain is felt in the front (anterior) aspect of the shoulder when the arm is overhead. Reaching and pulling on undercuts above

your head seems to be particularly provocative for pain. The tendon becomes inflamed, swollen, frayed and can eventually tear or rupture[145]. When the tendon ruptures, the long head of biceps retracts downwards into the arm, making the muscle bulge (Popeye style) more than normal, with bruising and weakness, especially with the forearm in supinated (palm up) position. Long head ruptures can be treated either surgically or conservatively and no consensus exists as to which gives better results[145]. Surgery is recommended for the young, but in adults I have seen several climbers who recovered quickly from the injury by undertaking a program of shoulder and upper arm strengthening exercises. Presumably, this injury responds comparatively well because the short head of biceps is still able to function.

As well as the biceps tendon, the ligaments that hold the long head tendon in place can also tear, allowing the tendon to sublux (move out of place) from its groove on the humerus. Another scenario is that the tendon pulls and tears the cartilage labrum to which it is connected. Both of these scenarios cause pain which seems unlikely to resolve without surgery in order to reconstruct the normal anatomy of the shoulder[146]. A good program of physiotherapy is essential following surgery to restore normal movement patterns in the shoulder and prevent recurrence or further shoulder pain.

Labral tears

The shoulder is, strictly speaking, a ball and socket joint. However, because it must have so much more mobility than other joints of this type, the socket is extremely shallow. Mobility in joints always comes at the expense of stability, and so additional stability is provided by a rim of cartilage which surrounds the socket, known as the glenoid labrum (Fig. 10.4). Sudden traction movements of the shoulder can tear the labrum. Labral tears do occur in climbers, and have been observed both as slow onset tears from repeated microtrauma, and as sudden tears[147, 148].

Labral tears are most often seen in gymnastics and throwing sports, with fast, aggressive and high force shoulder movements. It is not clear if there are any common mechanisms of injury in climbers, but various researchers report that there are two scenarios which seem most likely to cause the injury[131, 147]. Firstly, cutting loose suddenly or unexpectedly and trying to hang on has caused sudden tears in the labrum. Secondly, repeated eccentric loading, such as dropping down with two hands on the campus board may cause repeated microtrauma, eventually leading to symptoms appearing.

There are two common types of tear in the glenoid labrum: the SLAP lesion (acronym for Superior Labrum Anterior-to-Posterior tear) or the Bankart lesion, which is a tear of the anterior part of the labrum. Labral tears

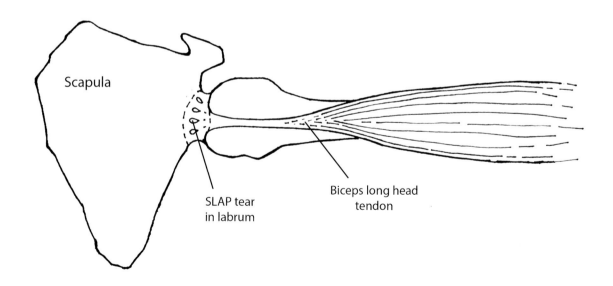

Scapula

SLAP tear
in labrum

Biceps long head
tendon

Fig. 10.4 A SLAP tear in the glenoid labrum.

can often occur at the same time as other (more common) shoulder injuries such as rotator cuff tears or shoulder dislocation, and thus can be easily missed during diagnosis. Shoulder subluxation (where the shoulder joint is pushed partially out of its socket but not fully dislocated) can also cause damage to the labrum. Even if a labral tear is suspected, there is some controversy over the effectiveness of various manual tests in confirming whether the labrum has torn or not[131]. Thus, seeking the opinion of more than one shoulder expert is a good idea. If you have previously suffered a dislocation or rotator cuff tear and have ongoing pain not consistent with the progress of the rehabilitation program, another diagnostic examination and MRI scan should be performed. Testing biceps strength in the injured shoulder, with the forearm supinated and after the injury has had a week of rest may be useful in raising suspicion of a SLAP tear if biceps is weak[30]. However, this test is rarely used among therapists.

The symptoms of labral tears seem to vary between individuals. Some individuals experience no pain and little instability. Others have dull or throbbing pain, worsened by overhead activities and a feeling of instability in the shoulder. There can be a painful clicking in the shoulder with certain movements. Minor labral tears may be treated by strengthening the muscles around the shoulder and improving range of motion. However, more serious tears require surgery. In recent years the development of arthroscopic (keyhole) surgery techniques has improved the outcomes and risk profiles of surgery significantly. Volker Schöffl and colleagues also report good results with an alternative surgical method to arthroscopic SLAP lesion repair[148].

Shoulder dislocation

The shoulder is the most commonly dislocated joint in the body and is quite a serious injury for any sportsperson since it tends to leave the athlete with chronic instability of the shoulder and a high risk of further dislocations. Although there are no data available, it seems that dislocations in climbing are not uncommon in falls and so all climbers should be aware of the high risk situations.

Prevention

Since non-surgical treatments for shoulder dislocations are far from satisfactory at reducing chronic risk of recurrence, prevention is an important concern. In climbing, there are probably two main causes of shoulder dislocations: falls onto the ground or mats and attempting to hold on with one hand when a sudden slip occurs. In the case of falling, it seems likely that the incidence of dislocations will rise with the advent of higher indoor bouldering walls with more dynamic moves. It is imperative that boulderers learn to fall well and react quickly to an uncontrolled fall, taking it seriously as a risky situation. Shoulder dislocations have been described in situations when climbers attempted to hold on when the feet or other hand slipped off, especially in situations when they did not have full trust in their belayer or protection, or when simply too scared to fall even in a safe situation. In short, anticipation of the high risk moments in climbing is key. Strengthening the muscles which act on the head of the humerus (arm bone) may lessen the risk of the dislocation occurring in an injury situation, but probably only if this is combined with greater awareness of 'engaging' the shoulder muscles at appropriate moments in climbing. For those in the early years of their climbing, or who don't maintain a steady level of climbing form, this is probably best done by slowly building up volume of steep powerful moves on overhanging terrain. This should be combined with plenty of falling practice to ensure confidence is developed simultaneously. However, additional exercises for prevention of impingement syndrome (see above) may well be useful for preventing dislocations.

Initial treatment

If the shoulder is dislocated, there is significant pain, inability to move the shoulder especially moving the arm out to the side, and usually visible deformity of the shoulder. There may also be numbness in the arm.

It is important that the dislocation is reduced (returned to its normal position) quickly, but this should be done by a professional since there is a risk of nerve and increased ligament damage if correct procedure is not followed for the type of dislocation. 97% of all dislocations are 'anterior', but posterior and inferior dislocations are also possible. If a suitably qualified doctor cannot perform the reduction at the scene, it should be placed in a sling in its current position and reduced in A&E under anaesthetic. Afterwards, X-ray will confirm that the reduction was successful and will check for other injuries.

Post reduction treatment

The longer term treatment of shoulder dislocations in athletes is still controversial[65]. The shoulder is likely to remain unstable and significantly more vulnerable to further dislocations, especially during the same types of activities that caused the initial dislocation. The data on the incidence of further dislocations is striking. In non-sporting populations, the rate of recurrence is between 20 and 30%. It is likely this is because they are less exposed to high risk situations for dislocation and more willing to modify their activities to protect a vulnerable shoulder. However, in sportspeople the rates are very high, some studies reporting between 50 and 96% incidence of recurrence, depending on age and the type of sport played[149]. Younger athletes have significantly higher rates of recurring instability. It seems that a majority of young athletes require shoulder stabilisation surgery in order to continue sport at the same level, but some decide to change sports or continue at a much lower level. If you are over 25, the risk of recurring instability is substantially lower, but still significant. Unfortunately there has not been enough research in the area to provide a clear picture of the risk. One thing that can be gleaned from the research is that contact or overhead sports carry a greater risk. There is no research on climbers, but it seems plausible that the overhead and varied shoulder positions used while supporting bodyweight during dynamic movements would present a high risk of subsequent dislocations.

The best available advice following a first time, or subsequent, dislocation is to have a discussion with a good orthopedic surgeon specialising in the shoulder who is used to treating athletes, and is aware of the increased risk of recurring instability in this subpopulation. The mechanism of injury and age must be taken into account and there must be a frank discussion about your ambitions for future climbing. Opting for non-surgical treatment is likely to impact on your confidence in climbing, and may severely inhibit what you are able to do. Even if you opt for non-surgical treatment but continue to climb without hard training or regular falls in bouldering situations, there is the risk that a dislocation could occur during a route in a situation where this would cause significant danger (trad climbing, mountaineering). There are reported cases of this happening to climbers during easy trad leads, leading to serious fall and rescue situations. Another factor to consider is that subsequent dislocations may be accompanied by additional injuries such as labral or rotator cuff tears that will require surgery anyway. Since medical opinion differs on the best course of treatment, it may be useful to seek a second opinion.

Surgery involves tightening the shoulder joint capsule to reduce instability. Any other damage to the shoulder joint structures are repaired at the same time. Shoulder stabilisation surgery has been shown to be effective in substantially reducing the recurrent dislocations. The reduced odds of recurrent instability are difficult to judge given a lack of good research in this field. However, one review suggests that shoulders in athletes treated surgically are between 5 and 10 times less likely to suffer subsequent dislocation.

Non surgical treatment usually involves immobilising the shoulder for a period of time, followed by a rigorous programme of progressive strengthening of the muscles that control the shoulder. However, the research has so far failed to show that exercise therapy reduces the risk of subsequent dislocations. The length of the immobilisation period and content of the rehab program depends on the nature of the dislocation and if there was additional damage to the rotator cuff or labrum. There are also controversies in how to best treat a dislocation non-surgically. Traditionally, the shoulder is immobilised in a sling for either 3 or 6 weeks, with the arm in internal rotation (i.e. with the forearm held against the body). However, some studies suggest that a shorter time period or even no immobilisation at all gives equivalent results. There is some evidence appearing that immobilising the arm in a position of external rotation (forearm pointing outwards, away from the body) results in a significant reduction in risk of subsequent dislocations. Although this is a little less practical for activities of daily life, it may be worth it. A 2003 study reported a reduction in recurrence of dislocation from 30% using internal rotation to 0% using external rotation[150]. For those under age 30, the difference was even greater; 45% recurrence with internal rotation and 0% with external rotation.

Frozen Shoulder

The correct name for frozen shoulder is adhesive capsulitis. It is a common problem in adults, especially those over 40, with 2-3% of the population affected. The condition causes a gradual restriction of shoulder movement with the growth of fibrous bands and adhesions around the shoulder joint capsule. It is also a painful condition, and recovery takes a long time. However, diligent physiotherapy over several months can reverse it in most cases.

The causes are essentially unknown. Some people develop it slowly with no obvious cause, while others develop the condition after suffering some other traumatic shoulder injury such as rotator cuff tear or shoulder surgery. The shoulder capsule becomes thickened and the fibrous tissue which grows around the shoulder joint adheres to the rotator cuff tendons and the humeral head, limiting movement of the arm progressively over several months. The early stages of the development of adhesive capsulitis are also painful, although pain becomes less of a problem than limited range of motion (ROM) later on.

If caught early, aggressive mobilisation can limit progression of the condition, but for many cases the progression through the three stages of the disease (freezing, frozen and thawing) takes many months or even upwards of two years. A comprehensive and labour intensive program of physiotherapy, both home exercises and mobilisations with a therapist, are essential to regain pain free shoulder ROM. 90% of those who comply with the program of treatment report a satisfactory outcome in the end. If left untreated, at least half of sufferers will be left with limited shoulder ROM in the long term.

The physiotherapy program begins with gentle pendular swinging of the arm, mainly with the aim of reducing pain in the sensitised joint. Later, careful stretching, strengthening exercises and joint mobilisations begin to reverse the joint movement limitation. This must be done carefully under supervision in order not to irritate the joint further. Various other treatments are available such as manipulation under anaesthetic, which essentially breaks the bands of scar tissue. Hydrodilatation (injecting the joint space to stretch the capsule) can also be effective. Various treatments will probably have to be used in combination. Corticosteroid injections were also popular in the past for rapid pain relief, but as with its use for other conditions, the treatment is much less favoured now given its poor long term outcomes.

An important issue facing sufferers of adhesive capsulitis is the intensive nature of the treatment required. Good private treatment will likely lead to a better outcome, but large numbers of sessions may become expensive. However, for those involved in sport, treatment under state healthcare provision may not be aggressive enough to achieve the best and fastest possible resolution of symptoms. If you can find a good and supportive physiotherapist, be appreciative for their help and they may even take a special interest in offering you extra treatment or staying in touch with you, advising you on how to do the treatments by yourself or with a partner.

Thoracic outlet syndrome

Strictly speaking, thoracic outlet syndrome is not a shoulder injury. The problem originates in the neck and the symptoms (numbness and/or pain) are felt down the arm. However, it is posture of the muscles around the shoulder that cause the problem.

It appears to be fairly common among climbers. The main symptom is numbness in the hands and forearms, particularly on the ulnar side (little finger side of the hand). There may also be pain, exacerbated by any overhead activities, carrying heavy rucksacks or various sleeping positions. The problem occurs in an area of branching nerves travelling from the neck to the shoulder and supplying the arm, called the brachial plexus. The nerves pass through a narrow space behind the clavicle (collar bone) which is prone to becoming compressed by poor posture or muscle imbalance caused by participation in many sports. As well as nerve compression, there may be compression of an artery supplying the arm, resulting in coldness of the arm and white or even blue skin.

Holding the arms overhead usually provokes the symptoms, and the presence of the condition is usually consistent with a posture of depressed scapulae and poor shoulder range of motion. The treatment is to remove the cause by correcting the misalignment. The most important task is to elevate the scapulae by learning to hold the shoulders in the correct position and stretching posturally shortened muscles (often lats and pec major). Even a one-off session with a good physiotherapist will help you to appreciate the correct postural position. After this, religious practice of scapular repositioning, and stretching and strengthening of the muscles which have become misaligned is essential. Sufferers also find that stress exacerbates symptoms, probably because this contributes to postural strain, so controlling stress levels may help. Manipulation of the spine by a chiropractor, and soft tissue massage or trigger point therapy may also be useful, but always in conjunction with correction of the underlying postural causes[151]. Otherwise symptoms will only be kept at bay and are likely to return when you stop paying for the treatments. Your visit to a good physio is also essential to establish whether it really is thoracic outlet syndrome you have; there are other, less common nerve compression syndromes around the neck that also give similar symptoms.

Shoulder and neck trigger point pain

Painful trigger points appear to be a common problem associated with the various shoulder injuries discussed above. Although the primary pathology may be a connective tissue injury such as a rotator cuff tear or adhesive capsulitis, the rotator cuff muscles themselves may become painful. The mechanism for this is not understood. However, trigger points may become the main source of pain in some individuals. Pain in the muscle belly of the rotator cuff muscles which lie across the back and top of the scapula may indicate the presence of trigger points. Some of the rotator cuff trigger points may refer pain down the arm to the elbow.

Trigger point therapy (see section 4 for details) with continuous pressure or muscle stripping techniques may be of great benefit in relieving this pain and allowing normal muscle function to return. However, the benefit may be less likely to last unless the underlying causes of the original injury are addressed simultaneously. Track down a good therapist to help you assess whether you have painful trigger points and their precise location. After that you might be able to treat yourself with continuous pressure treatments.

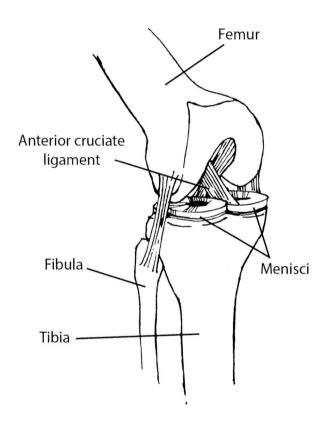

Femur

Anterior cruciate
ligament

Menisci

Fibula

Tibia

Lower body injuries

Section 11

The most common lower body injuries are generally better researched in sports medicine since they occur in many mainstream sports. Because the purpose of this book is primarily to present climbing specific information that is so far not widely known or accessible to climbers, I have not explored this area in great detail. However, there are a handful of lower body injuries that climbers commonly suffer which I have described so that climbers can be more aware of high risk situations and hopefully prevent their occurrence. The same diagnostic challenges apply for climbers who suffer a lower body injury; many are still routinely misdiagnosed or poorly treated by non-specialist medics or therapists.

Foot pain in climbers

Overly tight or poorly fitting rock-shoes are the cause of several painful foot injuries that climbers should be aware of. Prevention of most of these comes down to diligent experimentation with many different models when buying new shoes, and not persisting with painful shoes that were a purchase error. The pain of a foot injury will be the higher cost in the end. Common sense applies if you are wearing rock-shoes for half the waking hours of your life - it is no surprise that cramming your feet into tiny shoes causes problems in the long term. Taking them off while resting and wearing a slightly less tiny pair when maximum performance isn't critical or when the weather is warmer will help keep your feet healthy. Naturally, falls are also an important cause of foot injuries for climbers. Finally, if you must partake in that other injury plagued sport of running, some of the common running injuries may affect or even become worsened by climbing.

Plantar fasciitis

Plantar fasciitis is a very common injury in runners, and sometimes occurs in climbers doing lots of walking in the mountains or even from a nasty landing onto a hard surface from bouldering. It is pain in the sole of the foot originating from the tendinous fascia that runs from the heel bone to the toes, forming the longitudinal arch of the foot (Fig. 11.2). Pain is often felt under the medial (inner) aspect of the sole of the foot, near the heel. It is often most noticeable when getting out of bed in the morning, or after prolonged sitting. Those with either high arches or flat feet may be more at risk from developing the condition although it occurs in normal arches as well. A significant cause in climbers could potentially be reduced ankle range of motion and/or poor movement biomechanics following ankle sprains.

The causes of plantar fasciitis in the general population are not understood, and seem likely to involve several risk factors working together[152]. Just as with the height of the foot arch, research has failed to clearly show that other commonly blamed characteristics of athletes such as tight calves, loose calves, calcaneal (heel) bone spurs or 'overpronation' of the foot directly cause plantar fasciitis. Like many sports injuries with possible biomechanical causes, the faulty mechanics may be much more complicated that simply 'overpronation' and involve several joints of the body. Excessive pronation of the foot may be a risk factor for plantar fasciitis, but plenty of runners have excessive pronation but do not develop plantar fascia pain. Moreover, correcting excessive pronation will probably not be an effective treatment on its own for chronic cases.

Oversimplification of biomechanical faults may introduce more problems than it solves. This seems to be illustrated by the attempts of running shoe manufacturers over the past 30 years to design shoes that correct problems like overpronation and hence reduce injury development. Despite trying every conceivable design variation, injury rates in runners have remained just as high over this period, and no single design has emerged that demonstrates reduced risk of injuries such as plantar fasciitis.

However, there are two interesting findings from the world of running shoe design and injury research that are relevant for identifying and eliminating contributing causes of plantar fasciitis. Firstly, according to the prolific researcher and author in biomechanics and running shoe design, Benno Nigg, comfort seems to be pretty much the only aspect of a running shoe that leads to noticeable reductions in injury rates. If you walk into a 'good' running shoe specialist shop to choose a pair of shoes, much of the discussion from the sales assistants will probably focus on finding a shoe that corrects overpronation and returns the foot to a neutral position. While it is true that many people have pronated feet relative to the neutral position, there is no evidence that this directly causes injury. So the term 'overpronation' is a bit of a misnomer. Moreover, when 'overpronating' runners were given running shoes that countered the overpronation in a research study, they developed more injuries than runners who chose shoes based on comfort alone. From his career in studying the biomechanics of running and shoe design, Nigg's main recommendation to runners is to choose the shoe that is most comfortable[29].

Secondly, Nigg states that even if we could disentangle the immensely complicated biomechanics of human locomotion enough to point out exactly what was causing injury, it is still only a minor player in lower body injury development. The much more significant cause is likely to be the factors affecting the stress that must be absorbed by the foot per unit time: volume and intensity of training, rate of increase of training, running surface and amount and quality of rest. This is not to say that inadequate footwear cannot contribute to developing plantar fasciitis; it probably does. It is most likely to be just one of many contributing factors.

This seems to tie up with the fact that most mild cases of plantar fasciitis heal well with a little rest and then a resumption of training with a more modest progression. I developed plantar fasciitis after doing a lot of hill running in hillwalking boots. I chose sturdy boots to run in the tussocky grass and uneven bouldery terrain of the Scottish mountains because my battle scarred weak ankles needed the extra stability. It seems reasonable to conclude that the harder midsoles of my boots may have contributed to the plantar fascia pain. However, when I backed off and progressed the mileage of hill running more slowly (without changing the footwear - I had little choice), the pain disappeared. Perhaps the most important factor was that I acted to adjust the training

before the problem became more than an annoying niggle.

Plantar fasciitis sufferers will often allow the condition to progress to chronic degeneration which is much more difficult to recover from. It does also seem that some sufferers will not respond even if they do intervene early with rest and training modification. Since the causes are so poorly understood, it is not possible to say why this happens. There are many available treatments which should be used in combination to throw everything you can at the condition. Here is a list of treatments which either have some evidence behind them, or simply have a plausible mechanism to explain why they could work. Until the condition is better understood, this is the best advice on offer:

- Serious rest. Arguably the first port of call for a failure to recover from the initial appearance of plantar fasciitis is to rest, properly this time. Many runners consider 'rest' to be dropping their weekly mileage by 10%. This sort of reduction may be far from adequate. If 'relative rest' fails, total rest from long walking, running and climbing for several weeks, in combination with other therapies might work better. Resume training with a slow and cautious progression over many weeks.

- Stretching/splinting. Stretching the calves and plantar fascia seems be useful for many sufferers[153]. Remember to stretch both muscles of the calf musculature: gastrocnemius and soleus. Most people keep their knee locked and hence only stretch gastrocnemius. A separate stretch must be done with the knee bent to stretch the soleus. The plantar fascia itself can be stretched by placing your toes and the ball of your foot flat against a wall with your heel on the ground. By leaning forward the plantar fascia is stretched. For high arched sufferers, night splints are commonly used to slowly lengthen the plantar fascia while you sleep. The splint is known as a Strasbourg sock and there is some evidence that it provides improvements in symptoms.

- Orthotic arch supports. The research is

inconclusive on whether they are effective. There is also a powerful fashion among runners for barefoot running: the opposite of more support. The rationale is that this strengthens the foot structures and protects against injury. However, reviews of the research on barefoot running point out that there is no evidence that it reduces injury rates. Taping to support the foot arch may give temporary relief but is no substitute for rest and better training design.

- Friction massage. DTFM (deep transverse friction massage) may be important to break up the poorly arranged scarring in the plantar fascia and encourage the tissue to strengthen.

- Trigger point therapy. Some sufferers seem to have relief by using trigger point therapy of the muscles of the lower body, especially the calves.

- Pain relief. Analgesia using ice or NSAIDs could be important if used carefully. As with other injuries, if used to mask pain and carry on regardless, it will probably make things worse. NSAIDs may also interfere with tissue healing. However, short term pain relief may allow healing to progress and perhaps even reduce sensitivity in this chronic pain condition.

- Steroid injections. These often provide rapid short term relief, but have high recurrence rates, possibly because steroids cause atrophy of soft tissue. This is of particular concern for plantar fascia, since atrophy of the heel fat pad caused by poor injection technique can give permanent loss of function. The heel fat pad is an essential part of the heel anatomy for absorbing the impact forces of walking and running. The dangers of complications from steroid injections may be partially offset by using ultrasound guided injection by a sports medic who is well trained in the technique. It is also important that a minimum of injections are used and the treatment is used in combination with the other treatments, especially rest, in order that it gets the chance to actually work. Despite these precautions, steroid injections are not recommended by most researchers these days.

- Surgery. There are various options, with reasonable but far from ideal success rates. The most popular procedure is to cut the plantar fascia to lengthen it and relieve some of the pressure. There have been some good results reported from surgery which involves drilling into the heel bone to relieve pressure inside the heel bone. Surgery should be considered as a last resort and only when multiple rounds of the above treatments, especially rest and modified activities, have failed[153].

Photo 11.1 Calf stretch for gastrocnemius.

Photo 11.2 Calf stretch for soleus.

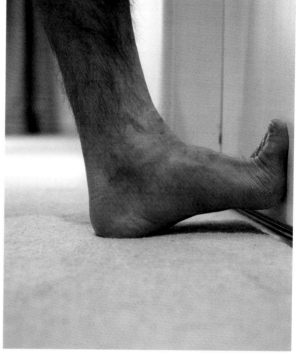

Photo 11.3 Plantar fascia stretch.

Other treatments which are sometimes offered by therapists such as standard sports massage, ultrasound, strengthening of various lower body muscles, and manipulating running gait seem to have at best disappointing and at worst no results in research. However, one thing that seems clear is that plantar fasciitis is a complex condition and when the most important treatments fail, it is worth trying everything as there are sometimes good results in individual sufferers. It may not be the actual treatment, but something else that you unwittingly did differently in the process that triggered improvement in the condition.

When you first realise you are developing plantar fasciitis, the first priority will be to have a think about what has caused it to come on. If there is a smoking gun such as starting a programme of running, running on different terrain, walking up a lot of mountains, new footwear, carrying heavier rucksacks or getting a job that involves lots of standing or walking, then take a break from these activities. Where that is impossible, at least modify them to reduce the stress. If the symptoms improve, reintroduce the loading more slowly. For fairly acute cases where a sudden cause brings on the condition quickly, a few days of complete rest followed by a few weeks of careful build up might be enough. If the damage is more severe or has developed over a long period, a couple of weeks of complete rest, followed by gradual return of training over 2-3 months might work. For chronic cases, several months of complete rest followed by over a year of gradual loading may be necessary.

The common reason for failure is probably inadequate understanding of the meaning of rest. To 'rest' injured runners go cycling instead, which can also irritate an injured plantar fascia. Occupational contributions such as standing all day, sometimes in uncomfortable shoes, are ignored, when they may be the main contributor.

Ingrown toenails

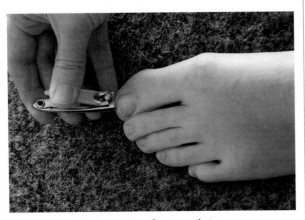

Photo 11.4 Toenail cutting technique.

Ingrown toenails are particularly common among sportspeople. The main causes are incorrect toenail cutting and sports shoes which are too narrow. Jumping and other explosive movements on the toes can also cause it. It is fair to say climbers are particularly at risk. The toenails should be cut straight across or to the shape of the toe, without cutting the sides too much. There must be no splintering at the edges and the nail must not be cut too short. Once the nail becomes ingrown, the splinter and any infected tissue can be removed by

your doctor with a scalpel. Climbers who repeatedly suffer from ingrown toenails despite giving previous occurrences a chance to heal and cutting their nails correctly, should consider experimenting with different rock-shoe models and sizes.

Heel pad bruising

The base of the heel is covered in a layer of elastic fatty tissue in the same way as the fingertips (Fig. 11.2). The fat pad acts as an effective shock absorber. However, hard landings or falls in poorly cushioned shoes can bruise this area. More substantial falls onto hard ground in rock-shoes, such as missing mats in bouldering or a violent swing in after a sport climbing fall can cause more serious damage. The fat cells are arranged in columns which bulge and spring back in normal landings. But they can rupture in falls and may recover poorly, causing pain and leaving the heel bone more susceptible to further bruising. The fat pad also naturally thins and becomes less elastic with age, regardless of injury. Taping the heel to prevent the heel pad spreading is a short term treatment. However, the most important treatment in both the short and long term is extra padding. This is straightforward in normal running shoes, but climbers with ongoing heel pain may need to use a shock absorbing heel orthotic in their rock-shoes to make them more comfortable to wear.

Sesamoid injuries

The flexor tendon running under the big toe contains two sesamoid bones (Fig 11.1) which sometimes become painful or injured in climbers. A sesamoid bone is one that is contained within a tendon. The largest sesamoid in the body is the patella on the front of the knee. The sesamoids under the bones of the foot absorb most of the weight on the medial side of the foot. They run in a groove and can become dislocated or fractured. I dislocated my sesamoid by landing on a sharp stone while running. However, as we will see below, the susceptibility

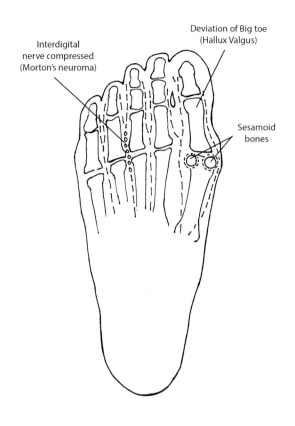

Fig. 11.1 Anatomy of the forefoot showing hallux valgus, sesamoids and Morton's neuroma.

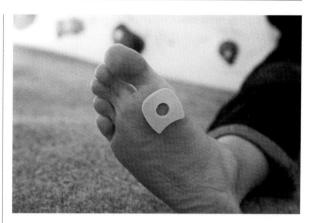

Photo 11.5 Ring shaped orthotic to relieve pressure on an injured sesamoid.

to this injury may have been secondary to many years of wearing tight rock-shoes. I have seen other cases of fractures from jamming cold-numbed toes into cracks or jumping down onto hard ground. Injured sesamoids produce pain under the ball of the foot, behind the big toe. Walking on the outside of the foot may be needed to relieve pain during walking. X-rays should be performed to assess whether the sesamoid is fractured. My own dislocation was x-rayed but the dislocation was missed. The doctor could only offer that my "foot looked weird".

Depending on the injury to the sesamoid, surgery may or may not provide better results than rest and foot orthotics and should generally be considered a last resort. A ring shaped orthotic can be placed on the foot to relieve pressure on the sesamoid. Alteration of walking gait and foot strike during running by 'gripping' the ground more with the toes may help to relieve pressure on the sesamoid. Some rock-shoe designs can also be very painful for injured sesamoids. For acute or stress fractures, sufficient rest is critical as sesamoid fractures are prone to non-union and subsequently much longer or incomplete recovery. Ongoing low-level pain from previously injured sesamoids can be managed by taking care to engage the toes and arches and avoid excessive foot pronation during walking, running and climbing.

Hallux valgus

Pain in the area of the big toe can also come in the form of hallux valgus, a big toe deformity which is usually caused by abnormal foot shape or hyper-mobility of the joint connecting the big toe to the foot (Fig. 11.1). Tight or ill-fitting rock-shoes may also be a contributing cause. In hallux valgus, the big toe is gradually deformed so as to point towards the second toe, with formation of a bunion at the joint. The sesamoid bones, which cannot move freely in their grooves in the base of the foot bones, cause erosion and pain. Eventually, the faulty movement pattern causes arthritic changes in the big toe joint or sesamoids. The main treatment for hallux valgus in sports with 'normal' sized footwear is to change to better fitting sports shoes and correct any overpronation.

A Dutch study interviewed 30 climbers about injuries relating to rock-shoe design[154]. While the incidence of foot injuries was generally greater with the higher level of climbing ability, all of the climbers showed evidence of hallux valgus development. It may be that hallux valgus is worsened in better climbers because of a combination of increased time spent in rock-shoes, together with a tendency to tolerate smaller and more painful shoes for the perceived performance advantage. The best prevention and treatment of the condition for climbers may be to experiment with different rock-shoe designs and take their shoes off between climbs more often. In severe cases which don't respond to the interventions above, surgery to remove the bunion and realign the toe may be required[155].

Morton's neuroma

Pain in the forefoot, most often near the third and fourth toes, may be swelling and irritation of the nerves that pass between the metatarsal bones, known as Morton's neuroma (Fig. 11.1). As well as pain radiating into the toes, there is often numbness, and pins and needles. The most common cause is overly narrow or short footwear, but excessive pronation of the foot is also an important cause. Removing the cause (the offending footwear) may resolve acute cases quickly. Padding under the metatarsals, in the form of specifically designed orthotics, may help to spread the load and improve symptoms. If pronation of the foot is contributing, a shoe orthotic can also be used to correct this. Severe cases occasionally need steroid injection or even surgery.

Ankle injuries in climbers

A large proportion of the climbing population in the 30+ age category is walking around with battle-scarred and weak ankles. Climbing can involve falling from ankle-destroying heights, a lot. Bouldering mats initially made things safer, until highballing became cool and the boulder problems just got higher. Indoor matting has got better too, but the height of bouldering walls has increased in parallel, as has the frequency of 'big last moves' to jugs that, just occasionally, spin. Part of the problem is that the foot is a lot less stable when crammed into a small rock-shoe and the foot cannot spread to absorb the impact. So falls that would be fine for skateboarders throwing themselves down sets of stairs or off walls in well padded sports shoes, are catastrophic for feet shod in tight rock-shoes.

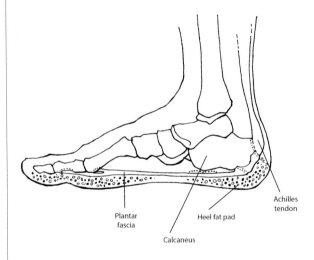

Plantar fascia

Calcaneus

Heel fat pad

Achilles tendon

Fig. 11.2 Anatomy of the rearfoot showing the heel pad, plantar fascia, Achilles tendon insertion and ankle joint capsule.

Generally speaking, the bone and ligament injuries in ankles are not career ending for climbers. Once you've got over the short term lay-off and rehab, they just leave you with a nuisance limitation in the long term. However, there are some exceptions. Cartilage damage in the ankle frequently occurs with falls from a height, and there are plenty of climbers who have been severely limited by having to get an ankle surgically fused after a fairly innocuous fall. Thus, prevention is important.

Prevention

If you are bouldering indoors, expect the unexpected. This doesn't mean altering your climbing much, if at all, from the 'gung ho' ideal of teenage males. It just means being ready for a hold to spin, anticipating and planning for a sudden fall, and reacting decisively to land like a cat. Those who boulder indoors but are scared to fall are arguably just as much at risk as the over-zealous. Fear tends to make you try to stay on beyond the point where the fall is inevitable, so you don't take control over the fall until it is too late to stop an uncontrolled landing. You also don't get enough practice with straightforward falls to learn to do it well.

Carrying huge mats around for outdoor bouldering can be awkward, but you might thank yourself for it. However, if your mat is several years old and the padding has degraded, it is going to be worse than useless for protecting your ankles. It will merely lull you into a false sense of security. If you are bouldering on someone else's mat, make sure you give it a good bounce to test its integrity and climb above it accordingly. It might pay to have a quick, controlled, practice jump from the crux of the problem you are trying before you totally go for it and come off out of control.

Leader falls on routes cause ankle injuries for climbers, too. A violent swing into the rock can have enough force to cause both fractures and ligament sprains. It is important for your belayer to give you a soft catch by moving appropriately as the rope comes tight. It may even be desirable to have more slack out so that you miss protruding rock features. If you don't trust that your belayer knows the score, climb accordingly or wait for another day.

Treatment

There are a multitude of possible ligaments and tendons to tear and bones to break in the foot and ankle, so your plan for treatment should follow a thorough diagnostic investigation with a professional. Serious ankle injuries are not always extremely painful. Badly sprained ankle ligaments (partial tears) are often more painful than complete ruptures. Similarly, it can be possible to walk on a broken ankle depending on the nature of the fracture. So, judging whether to seek immediate treatment based on pain and swelling is not a good idea. It is prudent to present at A&E for an X-ray even if you are able to walk. Make sure you mention the height you fell from, whether the fall was onto a mat or not. Climbers have a nasty habit of being so stoic that doctors sometimes opt to not bother with the X-ray, only for the problem to emerge on the next visit after a week of no progress. If a fracture involves the articular cartilage surface, this can have disastrous consequences.

For simple fractures, the ankle will generally be casted for six weeks, followed by rapid mobilisation and an aggressive program of physiotherapy. Six weeks of casting is essential for fracture healing. More complex fractures that occur with climbing falls, such as fractures of the talar neck may require surgical fixation. Unfortunately, the immobilisation period for healing fractures is not good for the surrounding soft tissue which atrophies rapidly. It is crucial to comply with your program of strengthening, stability and balance exercises, even though they can be a big daily commitment. If you are lazy with the exercises, the result may be weakness or tendon pain once you start to climb or walk in the mountains again, and much greater likelihood of suffering subsequent sprains. Exercising the healthy leg with one-legged cycling on an exercise bike has been shown to offset some of the atrophy in the injured leg while it is immobilised. So long as you are very careful, one-legged climbing will also be very useful for climbers for obvious reasons. It would also be a great way to make it a lot worse if you were silly enough to fall onto it or try to weight the affected leg.

The treatment for ligament damage depends on the extent of the injury. The common view that severe ligament damage can be a more serious injury than a simple fracture is true in many cases. Most ankle sprains result in damage to the lateral (outside) ligaments, with the anterior talofibular ligament the most commonly torn. If several ligaments have ruptured, surgery may be necessary, but there is some research that shows similar outcomes for surgical and non-surgical treatment. Recovery may be faster with surgery, and some multiple ruptures may result in long term instability of the ankle that will eventually require surgery anyway. It is important that the surgeon treats you as the serious sportsperson you are. Don't be afraid to book a private consultation for another opinion if you are not sure. It is an important decision.

The RICE protocol is important for most ankle sprains, which are often accompanied by a fair bit of swelling. Elevation, ice and compression will all help to limit swelling, as well as preparing the ankle for the first gentle sessions of exercise therapy. These methods are needed less once mobilisation has started, as movement is more effective at draining swelling from the area. However, ice and compression may still be required for pain relief and to limit post exercise swelling.

When exercise should begin depends on the injury. If it has been immobilised due to a fracture, exercises begin immediately after the cast is removed. For mild sprains, gentle exercises may be possible after a few days. Proceed under the guidance of a good physiotherapist. As with any sprained joint, the first task is to restore range of motion, followed by progressive strengthening exercises. Restoration of ankle range of motion can be a labour intensive task. Restoration of proprioception is especially important in ankle sprains. Wobble board/ cushion exercises are very important to improve long term stability and protection against future sprains. Progress from simple exercises to more difficult ones such as brushing your teeth while standing on one leg on the cushion, with your eyes closed. The research clearly shows that these exercises dramatically reduce chronic ankle instability and improve reaction time of the muscles which stabilise the ankle. Sufficient stress to tear ligaments in an inverting (rolling) ankle can build up within 0.1 seconds. In normal ankles it takes about half that time for the peroneal muscles to begin contracting in response. This reaction has been shown to be lengthened in injured ankles. Since it takes nearly 0.2 seconds for the peroneal muscles to build up to maximum tension, any deficit in their reaction time is likely to have a large effect on the risk of further sprains to a previously injured ankle[24].

Climbing provides a good rehab exercise for ankle strength and proprioception, once you are ready[156].

However, it is not enough on its own. It is important to follow through a complete progression of exercises to include dynamic and plyometric exercises in the later weeks of the rehab program. These include hopping, running in circles, figure of eights, plyometric jumps and other dynamic exercise drills.

Taping or using a brace on the ankle during rehab, and even during the later stages of remodelling when the ankle has regained most of its strength can be useful in preventing subsequent sprains. For common inversion ankle sprains, a 'stirrup' arrangement of tape or bracing has been shown to be effective. Run overlapping lengths of tape vertically from your inside leg, under your foot and up the outside of the lower leg, holding your foot upwards and outwards in the opposite direction from the sprain. Finish by wrapping tape around the ends of the stirrups to anchor them. And yes, shaving the ankle before applying the tape is a good idea. Contact dermatitis, where the adhesive in the tape (especially cheaper brands) irritates the skin can be a problem. An ankle brace such as the Aircast A60 may be a more practical alternative.

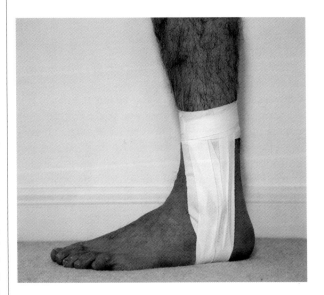

Photo 11.6 Stirrup taping to protect a healing inversion ankle sprain.

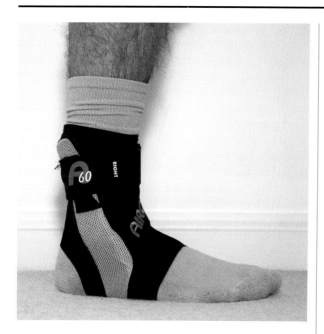

Photo 11.7 A commercially available ankle brace (Aircast A60).

Cartilage injuries

Probably the worst ankle injuries are those that involve the articular surface of the joints themselves. The cartilage that covers joint surfaces and allows the bones to glide over each other and absorb shocks does not have any healing capacity in adults. The challenges to treat and recover from joint injuries are complex and should be taken rather seriously. Cartilage injuries are comparatively rare because other structures such as bone and ligament generally break before the joint surface does. However, cartilage is most commonly damaged during unanticipated or uncontrolled falls which happen more quickly than muscle reflexes. Unfortunately, this is frequently the situation with ankle-spraining falls in climbing. I have suffered cartilage injuries in both ankles, from each of the most common situations for this injury in climbing. The first was in my left ankle when a hold broke while soloing. The other was after being lowered off the end of the rope by my belayer on a sport climb.

There are several types of cartilage injuries with different consequences in each case. Cartilage is composed mostly of water in a collagen matrix which behaves in a gel-like manner to absorb impact forces during movement. Cartilage has no blood supply or nerve fibres. It receives nutrients from the synovial fluid which fills the joint space. Cartilage tears which are partial thickness (do not extend down to the bone) tend not to heal in adults. If left untreated, they can cause long term degeneration of the joint and arthritis. Full thickness tears heal poorly with fibrous and bony tissue, but the flap of torn cartilage may still cause locking with twinges of pain and degeneration in the long term. When the damage involves a piece of the cartilage surface breaking off with some bone underneath, this is called an 'osteochondral fracture' (osteo - bone, chondral - cartilage). In teenagers, osteochondral fractures may heal well providing there is a sufficient (long!) period of non-weight bearing so the fragment does not become detached. In adults, surgery will generally be required and the technique used to repair the damage depends on the size and nature of the fracture[7].

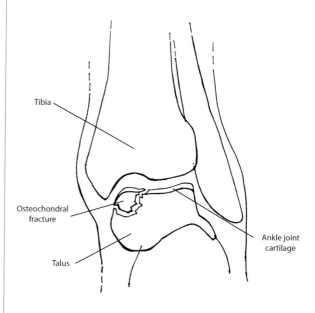

Fig. 11.3 Osteochondral fracture of the talus bone in the ankle.

A significant problem for cartilage injuries is that they are often missed at the initial presentation for treatment, sometimes with serious consequences. Torn flaps of cartilage are not visible on X-ray and are not always seen even on MRI scans. Even osteochondral fractures may be invisible on X-ray soon after the injury but will be visible if a further X-ray is taken several days later. It is important that you describe carefully to the doctor in A&E how the fall happened and that you were wearing very tight, non-padded footwear so that they carefully inspect the articular surface on the X-ray films.

When cartilage injuries are missed, the patient with a diagnosis of a simple ankle sprain is advised to proceed with weight bearing and exercises as soon as pain allows. With small cartilage tears, it is possible to make some initial progress with weight bearing and exercises. However, once walking and training activities resume after some weeks, progress fails and eventually this causes you to go back to the doctor reporting the unexplained pain deep in the ankle joint. This situation is referred to in sports medicine as 'the problem ankle', which basically means 'something has been missed or misdiagnosed'[13]. There are numerous possible causes of failure to progress with recovery from an ankle sprain or fracture. Small fractures of various bones around the ankle or chronic ligament instability are significant causes. However, cartilage damage is a frequent cause in climbers and, if suspected, it must be properly investigated.

Since many cartilage injuries will require surgery to allow the athlete to continue in sport at a high level, it is a serious setback if the diagnosis is delayed, especially if the athlete has already had several weeks of immobilisation for another fracture. If early weight bearing causes an osteochondral fracture to detach, this can affect the outcome even more. An MRI scan would prevent late discovery of cartilage damage accompanying an ankle sprain or fracture in many cases. So for those with the opportunity to get a scan, it may be a good idea to discuss this with your doctor, taking into account the circumstances of the accident, the level at which you climb, and the options (or costs) of getting an MRI scan.

If left untreated, torn flaps of cartilage or osteochondral fragments may come loose in the joint, causing locking, instability and pain. True locking of the joint is an indication for an urgent MRI. The symptoms are unlikely to improve and in many cases will get worse as the damaged cartilage degenerates and progresses to arthritis. However, the location and size of the damaged area is important in determining the long term outcome if left untreated.

Generally, non-surgical treatment is only advised for sportspeople if there is minor damage to the bone underlying the cartilage and no disruption to the articular surface itself. The treatment consists of non-weight bearing with passive movement of the joint, which helps to nourish the cartilage and prevent degeneration.

Surgical treatment generally involves scraping away damaged or torn cartilage ('debridement') and removal of any loose bodies floating in the joint space ('lavage'). There are several techniques used to encourage healing of the damaged area with new cartilage. In adults, the bone exposed where the torn cartilage is removed is drilled at 2-3mm intervals until it bleeds[7]. This allows a normal inflammatory healing process to occur. Stem cells from the underlying bone are allowed to come to the surface and heal into an adequate repair. The surgery can often be done as an arthroscopic (keyhole) procedure with no overnight stay in hospital. However, open surgery, despite its longer post surgical recovery, may allow the surgeon better access to the damaged area and thus make a better repair. Depending on the damage, there may or may not be a period of non-weight bearing after surgery, but return to sport is generally quite rapid. However, climbers must take care not to subject the joint to impact or shearing forces (jumping or falling) for around four months.

Unfortunately, the repaired cartilage is 'fibrocartilage' which is not the same as normal ('hyaline') cartilage which is found in joints[24]. Fibrocartilage is not so resistant to compression or shear forces as normal hyaline cartilage. Again, what this means for the long term outcome depends on the location and size of the original damage. If the damaged area is small and/or at the periphery of the joint, there may be few long term problems. There may or may not be longer term degeneration and appearance of arthritis symptoms many years or even decades down the line. More extensive damage to the articular surface may progress to painful arthritis much more quickly, causing significant limitation for any sport or activity. Where surgery has failed to prevent joint degeneration, fusion of the ankle may be necessary and there are numerous cases of this outcome in climbers.

Again, the location and extent of the damage is the key factor in determining outcome. The ankle joint itself (the top surface of the talus) seems to be able to function better with some disruption to the articular surface than other joints, because it is a very congruent joint. That is, the bones fit together very closely with movement only in one direction (moving the foot up and down). If the injury has been treated surgically but the damage is so bad that complete recovery is not possible, a careful approach to setting realistic goals may be the best way forward. Lots of walking or running, especially carrying loads, is likely to aggravate the joint more rapidly. However, climbing at venues involving less walking may be possible indefinitely, with few limitations. Careful choice of footwear and professional advice on orthotics may also be important in reducing the stress on the damaged joint, allowing continued participation and training despite the impaired joint. It is critical that your rehab program is supervised by an experienced sports physiotherapist in order to restore correct alignment and movement of the joint. If ankle joint mechanics are corrected, the force is well spread over the cartilage surface on the talus bone. However, even very small (1mm) deviations from ideal alignment causes huge imbalances in the force distribution which will wear the joint out much faster. Assessment and correction of joint mechanics definitely requires professional help and ongoing monitoring.

In teenagers, the situation is rather better. The body is able to repair cartilage damage with more normal cartilage, and osteochondral fractures will heal rather better. My own osteochondral fracture healed successfully, with no further joint pain over the following 15 years. However, it did require 3 months of immobilisation in a cast to prevent the fragment from becoming detached and was painful on long mountain days for the first year. If there are detached fragments of bone or cartilage in the joint space, these require surgery to be removed. The defect in the articular surface can be repaired using a graft of cartilage from the knee which gives good results.

Because of its inability to heal in adults, cartilage injuries are one of the more serious injury risks for climbers. Hopefully in the future, stem cell technology will improve to the point where a cure for cartilage injuries, and the resultant arthritis, is a reality. At the moment, stem cell therapy is still in its infancy although developments in the field are moving rapidly.

Ankle impingement syndrome

Gymnasts, footballers, ballet dancers and other athletes who land from jumps at the extremes of ankle range of motion all suffer from ankle impingement syndromes, and there are some reports of this occurring in climbers. The joint capsule becomes repeatedly trapped between the bones which are forced together at the end of their range of movement. The area becomes irritated with some pain and swelling, although this isn't usually debilitating. The repeated pressure on the bony surfaces at the edges of the joint cause bone spurs (osteophytes) to grow and these can be quite large. Eventually they may break off and come loose in the joint capsule. If they are large and unable to float freely, they may not cause symptoms and can be left as they are. However, if they do cause symptoms they must be removed by arthroscopic surgery. The surgery is a simple procedure with a short recovery, providing there is no additional damage inside the joint. I had a large ankle osteophyte which partially detached during a fall and had to be surgically removed.

Ankle impingement can occur at the front (anterior) or back (posterior) edges of the ankle joint. It seems plausible that climbers may suffer from either condition due to the diverse demands on the ankle from both climbing itself and from landing in bouldering falls. Posterior impingement syndrome can also be caused by irritation or fracture of the posterior process of the talus which can develop over time or break off to form a discrete 'extra' bone called the os trigonum. Posterior impingement syndrome can initially be mistaken for

Achilles tendinopathy, but it can be distinguished by the presence of pain when the foot is moved passively to its limit of plantarflexion (the foot pointing downward) by a therapist. Conversely, Achilles tendinopathy will produce pain when plantarflexion is actively resisted, such as performing a heel raise.

Achilles tendon pain

Achilles tendinopathy is one of the most common injuries in among runners, with a 52% lifetime risk of developing the condition in top level runners. The risk may be much lower (9%) among runners as a whole. Its contributing causes are still poorly understood. Interestingly, the injury was very uncommon until the 1950s and is still very rare in China. It has been suggested that modern lifestyles, resulting in both heavier bodies and longer periods of inactivity, even in sportspeople, could be to blame.

Climbing alone doesn't appear to cause many cases of Achilles tendinopathy, so a detailed discussion is outside the scope of this book. However, the Alfredson protocol for eccentric training therapy (180 reps of heel drops per day for 3 months) which is now being used to successfully treat many different tendons of the body was originally developed to treat degenerative Achilles tendons and this development appears to have offered significant improvements or cure for many long term sufferers in recent years. The development of the protocol is described in section 4. Eccentrics for Achilles tendinopathy take the form of heel drops; standing on the edge of a step and using the unaffected foot to raise up onto the toes, before eccentrically dropping the heel while weighting the affected leg. Extra weight, usually in a rucksack or holding a dumbell, is used to increase the loading to provoke some moderate pain in the tendon during the exercises and thus create sufficient stimulus for healing in the tendon. Crucially, the exercise must be adjusted depending on whether the pain is coming from the mid-portion of the tendon (the part of the Achilles most prominent above the heel) or the insertion, close to the junction with the heel bone. With mid-portion

tendinopathy, the heel drops should be performed through the whole range of motion, i.e. allowing the heel to drop below the level of the step. However, with insertional tendinopathy, which seems to be more difficult to recover from, results appear to be better when the heel drops are performed on a flat surface so that the heel cannot drop too far. It is thought that this avoids compression forces which may further irritate damaged tendon tissue at its insertion onto the bone. Perform 3x15 reps, morning and night, for both the gastrocnemius and soleus exercises. Minimally invasive scraping and sclerosing injections to obliterate the neovessels which form around the surface of chronically painful Achilles tendons which fail to respond to eccentric exercises is showing promising results in early trials[95].

Photo 11.8 Eccentric heel drop for Achilles tendinopathy, starting position. Note the knee is locked straight, targeting the gastrocnemius muscle. A rucksack is used to add extra resistance and the heel should be dropped slowly. Performing heel drops on a flat surface is recommended when the tendon damage is near the insertion onto the heel bone.

It is not uncommon for the Achilles tendon to rupture altogether, especially in middle aged runners with a history of Achilles tendon pain. Where the Achilles has ruptured, surgical repair lowers the risk of re-rupture in the long term from 15-20% to 1-4% compared with conservative treatment with a long program of physiotherapy[8]. However, surgery comes with a not insignificant 11% risk of other complications such as infection and altered skin sensitivity. For those wishing to return to sport at their previous level, surgery is more likely to be the treatment of choice. I know of one climber who opted for a year of conservative treatment following Achilles rupture only to re-rupture while walking up stairs, naturally opting for surgery the second time round.

Another type of Achilles pain that is relevant to climbers is calcaneal (heel) bursitis. The anatomy of the area where the Achilles tendon attaches to the heel bone is quite complex (Fig. 11.4). Behind the Achilles tendon, just above its insertion is the retro-calcaneal bursa, which allows the tendon to move freely over the heel bone. The tendon and bursa are closely integrated and pathological changes in one structure tend to affect the other. A proportion of the population have an unusually prominent rear edge of the heel bone, known as Haglund's deformity. It seems to predispose development of insertional tendinopathy in sportspeople. Tight rock-shoes obviously compress the Achilles tendon against the heel bone and may contribute to irritation of this

Photo 11.9 Eccentric heel drop, end position. Once you reach the end position, use the unaffected leg to return to the starting position.

Photo 11.10 Eccentric heel drop with knee bent to target the soleus muscle.

area. Some rock-shoe designs have an especially tight slingshot rand which makes matters even worse. As well as irritation of the retrocalcaneal bursa, the repeated rubbing of the shoe against the heel causes bursitis in the subcutaneous calcaneal bursa. This bursa lies between the Achilles tendon and the skin. Seemingly innocuous features of running shoes such as pull-tabs, stitching and even padding designed to relieve pressure on the Achilles seem to cause irritation here. Thus it seems logical that the extremely tight heel-cups of rock-shoes can cause the same condition. Perhaps the best treatment will be experimentation with different rock-shoes which are not so tight on the heel. Modification of the heel of the rock-shoe may also help: cutting off the irritating heel tab, loose material or stitching, or cutting away the heel over the affected area may reduce symptoms. It may be that cutting a few millimetres off the top of the heel cup, or even cutting a hole in the back of the heel may be required depending on the location of the painful spot. Alternatively, a horseshoe shaped rubber orthotic can be placed in the heel cup to relieve the pressure. Mild cases may resolve if you just change the offending shoes and give the heel a rest. Ignoring pain here is a bad idea because more advanced cases may need several months of complete rest from tight shoes, and possibly even surgery.

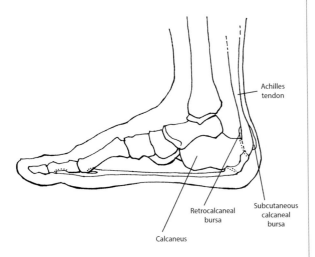

Fig. 11.4 The retro-calcaneal and subcutaneous bursa of the heel.

Finally, adolescents between 11-15 years old should look out for Sever's disease which gives pain in the Achilles area. It is sometimes misdiagnosed as Achilles tendinopathy, although the tendon can become diseased at the same time. Sever's disease is damage to the growth plate of the heel bone, immediately behind the Achilles tendon insertion. The treatment is a period of total rest followed by careful rehabilitation.

Knee injuries in climbers

The knee is a complex joint with a whole catalogue of possible injuries which are common in other sports, but outside the scope of this book. However, rock climbing does tend to cause three particular knee injuries which are worth a special mention. Drop knee moves and, less often, heel hooks or heel-toe locks are the most dangerous movements on the rock. Falls are also a common cause of knee injuries in climbers. Prevention of knee injuries in climbing may be difficult, as all these moves are essential in climbing. The following measures may help reduce the risk:

- It is challenging to strengthen all the ligament tissue around the knee because the movements of climbing are so varied. Drop knees, heel hooks, etc. are used comparatively infrequently by some climbers, yet demand large forces when they are used. Regular use of these movements throughout the year may be a protective measure to maintain strength and movement skill. Some basic functional exercises to strengthen the legs and knees may be important where a specific weakness has been identified. It will take a good physiotherapist to test reliably for these with manual muscle and stability tests. Applying generic, basic leg strengthening exercises may be too much of a shot in the dark and relatively ineffective compared to simply doing lots of varied lower body movements on the wall, either in normal climbing or in specific climbing drills.

- Ligaments are viscoelastic; they are stiffer if they are stretched more rapidly. At slow speeds, ligaments tend to pull a chunk of bone away (avulse). At faster speeds, the ligament itself tears. Thus, moves where you drop the knee and then move the hand all in one rapid motion may be particularly risky for knee ligaments.

- Ligaments are stiffer when cold, and more elastic or compliant when warm. Moreover, joint proprioception is poorer at lower tissue temperatures. Especially in bouldering, hard ascents are often done in cold conditions with the core body temperature, and especially lower limb temperature, rather low. Keeping the lower body and core temperature warmer may reduce the risk of tissue tearing and help increase moment-to-moment feedback and awareness of what is happening at the knee joint.

- Possibly the most important preventative measure of knee injuries in climbing is awareness and concentration during dangerous moves such as drop knees. A small part of conscious feedback should be maintained with the dropped knee even on the hardest moves. In other words, take the move seriously as a dangerous move and be ready to react instantly to let go if you feel an injury begin to occur. Awareness during the set up for the move may cause you to readjust and prevent the injury altogether. During the tenths of a second that it takes for the ligament tissue to tear, that awareness will help you let go of the tension quickly enough to reduce a potentially serious tear to a far more minor one. Often, once a ligament starts to tear in the knee, other structures will be damaged a fraction of a second later unless the force is removed.

- If a particularly deep knee drop is on a redpoint project, take a couple of non-committal tries, dropping off mid move, before fully committing to the move. This will help you learn the move and get a feel for whether it is safe and pain free.

Meniscus tears

Meniscal tears are a particular risk during drop knee or heel hooking moves and climbers should be aware of the risk presented by these moves. The menisci are elliptical pieces of cartilage inside the knee joint which add stability to the joint and help with shock absorption. A drop knee or heel hook move places a large force across the knee in an unusual direction. The edge of the meniscus can become pinched between the leg bones and either mildly frayed along its edge, or badly torn (Fig. 11.5).

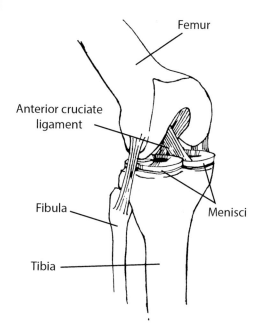

Fig. 11.5 The cruciate ligaments and menisci of the knee.

The pain experienced in the moment of injury varies greatly. Some small tears may cause no immediate symptoms but become painful and swollen over the next 24 hours. More serious tears are often accompanied by the feeling and sound of tearing in the knee and immediate pain. Pain can be reproduced by squatting or walking in a full squat position. The joint may lock and spontaneously unlock as the torn flap moves between the bony surfaces. The doctor will perform some manual tests such as McMurray's test or Apley's grinding test to help with diagnosis, but if a meniscal tear is suspected, an MRI scan will be required to see the extent of the tear and decide if surgery is needed.

Occasionally, mild tearing in certain parts of the meniscus with better blood supply can heal acceptably on their own. Some meniscal tears do not heal but cause no pain and do not require surgical repair. However, for painful tears, surgery may be beneficial to trim the frayed edges of the meniscus and stitch tears. Otherwise the frayed edges will tend to 'catch' in the joint giving pain and increase the risk of further tearing. Part of the surgeon's decision to opt for surgery comes down to the demands of the athlete. If you need full function, make sure you are emphatic about this during your consultation and point out that rock climbing involves regular deep twisting movements of the knee. The worst situation to be in is to avoid surgery when it ought to have been the treatment of choice to ensure your climbing activities did not cause further tearing. The length and content of the rehabilitation program depends on the extent of the tear, but return to climbing could be expected in 1-2 months following surgery. Damage to knee menisci causes the articular cartilage of the knee joint to wear out much faster, eventually causing osteoarthritis. Climbers with significant damage should be aware of this and choose their sporting activities carefully with advice from their orthopedic surgeon. Large volumes of mountain walking and running are likely to accelerate the development of knee arthritis.

Anterior cruciate ligament tears

Rupture or tearing of the anterior cruciate ligament (ACL) is a serious and common knee injury which unfortunately happens to many sportspeople. Over 100,000 ACL reconstruction surgeries are performed in the USA every year[157]. Chris Sharma had an ACL reconstruction early in his career (age 16). The ACL runs through the centre of the knee joint and is essential for providing stability during many knee movements.

The ACL is one of four knee ligaments that stabilise the knee (Fig. 11.5). It is the most commonly injured and the most likely to need surgical repair since it has very poor healing capacity. When a tear occurs there is often a snapping or popping noise with immediate pain. The knee tends to swell and often has a feeling of being unstable and prone to giving way. Diagnosis is frequently missed by many medical professionals and many cases only come to light after symptoms of instability persist for many months after the initial injury. One study from 2004 suggests that correct diagnosis was only made in 13% of cases at A&E departments, 30% by those seen by their GP and in 57% seen by an orthopedic consultant[65]. This clearly underlines the need to be seen by a consultant specialising in sports injuries, or the knee joint in particular. There are a range of manual tests that should be performed to assess whether the ACL is intact. If a tear is suspected, it may be confirmed by an MRI scan. Lack of awareness of the manual knee stability tests among doctors and the need for MRI scanning may be why to so many tears are being missed, with disastrous consequences for sportspeople. Another reason may be that the knee is assessed acutely, while still swollen and painful. Even if the tear is not apparent at first, you should have a further assessment at a later stage, especially if you do not have an MRI scan.

In sports involving running and jumping, ACL ruptures seem to happen during normal, regular movements, but especially those involving twisting over a planted foot or suddenly decelerating. In climbing, it tends to happen during heel hook or drop knee moves, but also during seemingly innocuous drops onto bouldering mats. In the latter situation, it could be that landing on straight locked knees or failing to judge the angle of slope of the mat or ground surface may precede the injury. Walking in powder snow through bouldery terrain is also a high risk situation, especially with a heavy rucksack. A meniscal tear will often occur at the same time as the ACL tear.

The main thing climbers can do to help prevent ACL tears is to build up specific strength across the knee by making sure their climbing involves the full spectrum of foot moves, performed in a controlled manner, on a regular basis, e.g. drop knees, heel hooks, rockovers, toe hooks and heel-toe bars. Too many climbers do not perform enough of these moves and are thus weaker across the knee than they should be, and are vulnerable to making technical errors that cause knee injuries. Boulderers should also take landing onto mats seriously, as ACL tears do happen in the most innocuous of falls. They should also practice how to anticipate and react to falls quickly, and to land well.

Treatment

ACL sprains which do not involve a full rupture can require surgery to completely restore function. However, even if the ACL has ruptured completely, surgery may not be the mandatory treatment. It is possible for the knee to function without the ACL if sporting activities are restricted and a knee brace is worn. Thus, during the consultation, the surgeon will ask about your level of involvement in sport and use this to help decide whether to operate. Older athletes who are sometimes happy to reduce the sports they do may opt to avoid surgery, and can still do some types of exercise such as running and cycling. But most younger athletes who want to continue pushing themselves in sport opt for surgery. Only 18% of those with ACL injuries treated conservatively are able to participate in 'very stressful' sports. Since climbing involves lots of twisting and application of force in many directions across the knee, surgery would likely be considered for a climber.

Surgery generally involves reconstruction of the ligament using tissue from the hamstrings or patella. Both surgical techniques seem to give good results, and the choice is usually down to the preferences of the surgeon and patient. Usually, the surgery is performed 4-6 weeks after injury to allow the joint inflammation to settle. There is a lengthy and intensive rehab program to be followed for 6-12 months after surgery to strengthen the reconstructed ACL, so it can cope with the demands of sport. Compliance with the regimen is essential to secure a good outcome. Beyond that, maintenance of good strength of the muscles across the knee and extra care to 'engage' the muscles during an aggressive move such as a heel hook will be the order of the day for climbers[151].

Conservative management of ACL tears basically involves wearing a knee brace for sport and avoiding sports or activities with knee twisting since the knee will have ongoing instability. Intensive physiotherapy to build strength, especially in the hamstrings, and to improve proprioception is also important. Absence of a functioning ACL is associated with the development of osteoarthritis of the knee. 20% of sufferers have significant cartilage degeneration after 10 years, rising to 35% after 14 years. There is also a higher risk of subsequent meniscal tears. Since these often require surgery, avoiding surgery for the initial ACL injury will be a false benefit for these people. There is poor and conflicting evidence for any beneficial effect of wearing a knee brace to stabilise the knee.

The available data suggests that non-surgical treatment for all but minor tears of the ACL is not very attractive for climbers. It seems likely that the risk of instability or further injury would be too high, given the demands of many rock climbing movements on the knee. However, surgical treatment does appear to give good results for many athletes in different sports. Provided the injury causes the climber to address strength deficits in the knee and use excellent technique with heel hooks, drop knees and other strenuous knee movements, it seems to be possible to continue to climb with little if any long term limitation.

Medial collateral ligament tears

The medial collateral ligament (MCL) stabilises the inner part of the knee and is placed under great strain during drop knee moves, especially very deep drop knees. The MCL is a large ligament and different parts of it are under tension, depending on how much the knee joint is flexed. Tears during drop knees are usually partial and the ligament tends to heal better than other knee ligaments such as the ACL. The length of the rehabilitation depends on the severity of the tear. Minor tears may only require a few weeks of restricted climbing (no drop knees or jump landings). More serious tears will require progressive loading for many weeks or months before normal climbing can begin.

A partial tear will cause pain across the inside of the knee joint, some swelling and possibly some instability in the knee, especially when it is flexed. Thorough diagnostic testing must be performed by a physiotherapist to exclude damage to the menisci and other ligaments on the medial side of the knee. The extent of laxity in the knee is the primary measure of how badly the ligament is damaged and will dictate the progression of rehabilitation. Complete rupture of the ligament may be less painful than a partial tear, with no end point to the laxity in the medial aspect of the joint. The posterior oblique ligament lies close to the MCL, and if ruptured may need surgery to heal properly. If damage beyond the MCL is suspected, an MRI should be performed to establish which structures have been injured. I suffered a partial MCL tear during a deep drop knee move on a climbing wall. At the moment of injury, I heard two small cracking noises. Only once the injury had settled after a week was it established that I also had a partial tear of the semimembranosus tendon (one of the hamstring muscles).

Treatment of even complete tears is usually conservative since the outcome is as good as with surgical repair. Progress through the stages will be dictated by the extent of the damage. In my own case, I was able to begin gentle walking from day one while still following the RICE protocol to reduce swelling. Once I was able to move the knee through its whole range of motion without pain, after two weeks, I could begin running, and climbing without drop knees. However, full restoration of strength for deep drop knee and heel hook moves still took several months. A hinged knee brace may be useful during the early stages to prevent re-injury. This may be particularly important for climbers using easy and restricted climbing as part of the rehab process to at least partially replace the basic functional exercises used in generic physiotherapy programs. Since climbing does not require competitive match play, it is easier and more motivating to use its movements to gain strength. However, this is balanced against the risk of over-stressing fragile, healing tissue and re-injuring it.

Progress through physiotherapy can be split into four distinct phases. The decision to move to the next stage, and how much exercise should be undertaken, depends on the injury and you should plan this with a physiotherapist and make adjustments based on symptoms.

Phase 1 - Use the RICE protocol to reduce swelling and progress to full weight bearing and normal walking. Gentle exercises such as unweighted knee flexion, supported 2-leg calf raises, hip abduction/extension and gentle hamstring exercises.

Phase 2 - RICE protocol may still be required. Progress to straight line jogging if the swelling has subsided, swimming (no breast stroke), and road biking with a hinged knee brace. Some climbing may be possible too, on a top rope with no bouldering falls. Basic exercises should be progressed to include partial squats and lunges, single leg calf raises, step-ups and single leg balance exercises.

Phase 3 - Increased load of running/swimming/biking/climbing and introduction of agility drills such as fast running, jumping, hopping, changing direction.

Phase 4 - Controlled climbing drills involving drop knee, body tension and heel hook moves on steep terrain, gradually progressing to normal climbing.

Previously injured MCLs may well continue to be vulnerable to re-injury even after healing is apparently complete. Even more care than normal should be taken during aggressive drop knee moves. While normal function should be possible on the vast majority of moves with care, it may be prudent in some cases to avoid the occasional move that feels particularly 'wrong'.

Hamstrings tear

Damage to the hamstrings muscle is a very common injury in running, but also occurs in climbers from hard heel hook moves. An acute tear sometimes happens, but often it can take the form of low-level, lingering pain around the back of the knee, and may be more reluctant to resolve in climbers who run. Manual therapy appears to be effective in stimulating healing, although failure to respond may indicate a more complex injury here, such as damage to the polpiteus muscle, polpiteal bursitis, or a lateral meniscus tear.

Hernia

There is a long list of potential causes of groin pain in athletes. Pain can come from muscles, tendons, bursae, fascia, nerves or joints in the abdominal area. Since climbing involves forceful contractions across the hip joint and movement in many complex directions, there are many possible diagnoses that must be explored to identify the cause of pain. However, hernia is a particular concern since it seems to be a particularly common injury.

Surgical repair of abdominal hernias is the most common operation performed in general surgery, with 80,000 operations in the UK every year (700,000 in the USA). In sportspeople, true hernias are comparatively rare, where the abdominal contents bulge through a complete tear in the abdominal wall. The lower part of the abdominal wall is formed from a sheet of tendon arranged in three layers. Tearing in one layer, without obvious bulging, is known as the 'sportsman's hernia' and it appears to be a common injury in many sports, and does occur among climbers. Repetitive kicking is a frequent cause among footballers. In climbing, footwork involving stabilisation of the lower body places stress on this area. Moves such as holding the swing while cutting loose or walking in uneven winter mountaineering terrain with a heavy rucksack are likely stressors.

There is usually a slow onset of groin pain that worsens with certain aggravating movements. As mentioned above, careful examination and manual testing is essential to establish the exact location and cause of the pain. Sportsman's hernia does not tend to respond to conservative treatment and surgery is usually necessary[158, 159]. If you take a long lay-off from sport, the symptoms usually subside, only to return when sport is resumed[159]. The surgical procedure has improved a lot in recent years, often using laparoscopic (keyhole) rather than open surgery. Today, a polypropylene mesh is usually introduced over the damaged area to support it, instead of simply stitching the defect together[160]. This results in more rapid post surgery rehabilitation and fewer recurrences[160]. Footballers are usually back to match play after 4-6 weeks. However, there are some reports of recurrences in the scientific literature, with the suggestion that incorrect or incomplete diagnosis of the damage may be involved in some cases. I had symptoms of a sportsman's hernia, but on examination, the surgeon felt the damage was too high to be located in the tendinous part of the abdominal wall. Rather, the damage was in the muscle belly and thus healed without the need for surgery. This experience underlines the need to see a good surgeon used to treating athletes in order to ensure a tailored treatment plan.

Further reading

Section 12

Further reading

It should be clear from this book that becoming the expert on your own injuries is an essential part of sustaining a lifelong career in climbing. Below I have collated a small list of textbooks that really should be on the shelf of every 'lifer' in climbing. They will allow you to match symptoms with potential conditions and take action early before things become worse than they need to be. I have also made some notes on using the web to track down reliable information and new research.

A good reference library for a climber

Brukner, P., K. Khan, *Brukner & Khan's clinical sports medicine*. 4th ed. Sports medicine series. 2012, Sydney ; New York: McGraw-Hill. xlvii, 1296 p, ISBN: 978-0070998131; An excellent and comprehensive reference covering injuries in all the areas of the body. It also contains a useful explanation of basic physiology and sports science for those unfamiliar with the subject. Essential on every climber's shelf.

Sahrmann, S., *Diagnosis and treatment of movement impairment syndromes*. 2002, St. Louis, Mo.: Mosby. xiii, 460 p, ISBN: 978-0801672057.

Specific or specialist textbooks

Simons, D.G. and Travell, J.G., *Travell & Simons' myofascial pain and dysfunction: the trigger point manual*. 2nd ed. 1999, Baltimore: Williams & Wilkins. v. 1, 2, ISBN: 978-0683307719; The leading text on muscle trigger point pain and trigger point therapy, but very detailed and may be difficult to use for some.

Kendall, F.P. McCreary, E.K. Provance, P. G. Rodgers, M. M. Romani, W. A., *Muscles: testing and function in posture and pain*. 5th ed. 2005, Baltimore: Williams & Wilkins. 479 p, ISBN: 9780781747806. A classic reference text with extensive details on how to test individual muscles of the body (useful in diagnosis) and a clear discussion of many human postural faults.

Baker, C.L. and Plancher K.D., *Operative treatment of elbow injuries*. 2001, New York: Springer. ISBN: 978-6610188086; Detailed discussion of the various surgical options for serious elbow injuries, including assessment of likely surgical outcomes and factors which influence this.

Butler, D.S. and Moseley G.L., *Explain Pain*. 1st ed. 2012, Noigroup Publications. 129 p, ISBN: 978-0975091005; A fantastic explanation of pain and how it affects us. Essential reading for anyone suffering a chronic pain syndrome.

Maffulli, N. Renstrom, P. Leadbetter, W.B. *Tendon Injuries, Basic Science and Clinical Medicine*. 2005, London: Springer. 332 p, ISBN: 978-1852335038; A cutting edge sports medical reference produced by prolific researchers in the field. Definitely for those with an advanced medical interest in the subject. If that doesn't put you off, the £200 price tag might.

Online resources

Good, reliable and relevant resources online for climbers are surprisingly hard to find. It is fair to say that the bulk of websites offering sports medicine information suffer from the same problem as clinical medicine: failure to update outdated advice, and failure to offer more than very general advice, mainly on treating symptoms.

Thus, searching online for comprehensive yet reliable and up to date advice is a challenging business. The main skills required are to resist taking any single source at face value and to use each source as a stepping stone to get closer to the original scientific research, or to identify prominent researchers to explore. This goes especially for advice posted on public internet forums, which should be treated with heavy suspicion of error, bias, ignorance or vested interest until proven otherwise by exploring the information more thoroughly elsewhere. They can occasionally be useful as a starting point, but beware!

Peer reviewed scientific journal articles are the best source of reliable information. However, building a picture of how to treat an injury from journals alone is a labour intensive task and might prove too difficult for those unaccustomed to digesting medical research. Where possible, seek out systematic review articles to get a clear picture of where the research is at right now and how the evidence from numerous small studies adds up to give balanced picture of the strength of evidence. Review articles are generally easier to read than raw research if you are not used to them.

Unfortunately, many scientific journal papers are hard to access unless you are a student or staff at an academic institution and have an 'Athens' or other relevant pass to access the full text of a wide range of scientific journals in biomedical and life sciences. If you don't have this access, you might be able to ask a friend or tutor who does to help you find papers on specific injuries.

Google can be useful to quickly find journal articles which are available full text for free online. Pubmed (www.pubmed.com) is a far more specific search engine to locate specific journal articles or explore a particular research subject such as eccentric exercise for tendinopathy.

A few particular researchers are worth singling out. Volker Schoffl, based in Bamberg, Germany, is the leading researcher on climbing injuries, especially finger injuries. He has published scores of articles detailing treatment of pulley injuries, growth plate fractures of the fingers and other injuries in climbers. Nicola Maffulli and Hakan Alfredson are two prolific researchers in the field of tendinopathy, and their work on tendinosis of the Achilles, patellar and elbow tendons has advanced the field immensely.

Finally, I have produced several online videos to demonstrate some of the treatments and climbing specific practical and technical skills I have explored in this book. You will find them, along with regular posts on new research and climbing performance at www.davemacleod.com

Getting access to good care

In the UK, the National Health Service still offers a great level of general medical care on the whole, given the pressures of ever increasing costs of care. However, the level of care is highly variable and in places falls far short of optimum. Climbers should be clear that it is not sports medical care. Many sports injuries will not be treated aggressively, if at all.

Good care can often be found and readily provided through the NHS if you are informed and prepared to argue your corner. A good relationship with your GP is a good place to start. Advice on how to make the most of your visits to your GP is in section 1. If you can find out in advance the name of a consultant who is an expert in your injury, it can often be possible to get a referral to see them, even if they are geographically remote.

Waiting times for surgery on the NHS can be disastrous for fitness and rehabilitation and contribute to a poor outcome. Physiotherapy care can at worst be non-existent. On the other hand, you might get lucky. It's up to you to decide whether getting lucky is a risk you can accept.

There is the option of private care, but for many in the UK, it is not even on their radar. There are a few reasons for this. For some, it's an ideological bridge too far. We already pay for the NHS, after all. Anyone would be sympathetic to this viewpoint. The other side of the argument is that one must be realistic about the limitations of the NHS. You only get one sporting career, so perhaps life is too short to deny yourself better care if you can afford it, even if it 'feels wrong' to have to pay extra for this. Affordability is the second reason private care is not considered by many. It's true that some treatments can be extremely expensive. However, it is definitely worth an hour of your time to find out exactly how expensive. In some cases you may be surprised to find it is not that bad. Moreover, switching to private care does not need to mean abandoning NHS care altogether. Usually, dealing with a sports injury involves several stages (e.g. GP, referral, consultant visit, scanning, surgery, physiotherapy). In many cases, dipping in to private care for one or more of these stages can not only be affordable, but ensure the best of both worlds: a solid diagnosis from an expert and prompt treatment where this is vital to the outcome.

For instance, If you need to see an orthopedic consultant specialising in a particular injury, the waiting list to see them on the NHS might be very long. Conversely, once they've seen you, the list for surgery might have a much shorter wait. Thus, you might be able to see the same consultant for £120-£150 privately within a week instead of three months, but still have the surgery on the NHS. Alternatively, it may be the wait for an MRI that holds up the process. MRI waits can be appallingly long for many sports injuries. It may be difficult to even get an MRI if it is not considered a serious enough medical problem by NHS standards. Private MRI scans vary wildly in price depending on the area to be scanned and the number of images required. Again, it is worth enquiring so you can make an informed decision. Note also that the quote may not be the final price. I was quoted £700 (2012) for an ankle MRI when enquiring via a private health care provider's call centre. But when I rang the hospital directly, I was quoted (and paid) £300.

A further consideration for those needing an expensive surgical procedure such as an ACL reconstruction is to source private treatment abroad. Many athletes from other sports regularly buy treatment on the European continent and further afield in countries such as India where the standard of care can often be very high but costs much lower than in the UK. Again, careful and thorough research into every aspect of the treatment is essential to make sure you know exactly what you are going to get.

If you are able to bear the cost, there is often a strong argument to take advantage of prompt treatment by the best experts available. Private health care companies are generally straightforward to contact for a quote for most treatments. Private health care insurance is also worth considering, although you must be very wary of the small print of health care policies which can have some nasty surprises in the exclusions section. If your employer provides, or might be persuadable to provide private health insurance for you, do it! It ought to be a good proposition for many employers; a healthy, happy employee does her best work.

Private sports physiotherapy (as well as podiatry, chiropractic, massage and other therapies) is increasingly readily available today. Where possible, choose a specific individual therapist (rather than just practice) by recommendation, to make sure you are seen by the most senior and skilled professional available. If you are lucky enough to find and see someone really good, build a good relationship with them. They are worth their weight in gold. See them as often as you can afford: it is money well spent. Good therapists truly want to see you overcome your injuries. They will spend extra time with you, send you information, keep in touch to monitor progress and generally bend over backwards to help you. But you have to make the investment in the relationship first.

The author's tale of woe/hope

As I write, at age 36 with 20 years of climbing behind me, 10 as a semi-professional climber, I carry more battle scars than I can even remember, and some fairly serious ongoing injury problems that affect how I move on mountains and rock every day. On the whole, I feel that I am doing pretty well and have been fortunate. Athletes in so many other sports, with good reason, consider age 35 to be positively geriatric for high level involvement in sport and training. Even more remarkable then, that like so many other climbers I have hit the ground from great heights several times and come through several years of repeated finger and chronic elbow injuries.

Climbing is quite hard on the body compared to many other sports. But it has two important things going for it: its variety as an activity and the freedom to reach your climbing goals whenever your body happens to be ready. The scheduled nature of other sports often dictates that training must be done according to a calendar and not according to feedback from the body. Being able to listen to your body and respond accordingly allows you to get away with a lot.

It is one thing to read all of the laborious, scientific details which fill this book, and another to hear the personal stories of others who have come through injuries to achieve their climbing goals. Overcoming climbing injuries requires a huge range of skills and strengths of character, which is why this book covers so many disparate fields. In the following paragraphs, I'll describe my own accomplished climbing injury career and try to highlight some key good decisions and lessons that were learned after a lot of mistakes.

My first climbing injury arrived at age 16, one year after starting to climb. It was a strain of brachialis or brachioradialis in my elbow, sustained after being challenged to an arm wrestle at school. Before this I was aware that climbers could get injured fingers or elbows and had to take long periods off climbing. The idea sounded terrifying, but at least injuries were something that happened to other people, usually old people. So when I found myself unable to climb for three weeks due to elbow pain, it felt like an eternity and served to make me even more scared of injuries. I was lucky to learn early that stupid feats of strength are, well, pretty stupid.

Still aged 16 I noticed an aching pain in my finger while bouldering over the course of a couple of sessions. I just ignored it. I let it get worse and worse until it stung so badly that pulling on crimps felt slightly nauseating and I gave in and admitted there was a serious problem. The A2 pulley tear I had must only have been partial. I was lucky I didn't rupture it altogether by ignoring it for two weeks. I went to my GP. He told me to take six weeks off. I was a 16 year old kid and he was my doctor, I trusted his advice 100%. Six weeks later I went back to tell him it felt exactly the same. He told me to take up a different sport. I'll never forget walking away from the clinic with a sense of total confusion. This just didn't seem right. In many ways, it was a defining moment in my transition to adulthood. I understood that there had to be something more and no one else was going to hand me the answers on a plate. I would have to take control by becoming the expert and understand that no single source of advice could be trusted implicitly.

The best place I could think of to access specialist sports medicine information was the Glasgow University Library book shop. I sat in a corner on the floor for two days and read everything I could find. After two short days I was much more in control, understanding the anatomy of the pulley system, the concept of progressive rehabilitation, the normal timescales for ligament healing, that increasing blood flow to the area may accelerate healing and that maintaining general fitness and sport skills will accelerate the return to form. All of a sudden, I had gone from sitting bored in despair at home to wondering how I would fit all the necessary rehab activities in. Moreover, simply knowing how long the recovery might take was so much better than not knowing. Before this, I wondered if my climbing could be over.

In the following two months, I still missed rock climbing movement desperately. But I had a whale of a time on the whole. I climbed mountains, had great adventures going out in bad weather, got fit, trained to be able to lock off on one arm and eventually do four one arm pull-ups and sat with my hand in countless pots of cold water. The routine of cold water treatment helped give me a sense of doing something every day that would add up to recovery. By pure coincidence, I also got another part of my rehab right. I cut myself off from crags and climbing walls 100%. I knew that the temptation to pull hard would likely send me backwards. However, I had my own little climbing wall, of sorts. I'd cut holds in the thick bark of a big tree in my mum's garden. Each day, I'd test the strength of the healing finger, with just a few pulls or problems. These were always done in a controlled and careful fashion, since it wasn't 'real' climbing and free from the influence of others. Only when I could climb my model of 'Hubble' (it was probably V8!) with no pain or tenderness the next day, did I dare venture back to my home crag of Dumbarton Rock. On my very first session back, I shocked myself by easily climbing two V8 projects I had been failing on before the injury. I sat on the train home on an indescribable high, one of the best of my climbing career. Not just because I was back to climbing and back to form, but because I had managed my rehab well and made it a success.

In my later teenage years, I suffered intermittently with pain around my brachioradialis muscles across the elbow. It wasn't a huge problem, but it did make me have to hold back a little in my climbing (which by modern standards was not very intense anyway, with plenty of rest days). This time, however, my searches for information on this very climbing-specific injury threw up virtually no information. It was only many years later that I discovered that more gentle progression of training intensity and maintenance of muscle balance across the elbow eliminated this constant bugbear for me.

Then, in my late teens and early twenties, I went through a most frustrating period of pulley injuries, one after the other, for five years! I lost count of how many I had, but it was definitely over 20, in all my fingers. I had a lot of time off, which became unbearable. Eventually I was driven to try and climb anything that didn't hurt. It was only then that I discovered that climbing completely openhanded, although it took a lot of discipline, still allowed me to push myself in a careful way while my injured pulleys healed. I had previously been one of the majority who crimped everything small. But after this experience, I found my openhanded strength had gone from zero to my preferred grip type for more than 50% of first-joint holds. In the subsequent decade, I have had only one or two very minor pulley tweaks, both from sudden slips while in hot and humid climbing walls. The openhanded strength also added a couple of grades to my climbing level.

At age 20, I had my first fall to the ground from a height. I top-roped what I hoped would be my first gritstone E8 six times in a row. Then, I pulled the rope and soloed it, only for the pebble on the crux to snap off. The ground was hard. My left ankle was the size of a football within ten minutes and I found myself in an orthopedic ward being told that I'd be spending three months in plaster and would likely get arthritis in my ankle within ten years. The lesson? Hard unprotected trad is dangerous. Do it enough and you will pick up injuries that could affect you forever. It is a balance of risk and reward I have tackled ever since. The experience of nearly a year to get back to climbing form gave me a deeper respect for life, mortality and the time it takes to become a solid trad leader. Who can tell, but perhaps if I hadn't had a serious, but not life threatening fall, something worse may have happened soon afterwards.

I was assigned to an NHS physiotherapy program for six weeks when I came out of plaster which proceeded to fail me miserably by simply ultrasounding me for a few minutes and standing me on the wobble board for a few minutes more while the physio went for a cup of tea. By

then I ought to have known better. But I failed myself by trusting the 'expert' again and being lazy with the exercises at home. The result was a permanently weak and inflexible ankle, which still fails to do what my right ankle can do to this day. What a stupid mistake.

After a year with a burning, aching foot I began several years of injury free climbing, during which I increased my level as a climber, but not as much as I feel I could have done. The 'fire' of motivation that burned my entire psyche while I was in lay-off with my first pulley injury was allowed to settle slightly, being fed with constant climbing.

But I was certainly not pain free. I have suffered with severe eczema on my feet all my life. Wearing shoes, especially sweaty rock-shoes or mountaineering boots, cold, heat and friction all seem to aggravate it. At its best it would only be sharply painful at the beginning of the climbing day. At its worst I used to dread putting on my mountaineering boots all the way from Glasgow to Cairngorm. Thankfully, the concerns and hardships of the winter climbing day always helped to make the pain drift into the background.

As I approached age 30, my worst injury fear struck: golfer's elbow. I had known several prolific climbers in the generation above me who had given up climbing because of this condition. There seemed to be no cure and once you had it, it seemed to be a chronic curse. At the end of a sport climbing trip, while climbing at my very best, I began to feel twinges in the medial epicondyle. I went through the usual phase of hoping it was just transient, but within a month I had to admit I was a sufferer. I could still climb, but intense training of any sort, especially deep lock offs or pull-ups, all made it much worse. Thankfully, I was sensible enough to not let it get very bad. I settled into a long period of reduced training, and going around climbing lots of dangerous trad routes. I hoped that it would settle over the course of a year. It didn't, and after the two year stage I was getting desperate for a solution and was even beginning to court the idea of giving up climbing for a long spell.

I had heard and read a little about eccentric exercises which sounded like a promising treatment among an array of other treatments that seemed wholly useless. I gave it a try. After two weeks of following the program, my elbow was worse than ever. This just felt wrong and so I backed off and stopped, only to try again several times. Each time, I became too concerned I was making it worse after a week or two of the exercises. In exasperation I managed to persuade my GP to refer me on the NHS to see Professor Nicola Maffulli in London. Maffulli is a prolific research author on tendinopathy and specialises in elbow tendinosis. I had no idea if he could offer me anything. In 15 minutes, he gave me the simplest, bluntest advice I could imagine. He recommended I continue with the eccentrics program, but this time push through and tolerate some worsening of the condition during the first several weeks. Moreover, he recommended I increase the volume of exercises 4 fold, to 180 reps per day! Meanwhile, he felt that the other treatments I had been trying (stretching, cold therapy, deep friction massage) were unlikely to make any impact.

I followed his advice and as expected my elbows (I had golfer's in both arms and tennis elbow in the other by then) became worse over the first two weeks, then stabilised in a pretty aggravated state for another two. However, in the 5th week, the level of pain during the eccentrics and climbing decreased markedly. After the 6th week I was able to perform an intense three hour bouldering session with no symptoms whatsoever for the first time in around three years. It was this experience that led me to begin working on this book.

I still have occasional symptoms of golfer's elbow to this day, and may always. However, it doesn't affect my climbing or training at all. Only the occasional hard day out with some really deep lock-offs or climbing in very bad conditions will elicit slight tenderness. I have had one or two flare-ups over the past three years. The last one was after my ankle surgery when I was doing two months of nothing but intense fingerboarding with some pull-ups. However, six weeks of eccentrics reversed the problem effectively once again.

I have dislocated my pinky, the sesamoids in my toes, broken my ankle twice with some permanent cartilage damage, suffered an excruciating nerve compression in my knee, torn the medial collateral ligament and hamstrings tendon of my knee during a drop knee, torn my hamstrings and quadriceps muscles, had some minor shoulder impingement syndrome, chipped the end off my radius falling onto my elbow, cut (partially) the digital nerve in my finger, suffered severe whiplash landing from trad falls, torn my plantar fascia and had multiple rounds of flexor unit strains in both ring fingers. As I write I am waiting my second ankle surgery in a year after hitting the ground from an unprotected trad route again.

A life of climbing gives everyone battle scars. Working with injuries is part of participation in sport. You should not feel isolated or excluded by injury. Quite the opposite. If you ask others at the climbing wall about their injuries, most will have a story to tell. Until you do this, it is easy to feel that you are suffering an unfair misfortune. What has amazed me about my own experiences with injury, and my study for this book, is that most of the injuries described in this book are no match for resourcefulness and determination to achieve your climbing goals come what may. You will have to work around your injuries to get to your climbing goals, and work through the frustration they will undoubtedly cause. By following the principles laid out in this book, you can not only maximise the effects of the body's ability to heal and regenerate, but enjoy the process of doing so.

Glossary of key terms

Glossary for some key terms you'll need to know to learn the detail of sports injury science:

Abduction: A movement away from the midline of the body, such as moving an arm out to the side.

Acute: Refers to a type of injury; sudden tearing or trauma to tissue. Alternatively used to refer to the initial phase of the healing response to traumatic injury, with inflammation triggering the later proliferative and remodelling stages of healing.

Adduction: A movement towards the body's midline

such as bringing an arm back down to your side from a raised position.

Agonist: A prime mover muscle that provides the major force to complete a joint movement and is opposed by an antagonist.

Anabolic: A body process that tends to build up body tissues, such as adding muscle or soft tissue.

Analgesic: Pain relieving.

Antagonist: A prime move muscle which opposes an agonist, for example causing extension of a joint rather than flexion.

Anterior: Forward or towards the front of the body.

Aponeurosis: A flattened tendon forming a sheet such as the lower part of the abdominal wall or the palm of the hand.

Atrophy: Loss of tissue such as muscle, tendon, ligament or bone due. The loss may be caused by disuse or other causes such as steroid injections.

Avulsion fracture: A bone fracture which occurs when a ligament or tendon pulls away a fragment of bone from it's attachment.

Bursa: Smooth areas of fibrocartilage between bone and overlying tendons which facilitate free movement between tendon and bone. Often inflamed by overuse, trauma, or excessive pressure.

Cartilage: The soft tissue which lines joints, allowing free movement of joints and absorbing shock. Joint cartilage is known as hyaline cartilage. Another type of cartilage known as fibrocartilage forms structures such as the nose and ears.

Catabolic: A body process that tends to break down body tissue such as atrophy of muscle and soft tissue.

Chronic: When used in the context of sports injuries, an injury is referred to as chronic when it has long lasting duration, usually of many weeks or months.

Clinical diagnosis: Diagnosis made on the basis of medical history and physical examination, rather than scanning or laboratory tests.

Collagen: The main structural protein of connective tissue. It is arranged in bundles of long fibrils in ligament and tendon tissue, but is also present in skin, bone, cartilage and blood vessels.

Concentric contraction: A muscle contraction where the muscle shortens during the contraction.

Conservative treatment: Less aggressive or risky treatment. Often used in sports medicine to mean non-surgical treatment.

Cryotherapy: Cold treatment of various types which is applied with the goal of reducing pain and limiting swelling accumulation.

Distal: Further from the centre of the body.

Eccentric contraction: A muscle contraction where the muscle lengthens during the contraction, such as lowering back down from a pull-up.

Enthesis: The tendon bone junction. It is a complex area where bony tissue makes a transition through fibrocartilage to tendon tissue.

Epiphysis: The rounded end of a long bone, at its joint with another bone. In growing youngsters, it is connected to the shaft of the bone by the epiphyseal cartilage or growth plate, which fuses into bone in adulthood.

Epicondyle: The bony ridges on either side of the humerus at the elbow.

Extension: A movement or position where a joint is straightened, increasing the angle across the joint. Reaching with the arm extends the elbow joint.

External rotation: Rotation of a joint or body part away from the centre of the body. Also referred to as lateral rotation.

Fascia: The layer of connective tissue surrounding muscles and body compartments.

Flexion: A movement or position where the angle of the joint is decreased, such as bending the elbow.

Hypertrophy: Tissue growth due to increase in the size of its cells.

Inferior: A structure which is lower on the body. The ankle is inferior to the knee.

Inflammation: The complex protective mechanism of the body to remove injurious stimuli and initiate the healing process. The classical signs of inflammation are pain, redness, swelling and loss of function.

Internal rotation: Rotation of a joint or body part towards the centre of the body. Also referred to as medial rotation.

Joint Capsule: The soft tissue envelope of a joint which holds in synovial fluid which lubricates and nourishes the cartilaginous surfaces of the joint within it.

Kinetic chain: A concept describing the interconnectedness of body segments and joints in producing body movements and applying force. For example, weakness or limited mobility further 'up' the kinetic chain in the back and shoulders may affect the demands on distal areas such as the elbow and forearm muscles.

Lateral: Further from the midline of the body. E.g. the lateral epicondyle is on the outside of the elbow. Also movement away from the midline of the body. Also referred to as 'external' i.e. lateral or external rotation describe the same movement.

Ligament: Connective tissue connecting one bone to another.

Magnetic Resonance Imaging (MRI): A scanning technique which can visualise soft tissue such as ligaments and tendons as well as bone, providing a very sensitive diagnostic tool.

Medial: Closer to the midline of the body. E.g. the medial epicondyle is on the inside of the elbow. Movement towards the midline of the body. Also referred to as 'internal'; Medial or internal rotation describe the same movement.

Orthotic: An externally applied device that modifies the functional characteristics of the musculoskeletal system. They are applied to relieve pain, alter joint motion, reduce loading or improve function. An example would be a heel-lift wedge in the shoe.

Palpation: The use of the hands to examine the body, often in diagnostic assessment to locate anatomical structures or injury sites and assess swelling or other characteristics.

Pathology: The study of the causes, processes and effects of injury or disease. Also used to describe abnormal changes in tissue.

Posterior: A structure located towards the back of the body.

Pronation: Rotation of the forearm so that the palm faces downward. Also rotation of the foot so that the arch flattens and the medial side of the foot is preferentially weighted.

Proprioception: The body's sense of joint positioning or location in space based on neural feedback.

Proximal: Closer to the centre of the body.

Pulley: Thickened ligamentous band of tendon sheath which holds the tendon against the bone. The annular pulley system in the fingers prevents the flexor tendons from 'bowstringing' away from the phalanges when the fingers are flexed.

Subluxation: Partial dislocation of a joint, where the bone slides part-way out of the joint. Most common in the shoulder.

Superior: A structure which is higher on the body.

Supination: Rotation of the hand so that the palm faces up. Also rotation of the foot so that the lateral side of the foot is weighted.

Synovial fluid: Viscous fluid which fills joint spaces, lubricating and nourishing them.

Synovium: The synovium or synovial membrane lines the capsule of joints and the sheaths of tendons, releasing synovial fluid into the synovial space.

Tendon: Connective tissue which connects muscle with bone.

Tendonitis: Acute inflammation of a tendon causing pain with rapid onset, usually following a particularly aggressive exercise bout or traumatic injury. The term is no longer used to describe slow-onset tendon pain from overuse.

Tendinopathy: A generic term that encompasses any abnormal condition of a tendon.

Tendinosis: Changes in tendons which are currently described as degenerative, causing pain on activity. Symptoms are usually slow-onset. There is ongoing argument about the nature and definition of the condition.

Trigger point: The correct name is myofascial trigger point. A hypersensitive focal area in muscle tissue or fascia which can also refer pain to distant areas. Often trigger points can be palpated as tight nodules in the muscle.

Thanks

Many people helped in one way or another to make this book happen. Thanks!

Tina Davenport
Rebecca Dent www.rebeccadent.co.uk
Mark Garthwaite
Alicia Hudelson
Susan Jensen
Barbara MacLeod
Claire MacLeod
Freida MacLeod
Katy MacLeod
Jenny Munro
John Ostrovskis www.919clinic.co.uk
Jacqui Parfitt www.lochaberphysiotherapy.co.uk
Readers of my blog, who commented so many thoughts and examples
John Sutherland www.crofteleven.co.uk
Liz Turner
Michael Tweedley
West Highland College, UHI

Also by Dave MacLeod

9 out of 10 Climbers Make the Same Mistakes

The bestselling book on improving your climbing performance. *9 out of 10* redefines what it means to train for climbing, sharpening your focus on the important, eliminating the unimportant and opening the door to the potential you already have.

References

1.   Wright, D.M., T.J. Royle, and T. Marshall, *Indoor rock climbing: who gets injured?* Br J Sports Med, 2001. 35(3): p. 181-5.

2.   Gerdes, E.M., J.W. Hafner, and J.C. Aldag, *Injury patterns and safety practices of rock climbers.* J Trauma, 2006. 61(6): p. 1517-25.

3.   Rooks, M.D., et al., *Injury patterns in recreational rock climbers.* Am J Sports Med, 1995. 23(6): p. 683-5.

4.   Schoffl, V.R. and I. Schoffl, *Injuries to the finger flexor pulley system in rock climbers: current concepts.* J Hand Surg Am, 2006. 31(4): p. 647-54.

5.   Schoffl, V., et al., *Pulley injuries in rock climbers.* Wilderness Environ Med, 2003. 14(2): p. 94-100.

6.   Schweizer, A., *Lumbrical tears in rock climbers.* J Hand Surg Br, 2003. 28(2): p. 187-9.

7.   Frontera, W.R., I.M. Commission., and I.F.o.S. Medicine., *Rehabilitation of sports injuries : scientific basis.* The Encyclopaedia of Sports Medicine. 2003, Boston, MA: Blackwell Science. x, 326 p.

8.   Maffulli, N., P. Renström, and W.B. Leadbetter, *Tendon injuries: basic science and clinical medicine.* 2005, London: Springer. xii, 332 p.

9.   Hamilton, B. and C. Purdam, *Patellar tendinosis as an adaptive process: a new hypothesis.* Br J Sports Med, 2004. 38(6): p. 758-61.

10. Lyman, J., *Strain Behavior of the Distal Achilles Tendon: Implications for Insertional Achilles Tendinopathy.* Am J Sports Med, 2004. 32(2): p. 457-461.

11. Arnoczky, S.P., M. Lavagnino, and M. Egerbacher, *The mechanobiological aetiopathogenesis of tendinopathy: is it the over-stimulation or the under-stimulation of tendon cells?* Int J Exp Pathol, 2007. 88(4): p. 217-26.

12. Scott, A., et al., *Sports and exercise-related tendinopathies: a review of selected topical issues by participants of the second International Scientific Tendinopathy Symposium (ISTS) Vancouver 2012.* Br J Sports Med, 2013. 47(9): p. 536-44.

13. Brukner, P., K. Khan, and P. Brukner, *Brukner & Khan's Clinical Sports Medicine.* 4th ed. Sports medicine series. 2012, Sydney ; New York: McGraw-Hill. xlvii, 1296 p.

14. Sahrmann, S., *Diagnosis and Treatment of Movement Impairment Syndromes.* 2002, St. Louis, Mo.: Mosby. 460.

15. Butler, D.S. and G.L. Moseley, *Explain Pain.* 2012: Noigroup Publications.

16. Maughan, R.J., *Basic and applied sciences for sports medicine.* 1999, Oxford ; Boston: Butterworth-Heinemann. xvi, 346 p.

17. Shiri, R., et al., *Prevalence and determinants of lateral and medial epicondylitis: a population study.* Am J Epidemiol, 2006. 164(11): p. 1065-74.

18. Silverstein, B., E. Welp, and N. Nelson, *Claims incidence of work-related disorders of the upper extremities: Washington State, 1987 through 1995.* Am J Public Health, 1998. 88: p. 1827–33.

19. Kurppa, K., E. Viikari-Juntura, and E. Kuosma, *Incidence of tenosynovitis or peritendinitis and epicondylitis in a meat- processing factory.* Scand J Work Environ Health 1991. 17: p. 32–7.

20. Verhaar, J.A., *Tennis elbow. Anatomical, epidemiological and therapeutic aspects.* Int Orthop, 1994. 18: p. 263–267.

21. Hochholzer, T. and V. Schoffl, *One Move Too Many: How to Understand the Injuries and Overuse Syndroms of Rock Climbing.* 2 ed. 2006: Lochner-Verlag. 230p.

22. Saunders, J., *Stretching, the truth.* Rock, 2005: p. 37.

23. Forster, R., et al., *Climber's back-form and mobility of the thoracolumbar spine leading to postural adaptations in male high ability rock climbers.* Int J Sports Med, 2009. 30(1): p. 53-9.

24. Norris, C.M., *Sports injuries : diagnosis and management.* 2nd ed. 1998, Oxford ; Boston: Butterworth-Heinemann. x, 498 p.

25. Saunders, J., *Bum wraps: the truth about taping.* Rock & Ice, 2006(148): p. 54-57.

26. Ellenbecker, T.S. and A.J. Mattalino, *The elbow in sport : injury, treatment, and rehabilitation.* 1997, Champaign, IL: Human Kinetics. xi, 202 p.

27. Larson, P. and B. Katovsky, *Tread lightly*. 2012: Skyhorse Publishing. 258p.

28. Lieberman, D.E., *What we can learn about running from barefoot running: an evolutionary medical perspective*. Exerc Sport Sci Rev, 2012. 40(2): p. 63-72.

29. Nigg, B.M., *Biomechanics of Sports Shoes*. 2010: University of Calgary Press. 300.

30. Kendall, F.P., et al., *Muscles: Testing and Function with Posture and Pain*. 5th ed. 2005: Lippincott Williams & Wilkins. 479.

31. Nirschl, R.P., *Tennis elbow*. Prim Care, 1977. 4(2): p. 367-82.

32. Olderman, R., *Fixing you: shoulder and elbow pain*. 2010: Boone Publishing LLC.

33. Ingraham, P. *Does posture matter?* 2013. http://saveyourself.ca/articles/posture.php.

34. Csapo, R., et al., *On muscle, tendon and high heels*. J Exp Biol, 2010. 213(Pt 15): p. 2582-8.

35. Saunders, J., *Shoulder Impingement*. Rock, 2005: p. 35.

36. Saunders, J., *Vertical addiction*. Sportslink, (2): p. 6-9.

37. Muyor, J.M., P.A. Lopez-Minarro, and A.J. Casimiro, *Effect of stretching program in an industrial workplace on hamstring flexibility and sagittal spinal posture of adult women workers: a randomized controlled trial*. J Back Musculoskelet Rehabil, 2012. 25(3): p. 161-9.

38. Petrofsky, J.S., M. Laymon, and H. Lee, *Effect of heat and cold on tendon flexibility and force to flex the human knee*. Med Sci Monit, 2013. 19: p. 661-7.

39. Daneshjoo, A., et al., *The effects of comprehensive warm-up programs on proprioception, static and dynamic balance on male soccer players*. PLoS One, 2012. 7(12): p. e51568.

40. Soligard, T., et al., *Comprehensive warm-up programme to prevent injuries in young female footballers: cluster randomised controlled trial*. BMJ, 2008. 337: p. a2469.

41. Soligard, T., et al., *Compliance with a comprehensive warm-up programme to prevent injuries in youth football*. Br J Sports Med, 2010. 44(11): p. 787-93.

42. Lauersen, J.B., D.M. Bertelsen, and L.B. Andersen, *The effectiveness of exercise interventions to prevent sports injuries: a systematic review and meta-analysis of randomised controlled trials*. Br J Sports Med, 2014. 48(11): p. 871-7.

43. Hart, L., *Effect of stretching on sport injury risk: a review*. Clin J Sport Med, 2005. 15(2): p. 113.

44. Brushoj, C., et al., *Prevention of overuse injuries by a concurrent exercise program in subjects exposed to an increase in training load: a randomized controlled trial of 1020 army recruits*. Am J Sports Med, 2008. 36(4): p. 663-70.

45. Pereles, D., A. Roth, and D. Thompson *A Large, Randomized, Prospective Study of the Impact of a Pre-Run Stretch on the Risk of Injury in Teenage and Older Runners*. https://www.usatf.org/stretchStudy/StretchStudyReport.pdf.

46. Mah, C.D., et al., *The effects of sleep extension on the athletic performance of collegiate basketball players*. Sleep, 2011. 34(7): p. 943-50.

47. Engle-Friedman, M., *The effects of sleep loss on capacity and effort*. Sleep Science, 2014.

48. Fullagar, H.H., et al., *Sleep and Athletic Performance: The Effects of Sleep Loss on Exercise Performance, and Physiological and Cognitive Responses to Exercise*. Sports Med, 2014.

49. Maughan, R.J., IOC Medical Commission., and International Federation of Sports Medicine., *Nutrition in sport*. Encyclopaedia of sports medicine. 2000, Osney Mead, Oxford ; Malden, MA: Blackwell Science. 680 p.

50. Cook, C.J., et al., *Skill execution and sleep deprivation: effects of acute caffeine or creatine supplementation - a randomized placebo-controlled trial*. J Int Soc Sports Nutr, 2011. 8: p. 2.

51. Kreider, R.B., et al., *ISSN exercise & sport nutrition review: research & recommendations*. J Int Soc Sports Nutr, 2010. 7: p. 7.

52. Antonio, J., et al., *The effects of consuming a high protein diet (4.4 g/kg/d) on body composition in resistance-trained individuals*. J Int Soc Sports Nutr, 2014. 11: p. 19.

53. Gerlach, K.E., et al., *Fat intake and injury in female runners*. J Int Soc Sports Nutr, 2008. 5: p. 1.

54. Paoli, A., et al., *Ketogenic diet does not affect*

strength performance in elite artistic gymnasts. J Int Soc Sports Nutr, 2012. 9(1): p. 34.

55. Bhutani, S., et al., *Effect of exercising while fasting on eating behaviors and food intake.* J Int Soc Sports Nutr, 2013. 10(50).

56. Paddon-Jones, D., et al., *Protein, weight management, and satiety.* Am J Clin Nutr, 2008. 87(5): p. 1558S-1561S.

57. La Bounty, P.M., et al., *International Society of Sports Nutrition position stand: meal frequency.* J Int Soc Sports Nutr, 2011. 8: p. 4.

58. van Buul, V.J., L. Tappy, and F.J. Brouns, *Misconceptions about fructose-containing sugars and their role in the obesity epidemic.* Nutr Res Rev, 2014. 27(1): p. 119-30.

59. Wandel, S., et al., *Effects of glucosamine, chondroitin, or placebo in patients with osteoarthritis of hip or knee: network meta-analysis.* BMJ, 2010. 341: p. c4675.

60. Notarnicola, A., et al., *SWAAT study: extracorporeal shock wave therapy and arginine supplementation and other nutraceuticals for insertional Achilles tendinopathy.* Adv Ther, 2012. 29(9): p. 799-814.

61. Kanaley, J.A., *Growth hormone, arginine and exercise.* Curr Opin Clin Nutr Metab Care, 2008. 11(1): p. 50-4.

62. Mountjoy, M., et al., *The IOC consensus statement: beyond the Female Athlete Triad--Relative Energy Deficiency in Sport (RED-S).* Br J Sports Med, 2014. 48(7): p. 491-7.

63. Prentice, W.E., *Therapeutic modalities in rehabilitation.* 4th ed. ed. 2011, New York: McGraw-Hill Medical ; London : McGraw-Hill [distributor].

64. Knight, K.L. and D.O. Draper, *Therapeutic modalities: the art and science.* 2008: Lippincott Williams & Wilkins. 399.

65. MacAuley, D. and T.M. Best, *Evidence-based sports medicine.* 2nd ed. 2007, Malden, Mass. ; Oxford: BMJ Books/Blackwell Pub. xv, 615 p.

66. Kaux, J.F., et al., *Current Opinions on Tendinopathy.* J Sports Sci Med, 2011. 10(2): p. 238-253.

67. Rees, J.D., M. Stride, and A. Scott, *Tendons - time to revisit inflammation.* Br J Sports Med, 2014. 48(21): p. 1553-1557.

68. Maffulli, N. and U.G. Longo, *Conservative management for tendinopathy: is there enough scientific evidence?* Rheumatology (Oxford), 2008. 47(4): p. 390-1.

69. Almekinders, L.C., J.H. Vellema, and P.S. Weinhold, *Strain patterns in the patellar tendon and the implications for patellar tendinopathy.* Knee Surg Sports Traumatol Arthrosc, 2002. 10(1): p. 2-5.

70. Cook, J.L. and C. Purdam, *Is compressive load a factor in the development of tendinopathy?* Br J Sports Med, 2012. 46(3): p. 163-8.

71. Rees, J.D., N. Maffulli, and J. Cook, *Management of tendinopathy.* Am J Sports Med, 2009. 37(9): p. 1855-67.

72. Benjamin, M., et al., *Where tendons and ligaments meet bone: attachment sites ('entheses') in relation to exercise and/or mechanical load.* J Anat, 2006. 208(4): p. 471-90.

73. Lyman, J., *Strain Behavior of the Distal Achilles Tendon: Implications for Insertional Achilles Tendinopathy.* American Journal of Sports Medicine, 2004. 32(2): p. 457-461.

74. Maganaris, C.N., et al., *Biomechanics and pathophysiology of overuse tendon injuries: ideas on insertional tendinopathy.* Sports Med, 2004. 34(14): p. 1005-17.

75. Andres, B.M. and G.A. Murrell, *Treatment of tendinopathy: what works, what does not, and what is on the horizon.* Clin Orthop Relat Res, 2008. 466(7): p. 1539-54.

76. Magnusson, S.P., H. Langberg, and M. Kjaer, *The pathogenesis of tendinopathy: balancing the response to loading.* Nat Rev Rheumatol, 2010. 6: p. 262-268.

77. Stanish, W.D., R.M. Rubinovich, and S. Curwin, *Eccentric exercise in chronic tendinitis.* Clin Orthop Relat Res, 1986. 208: p. 65-68.

78. Alfredson, H. and J. Cook, *A treatment algorithm for managing Achilles tendinopathy: new treatment options.* Br J Sports Med, 2007. 41(4): p. 211-6.

79. Rees, J.D., R.L. Wolman, and A. Wilson, *Eccentric exercises; why do they work, what are the problems and how can we improve them?* Br J Sports Med, 2009. 43(4): p. 242-6.

80.   Allison, G.T. and C. Purdam, *Eccentric loading for Achilles tendinopathy--strengthening or stretching?* Br J Sports Med, 2009. 43(4): p. 276-9.

81.   Jonsson, P., et al., *New regimen for eccentric calf-muscle training in patients with chronic insertional Achilles tendinopathy: results of a pilot study.* Br J Sports Med, 2008. 42(9): p. 746-9.

82.   Drew, B.T., et al., *Do structural changes (eg, collagen/matrix) explain the response to therapeutic exercises in tendinopathy: a systematic review.* Br J Sports Med, 2012.

83.   Magnussen, R.A., W.R. Dunn, and A.B. Thomson, *Nonoperative treatment of midportion Achilles tendinopathy: a systematic review.* Clin J Sport Med, 2009. 19: p. 54-64.

84.   Alfredson, H., et al., *Heavy-load eccentric calf muscle training for the treatment of chronic Achilles tendinosis.* Am J Sports Med, 1998. 26(3): p. 360-6.

85.   Woodley, B.L., R.J. Newsham-West, and G.D. Baxter, *Chronic tendinopathy: effectiveness of eccentric exercise.* Br J Sports Med, 2007. 41(4): p. 188-98; discussion 199.

86.   Saunders, J., *Dodgy elbows.* Rock & Ice, 2007(156): p. 77-79.

87.   van der Plas, A., et al., *A 5-year follow-up study of Alfredson's heel-drop exercise programme in chronic midportion Achilles tendinopathy.* Br J Sports Med, 2012. 46(3): p. 214-8.

88.   Joseph, M.F., et al., *Deep friction massage to treat tendinopathy: a systematic review of a classic treatment in the face of a new paradigm of understanding.* J Sport Rehabil, 2012. 21(4): p. 343-53.

89.   Ingraham, P. and T. Taylor, *Trigger Points & Myofascial Pain Syndrome.* 2013, Paul Ingraham & Regeneration Training: Vancouver. p. 265p.

90.   Houglum, P.A., *Therapeutic exercise for musculoskeletal injuries.* 3rd ed. 2010: Human Kinetics.

91.   Lewis, T., *Observations upon the reactions of the vessels of the human skin to cold.* Heart, 1930. 15: p. 177-208.

92.   Cochrane, D.J., *Alternating hot and cold water immersion for athlete recovery: a review.* Physical Therapy in Sport, 2004. 5: p. 26-32.

93.   Tsai, W.C., S.T. Tang, and F.C. Liang, *Effect of therapeutic ultrasound on tendons.* Am J Phys Med Rehabil, 2011. 90(12): p. 1068-73.

94.   Khan, M., et al., *Arthroscopic surgery for degenerative tears of the meniscus: a systematic review and meta-analysis.* CMAJ, 2014. 186(14): p. 1057-64.

95.   Sunding, K., et al., *Sclerosing injections and ultrasound-guided arthroscopic shaving for patellar tendinopathy: good clinical results and decreased tendon thickness after surgery-a medium-term follow-up study.* Knee Surg Sports Traumatol Arthrosc, 2014.

96.   Coombes, B.K., L. Bisset, and B. Vicenzino, *Efficacy and safety of corticosteroid injections and other injections for management of tendinopathy: a systematic review of randomised controlled trials.* Lancet, 2010. 376(9754): p. 1751-67.

97.   Pountos, I., et al., *Do nonsteroidal anti-inflammatory drugs affect bone healing? A critical analysis.* ScientificWorldJournal, 2012. 2012: p. 606404.

98.   Murrell, G.A., *Using nitric oxide to treat tendinopathy.* Br J Sports Med, 2007. 41(4): p. 227-31.

99.   Paoloni, J.A. and G.A. Murrell, *Three-year followup study of topical glyceryl trinitrate treatment of chronic noninsertional Achilles tendinopathy.* Foot Ankle Int, 2007. 28: p. 1064–1068.

100. Paoloni, J.A., et al., *Randomised, double-blind, placebo-controlled clinical trial of a new topical glyceryl trinitrate patch for chronic lateral epicondylosis.* Br J Sports Med, 2009. 43(4): p. 299-302.

101. McCallum, S.D., J.A. Paoloni, and G.A. Murrell, *Five-year prospective comparison study of topical glyceryl trinitrate treatment of chronic lateral epicondylosis at the elbow.* Br J Sports Med, 2011. 45(5): p. 416-20.

102. Rabago, D., et al., *A systematic review of four injection therapies for lateral epicondylosis: prolotherapy, polidocanol, whole blood and platelet-rich plasma.* Br J Sports Med, 2009.

43(7): p. 471-81.

103. Suresh, S.P., et al., *Medial epicondylitis: is ultrasound guided autologous blood injection an effective treatment?* Br J Sports Med, 2006. 40(11): p. 935-9; discussion 939.

104. de Vos, R.J., et al., *No effects of PRP on ultrasonographic tendon structure and neovascularisation in chronic midportion Achilles tendinopathy.* Br J Sports Med, 2011. 45(5): p. 387-92.

105. Gosens, T. and A.K. Mishra, *Editorial in response to the systematic review by de Vos et al: 'Strong evidence against platelet-rich plasma injections for chronic lateral epicondylar tendinopathy: a systematic review'.* Br J Sports Med, 2014. 48(12): p. 945-6.

106. de Vos, R.J., J. Windt, and A. Weir, *Strong evidence against platelet-rich plasma injections for chronic lateral epicondylar tendinopathy: a systematic review.* Br J Sports Med, 2014. 48(12): p. 952-6.

107. Layard, P.R.G., *Happiness : lessons from a new science.* 2005, New York: Penguin Press. ix, 310 p.

108. Stasinopoulos, D., et al., *Comparison of effects of a home exercise programme and a supervised exercise programme for the management of lateral elbow tendinopathy.* Br J Sports Med, 2010. 44(8): p. 579-83.

109. Schoffl, V., et al., *Evaluation of injury and fatality risk in rock and ice climbing.* Sports Med, 2010. 40(8): p. 657-79.

110. Faigenbaum, A.D., et al., *Youth resistance training: updated position statement paper from the national strength and conditioning association.* J Strength Cond Res, 2009. 23(5 Suppl): p. S60-79.

111. Schoffl, V.R., et al., *Radiographic adaptations to the stress of high-level rock climbing in junior athletes: a 5-year longitudinal study of the German Junior National Team and a group of recreational climbers.* Am J Sports Med, 2007. 35(1): p. 86-92.

112. Schoffl, V., T. Hochholzer, and A. Imhoff, *Radiographic changes in the hands and fingers of young, high-level climbers.* Am J Sports Med, 2004. 32(7): p. 1688-94.

113. Morrison, A.B. and V.R. Schoffl, *Physiological responses to rock climbing in young climbers.* Br J Sports Med, 2007. 41(12): p. 852-61; discussion 861.

114. Hochholzer, T. and V.R. Schoffl, *Epiphyseal fractures of the finger middle joints in young sport climbers.* Wilderness Environ Med, 2005. 16(3): p. 139-42.

115. Schoffl, V.R. and I. Schoffl, *Finger pain in rock climbers: reaching the right differential diagnosis and therapy.* J Sports Med Phys Fitness, 2007. 47(1): p. 70-8.

116. Saunders, J., *Ask Dr. J.* Rock & Ice, 2009(176): p. 68-69.

117. Struijs, P.A., et al., *Orthotic devices for the treatment of tennis elbow.* Cochrane Database Syst Rev, 2002(1): p. CD001821.

118. Baker, C.L. and K.D. Plancher, *Operative treatment of elbow injuries.* 2001, New York: Springer.

119. Alfredson, H., C. Spang, and S. Forsgren, *Unilateral surgical treatment for patients with midportion Achilles tendinopathy may result in bilateral recovery.* Br J Sports Med, 2014. 48(19): p. 1421-4.

120. Saunders, J., *Ask Dr. J.* Rock & Ice, 2008(169): p. 82-84.

121. Peters, P., *Nerve compression syndromes in sport climbers.* Int J Sports Med, 2001. 22(8): p. 611-7.

122. Vigouroux, L., et al., *Middle and ring fingers are more exposed to pulley rupture than index and little during sport-climbing: a biomechanical explanation.* Clin Biomech (Bristol, Avon), 2008. 23(5): p. 562-70.

123. Schoffl, I., et al., *The influence of concentric and eccentric loading on the finger pulley system.* J Biomech, 2009. 42(13): p. 2124-8.

124. El-Sheikh, Y., et al., *Diagnosis of finger flexor pulley injury in rock climbers: A systematic review.* Can J Plast Surg, 2006. 14(4): p. 227-31.

125. Schoffl, V., A. Heid, and T. Kupper, *Tendon injuries of the hand.* World J Orthop, 2012. 3(6): p. 62-9.

126. Moutet, F., *Flexor tendon pulley system: anatomy, pathology, treatment.* Chir Main, 2003. 22: p. 1-12.

127. Moutet, F., A. Forli, and D. Voulliaume, *Pulley*

rupture and reconstruction in rock climbers. Tech Hand Up Extrem Surg, 2004. 8(3): p. 149-55.

128. Schoffl, V., et al., *Surgical repair of multiple pulley injuries-evaluation of a new combined pulley repair.* J Hand Surg Am, 2012. 37(2): p. 224-30.

129. Schoffl, V. and I. Schoffl, *Isolated cruciate pulley injuries in rock climbers.* J hand Surg, 2010. 35E(3): p. 245-246.

130. Schoffl, V.R., et al., *Strength measurement and clinical outcome after pulley ruptures in climbers.* Med Sci Sports Exerc, 2006. 38(4): p. 637-43.

131. Saunders, J., *Ask Dr. J.* Rock & Ice, 2009(175): p. 68-69.

132. Yamaguchi, T., *Climber's Finger.* Hand Surgery, 2007. 12(2): p. 59-65.

133. Schoffl, V., et al., *Surgical repair of multiple pulley injuries--evaluation of a new combined pulley repair.* J Hand Surg Am, 2012. 37(2): p. 224-30.

134. Schoffl, I., T. Baier, and V. Schoffl, *Flap irritation phenomenon (FLIP): etiology of chronic tenosynovitis after finger pulley rupture.* J Appl Biomech, 2011. 27(4): p. 291-6.

135. Schweizer, A., *Biomechanical effectiveness of taping the A2 pulley in rock climbers.* J Hand Surg Br, 2000. 25(1): p. 102-7.

136. Warme, W.J. and D. Brooks, *The effect of circumferential taping on flexor tendon pulley failure in rock climbers.* Am J Sports Med, 2000. 28(5): p. 674-8.

137. Schoffl, I., et al., *Impact of taping after finger flexor tendon pulley ruptures in rock climbers.* J Appl Biomech, 2007. 23(1): p. 52-62.

138. Schoffl, V., T. Hochholzer, and I. Schoffl, *Extensor hood syndrome-osteophytic irritation of digital extensor tendons in rock climbers.* Wilderness Environ Med, 2010. 21(3): p. 253-6.

139. Saunders, J., *Ask Dr. J.* Rock & Ice, 2008(173): p. 74-75.

140. Logan, A.J., et al., *Can rock climbing lead to Dupuytren's disease?* Br J Sports Med, 2005. 39: p. 639-644.

141. Saunders, J., *Blondes have more fun and more injuries.* Rock & Ice, 2006(141): p. 40.

142. Saunders, J., *The big squeeze: navigating the slippery slope of wrist health.* Rock & Ice: p. 42-43.

143. Talebi, M., et al., *Effect of vitamin b6 on clinical symptoms and electrodiagnostic results of patients with carpal tunnel syndrome.* Adv Pharm Bull, 2013. 3(2): p. 283-8.

144. Elphinston, J., *Stability, sport, and performance movement : great technique without injury.* 2008, Chichester, England: Lotus Pub. . 351 p.

145. Schoffl, V.R., J. Harrer, and T. Kupper, *Biceps tendon ruptures in rock climbers.* Clin J Sport Med, 2006. 16(5): p. 426-7.

146. Saunders, J., *Ask Dr. J.* Rock & Ice, 2009(174): p. 74-75.

147. Haddock, M.C. and L. Funk, *Labral tears in rock climbers.* Clin J Sport Med, 2006. 16(3): p. 271-3.

148. Schoffl, V., et al., *Superior labral anterior-posterior lesions in rock climbers-primary double tenodesis?* Clin J Sport Med, 2011. 21(3): p. 261-3.

149. Bahr, R. and S. Mæhlum, *Clinical guide to sports injuries.* 2004, Champaign, IL: Human Kinetics. 451 p.

150. Itoi, E., et al., *A new method of immobilization after traumatic anterior dislocation of the shoulder: a preliminary study.* J Shoulder Elbow Surg, 2003. 12(5): p. 413-5.

151. Saunders, J., *Ask Dr J.* Rock & Ice, 2008(167): p. 72-73.

152. Ingraham, P., *Save Yourself from Plantar Fasciitis.* 2013, Paul Ingraham & Regeneration Training: Vancouver. p. 95.

153. Ingraham, P., *Save Yourself from Plantar Fasciitis.* 2013.

154. van der Putten, E.P. and C.J. Snijder, *Shoe design for prevention of injuries in sport climbing.* Appl Ergon, 2001. 32(4): p. 379-87.

155. Schoffl, V. and T. Kupper, *Feet injuries in rock climbers.* World J Orthop, 2013. 4(4): p. 218-228.

156. Schweizer, A., et al., *Functional ankle control of rock climbers.* Br J Sports Med, 2005. 39(7): p. 429-31.

157. Csintalan, R.P., M.C. Inacio, and T.T. Funahashi, *Incidence rate of anterior cruciate ligament reconstructions.* Perm J, 2008. 12(3): p. 17-21.

158.   Caudill, P., et al., *Sports hernias: a systematic literature review.* Br J Sports Med, 2008. 42(12): p. 954-64.

159.   Garvey, J.F., J.W. Read, and A. Turner, *Sportsman hernia: what can we do?* Hernia, 2010. 14(1): p. 17-25.

160.   McCormack, K., et al., *Laparoscopic techniques versus open techniques for inguinal hernia repair.* Cochrane Database Syst Rev, 2003(1): p. CD001785.

Index